P9-EER-772

DATE D

SAM HOUSTON

By Noel B. Gerson

Fiction

Nonfiction

SAM HOUSTON

A BIOGRAPHICAL NOVEL

By NOEL B. GERSON

1968

DOUBLEDAY & COMPANY, INC.
GARDEN CITY, NEW YORK

FOR
Oliver G. Swan

Sam Houston's contradictions actually confirm his one basic, consistent quality: indomitable individualism, sometimes spectacular, sometimes crude, sometimes mysterious, but always courageous. He could be all things to all men—and yet, when faced with his greatest challenge, he was faithful to himself and to Texas.

John F. Kennedy

Sir, Sam Houston is a patriot! No man has ever loved, or will ever love, the United States more than he.

Andrew Jackson

SAM HOUSTON

1863

No rain had fallen in more than a month, and the brown soil of Texas was parched and cracked. Grazing cattle were forced to make their way across the bone-dry plains and hills to the river banks, where grass still grew, and ranch owners checked the depth of the water in their wells at daybreak and again at dusk. There was still enough to drink, but housewives washed clothes sparingly, and small children who came home from play with dirty breeches and soiled shirts were sure to be spanked before bedtime.

At the Confederate Army's training camp two miles from the little town of Huntsville, recruits kicked up huge, rolling clouds of dust as they marched and countermarched. Exploding shells on the artillery range sent tiny particles of earth, as fine as sand, high into the air, and every dwelling within miles of the bivouac became accustomed to the thin, gritty layers of dirt that covered every flat surface. But no one in Walker County complained. The drought, like the reverses the Confederacy was suffering in the War between the States, were accepted in silence, combined with the hope that there would be a marked improvement in the immediate future.

The old man was one of the few who actually enjoyed the

weather. He sat in a creaking rocking chair on the porch of the rambling, clapboard house and the hot sun eased the aches that had been his constant companions for so many years. The pain in his shoulder from the wound he had suffered at the age of eighteen in the Alabama Territory campaign of General Andy Jackson against the Creek Indians was so much a part of him that he couldn't remember when he had been free of the discomfort it caused. But his leg, the leg that had been shattered at the climax of his own great Battle of San Jacinto, the leg on which he had learned to walk again without a limp, could be stretched to its full length after the sun beat down on it for an hour or two.

The house was badly in need of paint, and both the porch and picket fence that faced the road were almost bare of whitewash, but the old man didn't care about such trivia. Margaret was unhappy about the shabby appearance of the place, he knew, although she was too loyal to mention the subject to him, and some of the elder children, particularly Nan, who was a grown woman now, occasionally tried to buy paint in town, and became upset when none was available. But he just shrugged and smiled when they told him, and they knew that, as always, he was reserving his pride for the things that mattered.

The old man hated inactivity, so it was fortunate that the road from the city of Houston, less than seventy miles to the south, ran past the front fence. He was too tired to leave the property, no matter how hard he tried to hide his feebleness, but he could watch the world pass his gate, and had to be content.

There were few who passed without staring, and many stopped for a moment or two to shout a few words. Even now, when his days were numbered, it was impossible to ignore him, and his enemies said he dressed like a stage actor to call attention to himself. He ignored his foes, of course, as he had for so many years, and continued to wear what pleased him.

His broad-brimmed hat of white beaver protected his bald head from the sun and shielded his broad-cheeked face. Most Americans, and certainly everyone in Texas, had become aware of that hat and his panther-skin waistcoat through the years. As for the

2

serape, or embroidered Mexican Indian blanket that was draped over the shoulders of his still massive frame, he had worn it to the White House when he had called on President Jackson, and again, many times, when Jamie Polk had lived there, so he had no intention of putting it aside when sitting on his own porch. As he had so often said during the better part of his seventy years on earth, people had to accept him on his own terms or reject him outright. He had never pandered to the cautious or self-effacing, and had no intention of starting now.

The old man was glad he had refused the offer of Texas to accept physical protection, and he still grinned quietly when he remembered how he had cursed the representative of President Jefferson Davis of the Confederate States, who had wanted to provide him with a permanent bodyguard. For one thing, he had cordially disliked Jeff Davis since they had served together in Washington City, and knew that his distaste was reciprocated. Of far greater importance, however, was his conviction that he needed no troops to come between him and the people. There might be thousands of Texans who hated him, as did men in other parts of the Confederacy, but he had earned universal respect, and no one would attack him. If he was wrong, and some hothead took a shot at him, he wouldn't mind too much. He had been close to death so often that he could not worry about minor risks.

So far his faith in the people had been justified. Older men riding on the Houston road usually doffed their hats to him and called, "Good morning, Mr. President." Others, of all ages, referred to him as "Senator" or "Governor." And quite a few, among them high-ranking Confederate officers, often saluted and called him "General."

To be sure, not everyone was pleasant. Bodies of Confederate troops pretended he didn't exist, and men marching off to war looked straight ahead, never glancing in the direction of the porch. The returning wounded, making their way slowly across east Texas, were frequently savage in their denunciations of him, as were some civilians.

Margaret found it difficult to believe, but his feelings were not hurt when someone shouted, "You damned traitor!" He knew he was right, and was responsible only to his own conscience. It was enough that, although he was unable to agree with the overwhelming majority of his fellow Texans, who had insisted on taking the state out of the Union, he had done and would do nothing to flout their will. He had worked too hard on behalf of Texas' independence and had served her too long as a state, as well, to have any hand in setting neighbor against neighbor.

Democracy, as he had declared in countless addresses through the course of a half-century, was expressed through the active desires of the electorate. He was demonstrating those principles now, as a member of a small minority. He refused to fool himself, however, and his anguish was excruciating. But he felt for others, not himself; his day was ended, and the burdens of the future had to be carried by those who survived him.

He worried more about his eldest son than anyone else, which was natural. Young Sam was an officer in the Confederate Army, and it was strange to be pulled in two directions at once, to hope the boy would earn distinction in battle, while at the same time praying he would survive in a struggle that was hopeless.

The Confederacy, as he had predicted in the turbulent days before secession, had no chance to win against the heavily populated, industrialized North. Others were coming to the same conclusion, slowly, but it was too late for Texas and the rest of the Confederacy to change course now. Too much blood had been shed, too many sacrifices had been made, so the war would go on to its grim end, and thousands more would die. Shiloh had been clear proof of what would happen everywhere in the South, and thinking of the battle, he drew his serape more closely around him. He had not wept since Shiloh.

Even now, thinking of the slaughter, he felt his throat become dry. Thousands of the boys who had marched past his gate had died there, and so had Albert Johnston. Albert Sidney Johnston had been a first-rate general, perhaps the Confederacy's best, and a close friend since the days Texas had fought for her independence from Mexico. The old man didn't like remembering the occasion he had appointed Johnston field commander of the

4

Texas army, and the soldier had said, "I'll do my best, Mr. President." He had done his brilliant best by defeating Grant's troops at Shiloh, but he paid with his own life there on April 6, the year before, while fighting for this cause that he, like so many intelligent men, had known could not triumph.

The shouts of the younger children at play in the pasture behind the house momentarily aroused the old man from his reverie, and again he stirred. Soon young Andy would be old enough for military service, and some of the girls might marry men who would die in the field. Yet there was nothing he could do to prevent the tragedy from becoming worse. He was reminded of the plays of Sophocles and Euripides he had read during his years of wilderness exile. The gods had decreed that men should suffer, and they would. Caught in the tight web of their own making, humans were the victims of fate.

Perhaps he was wrong to have assumed that the inevitable could have been avoided. Perhaps he should have stood aside while the gods had planned their cruel work. No, not once had he abandoned faith, and he could not lose hope now. As he had said in his maiden speech before Congress, as a Representative from Tennessee, "Our Union is sacred. May Almighty God protect and preserve the United States."

Now the homely lawyer from Illinois was living in the White House, and the nation was split in two. It hadn't been President Lincoln's fault, of course, that the War between the States had broken out, although his election had guaranteed that the states of the South would secede. The old man didn't care for some of Lincoln's methods and thought he had made a major error by issuing his Emancipation Proclamation, freeing the slaves, the previous January. It had been a foregone conclusion that the slaves would be set free, but the move could have been postponed until the North achieved its victory.

By ordering emancipation now, the President had made it impossible for the moderates in the South to effect a compromise that would permit the states that had left the Union to save face. The Confederacy would be forced to fight to the end. The old man was willing to admit, however, that Lincoln might have been

5

compelled to take a strong stand by the Abolitionists who had played such a major role in his election. Unseen pressures often forced a nation's chief executive to act against his own better judgment, as the old man well knew, perhaps better than any other living American.

He had to concede, moreover, that Lincoln loved the Union, not in Jackson's way, but in his own, and was equally determined to save and restore it. Old Hickory had been just as uncompromising in his dealings with John Calhoun. The old man glowered, his eyes darkening, as he thought of Calhoun, the man who had held virtually every high office in the United States government except the presidency itself. While it was true that principles were more important than individual men, it was also true that men shaped and controlled the developments of history. So much violence could have been avoided had he given in to his instincts and put a bullet through Calhoun forty-five years earlier. When he thought about Calhoun, his hatred made the past come to life again, and the years rolled away.

"Samuel."

He looked up to see Margaret standing beside him, and all his other feelings vanished as he was engulfed by his compassion for her. She looked old for her years, and he knew that bearing and rearing their seven children, combined with all the other troubles he had caused, had aged her prematurely. "I thought you were resting," he said.

"The shouts woke me up."

The sun was in his eyes, and he squinted. "The children?"

"No, Samuel, those—young hellions who were threatening to hang you." Scarcely a day passed without its quota of threats and obscenities, and they always upset her.

The old man reached out to pat his wife's hand. "I didn't hear them, and I wish you'd shut your ears to them, too. There's no real malice in the lads, Maggie. They read the newspaper attacks that blame me for all the South's woes, and they don't know any better. Besides," he added with a chuckle, "I still have a neck tough enough to resist hanging."

"I wish you'd come into the house."

6

"I'll be along soon."

Margaret hesitated for a moment. "Would you like a drink of whisky?"

He smiled again, but his eyes remained solemn as he shook his head.

"The doctors said a drink now and again might do you good, Samuel."

"When I swore off last time, I promised you I'd never touch the damned stuff again."

"I release you from your pledge."

"Well, I don't." He changed the subject abruptly. "Are you sending one of the youngsters down to the post office soon?"

"Nan was there this morning. Are you expecting a special letter?"

"I've been hoping we'd hear from young Sam. The post office people have been putting military mail into the boxes at all hours lately, even when it arrives after the usual distribution time."

Margaret stroked his shoulder. "Stop fretting, Samuel. He said in his last letter to us that he didn't expect his regiment to go into action again until late in the summer."

"I just don't want him fighting my battles, that's all."

"Who has a better right? He's inherited your temper as well as your name."

"The boy needs to use common sense, Maggie. I tell him in every letter that he's got to stop challenging everybody who curses me. He's carrying an impossible load. He won't be a good platoon leader until he inspires the trust of his men. And he sure as all hell won't win their confidence defending the arch-traitor."

"I won't let you talk that way about yourself."

"At one time or another I've been called a damnsight worse, and it never did the slightest harm to my health or disposition. Young Sam has got to learn that I'm content to let history vindicate me."

"Andy Donelson told me that one time, when you were governor of Tennessee, I think it was, one of your political opponents made a slighting reference to your father. Not that he knew

7

anything about your father, of course. It was just an orator's trick. But, Andy said, you pounced on the man, right there on the rostrum, and would have scalped him if a half dozen men hadn't hauled you off."

"I don't rightly remember the incident, but I won't deny it happened, Maggie. I've never taken kindly to insulting remarks about my family." His grin became sheepish. "All right. I'll let young Sam do what he thinks is right, and I'll stop deviling him with lectures."

"He'll be grateful to you, Samuel. It isn't easy for the boy to keep quiet. He feels someone must defend you, since you won't say a word yourself."

"There are times," the old man confessed, "when I wish I was strong enough to ride down to Houston and make a speech on the courthouse steps."

Margaret became alarmed. "You'd be stoned."

"It wouldn't be the first time." A hint of amusement appeared in his tired eyes. "Besides, it's been my experience that the aim of mobs is notoriously poor. If I thought it would help end the war sooner and return Texas to the Union, I'd find the energy. But I have too few friends to do any good. There are just enough of them to cause a riot, and soon all the Union supporters in the state would be beaten to death."

"When I think that you can't even visit the city that's been named for you—"

"Where's your perspective, Maggie? They haven't changed the name of the town, and they won't. As sure as I'm sitting here, troops will march through Houston in my honor again, and people will line the streets cheering my name. Between you and me, I'm sorry I won't live to see the day. But that isn't what matters. I've spent my whole lifetime serving the United States and Texas, and I won't be here to see them reunited."

"You will, Samuel! You—" She saw the expression in his eyes, and stopped short. Obviously, he knew, even better than his doctors, that any day might be his last.

"I sit here, thinking of the things I might have done to prevent this war. Only this morning I was telling myself that if I'd agreed

8

to accept the nomination for the presidency—in '56, the last time it was offered to me—I might have kept the country together." He held up his hand to silence her when she tried to interrupt. "But I was right to refuse. No candidate from the South could have won when all his support was in the North. I'd have made things worse, not better." Slowly, with great effort, he hauled himself to his feet.

Margaret stood, watching him but making no attempt to help. Now, as always throughout his long life, he insisted on walking alone, unaided.

Holding the serape with one hand, he used the porch railing to steady himself as he gazed out across the vast expanses of the Texas he had done so much to create, whose people he had done so much to mold into a breed set apart from all other Americans, yet so similar to the men of both South and North. "My God, Maggie, I feel so sorry for Lincoln. He wants to bring this whole country together again, but the task is too great for him, just as it was for me."

Margaret touched his arm, and with a last, long look toward the horizon, he started into the house.

ONE

1805–8

The youngest of the boys pounded at the gong suspended from a tree near the kitchen well, and the sound reverberated across the Virginia hills. The three girls, who were helping their mother prepare noon dinner, the family's largest meal of the day, speeded their preparations. One added flour to the gravy, another took the dripping roast from its spit, and the third drained steaming water from the kettle of boiled potatoes, onions, and parsnips. The four eldest sons, all of whom had been working on the farm, promptly dropped their work and came to the house, a two-story clapboard building to which log cabin additions had been made as the family had grown. They cleaned their hands with soft, yellow soap and cold water from the well, then went to the kitchen outbuilding to help carry dishes to the dining room, which was located in the main house. Everyone had his or her chores, and performed them quietly, without fuss.

Elizabeth Houston, a tall, spare woman in calico, wiped her hands on her apron as she moved to her accustomed place at the foot of the table, and surveyed her brood. "Where is the Major?" she demanded.

"The last I saw of Pa," one of her sons said, "he was heading off into the woods to try his luck at a mite of hunting."

The woman sighed. "And Sam?"

Her children exchanged uneasy glances.

"Well?"

"He went with Pa."

She was silent for a moment. "Pass me the meat platter, and I'll carve. Even if those two heard the dinner call, which I think unlikely, they won't be home before sundown."

One of the older sons, a youth in his late teens, hastened to obey.

His sisters nudged each other, whispering, and finally one of them tried to soften Elizabeth's wrath. "They'll bring home a buck, Ma, or maybe a wild boar. You know how it is when Pa and Sam go a-hunting."

"I know how it is. I also know we can't afford a beef roast very often, so more's the pity for what they're missing. Eat hearty. I'm not saving them a single slice."

Her children averted their faces to hide their grins. Ma always made the same threat when Pa and his second youngest son went hunting or fishing, or sometimes rode into the nearby town of Lexington for a parade of Revolutionary War veterans, in which Pa marched. But, no matter how severe her threats, she always saved a choice dish for the errant pair.

"Wasn't Sam working in the wheat fields this morning? That's the chore I assigned him." Elizabeth carved the meat with the ease of long practice.

"He started there, Ma, but he ain't—"

"Isn't."

"—isn't very good at weeding. He gets to thinking of other things."

The woman's mouth formed in a thin, grim line. Sam's daydreaming was her husband's fault. It was he who put strange notions into the boy's head, spoiling him. "The rest of you earned your keep when you were thirteen years old. I expect Sam to do the same!"

"He knows, Ma, and he means to try hard." Inevitably, one or another of the girls came to the favorite's defense. "But he can't resist going a-hunting. He knows more about finding trails in the forest than all the rest of us together. And he has a way of smelling when there's game in the neighborhood. Pa says he's as good at it as any Indian."

"That's what he'll be someday, a savage! Now, eat! I don't like foolish chatter at table!"

Man and boy leaned backward on their elbows, their rifles beside them on the top of the flat boulder overlooking a small lake. Occasionally the father took a nip of whisky from a silver flask, then poured a little into his son's water gourd.

"It was a day like this, maybe a little warmer," Major Samuel Houston said. "The militia regiment was tuckered out after being on the march for six days, so the colonel told me to put the battalions at their ease for the day. Well, I followed orders, of course. Remember that, Sam. A soldier always does what he's told. He never disobeys, he never talks back to his superiors, no matter what he thinks. But I wasn't rightly satisfied with the arrangements."

"Is that when the Redcoats and the Ottawa from Canada attacked?" The boy, already taller than his father at thirteen, knew every word of the familiar tale.

"You let me tell this story, youngster," his father said with mock severity. "I took me three or four friends from the scout company—Willie Young, who lives yonder in Pine Hollow, was one of them—and we went out into the wilderness to satisfy ourselves there was no enemy nearby. Well, blamed if my hunch wasn't right. Not a quarter of an hour after we started out, I knew for sure there were Naturals in the area. How do you suppose I knew?"

"Because of the way the grass was bent." Sam scrambled down the rock to the ground, and illustrated in the ankle-high wild grass. "The stalks were pressed down, like this, all in the same direction. Not that they were bent over double. They'd started to move back toward being upright again. But they were leaning."

"Hell, I've told you about that surprise attack, and the way the Virginia militia fooled the enemy. I've told you so many times I reckon you could tell me." Major Houston yawned, sat upright

12

and stared out across the lake. "Virginia isn't what it was in those days, youngster. Right here, mind you, there was enough game to feed everybody in the area. But nowadays a man has to farm to feed his family, and when you have nine children, that's a heap of feeding. Sam, can you keep your mouth shut?"

"You know I never mention anything you say to me, Pa." The boy sounded reproachful as he climbed back to the top of the boulder.

"Ma knows about this, but nobody else. I'm aiming to move us to a place where it'll be easier to earn a living. President Jefferson does the best he's able, but he can't control costs, and everything we buy becomes dearer year by year."

Home represented security, and Sam was stunned. "We're not leaving Virginia, Pa!"

"Like hell we aren't. I'm selling the farm, and we're going across the mountains to the Tennessee country. Land is cheap there, and so fertile, the way I hear tell, that anything will grow there. It will be grand for all of us, boy."

Sam was torn. "How soon do we go, Pa?"

"You're as bad as I am. You don't have a patient bone in your body, and life will treat you right mean if you don't learn to bide your time. We aren't going tomorrow, nor next week, nor next month. First off, I've got to find me a buyer for the farm who'll pay a fair price. Then I've got to get me a patent to a claim in Tennessee. I have options on two parcels out there now, and I'd go to inspect them myself, if I could afford to leave the farm. But I'll have to take the word of some trader friends who are selling iron pans and suchlike to folks across the mountains. Maybe we'll go next year, maybe the year after that. But it can't be too soon for me, that much I can promise you."

The boy was silent, digesting the news. "There are Indians in the Tennessee country, aren't there, Pa?"

"Too many of them, the way I hear it. A half-dozen nations have their lands staked out in the wilds there, and don't aim to be moved. The Cherokee are the worst."

"I could learn a heap more about the forests from them, couldn't I?"

13

Major Houston remembered his obligations as a father. "You'll finish your education, Sam," he said sternly. "I'll grant that you do right well reading the Bible and the works of Homer, be they in Greek or English. But your mathematicals are a disgrace. You've been studying Euclid for three years now, and you're still hopeless at figures."

"I can't set my mind to studying Euclid, Pa." Sam made a simple statement of fact, without complaint.

The man softened, grinning. "To tell you the truth, youngster, I never cared much for Euclid myself."

"I want to be like you, Pa."

"That isn't good enough." The smile slowly vanished. "I'm nobody."

"You were a field-grade officer in the Virginia militia, Pa! You fought in six battles, and you were made chief inspector of the whole blamed state militia!" The boy spoke fiercely, his fists clenched.

"I'm a man who can barely scrape together a living for his family."

"But, Pa—"

"Hear me out, Sam. You don't take to farming, and I can't say as I blame you. Either a man has the feel for the land, or he doesn't. Your brothers, now, they're real farmers. They get a thrill watching plants grow. All you like is hunting—and riding across open country at a gallop. Ma and I have been talking about you of late." That wasn't strictly true, Samuel thought. Elizabeth had done most of the talking, while he had listened. "We're worried about what will become of you."

"I'll do fine."

"If we have anything to say about it, indeed you will. Ma is anxious to see you finish your education, youngster. You have a natural feel for reading, and we're proud of the way you can use big words. Nights, when you read to us from the Bible or from the *Iliad*, you sound like a preacher."

"I'd never be satisfied as a clergyman, Pa."

Major Houston nodded, sympathizing. He was well aware of a wild streak in the boy, and realized that Sam would not feel at home on a pulpit. "Your ma," he said, "has hopes you'll want to teach school someday."

"Like old Mr. MacPherson? I could beat him right now at wrestling or fist-fighting or no-holds-barred."

The man frowned. "Can you translate Ovid as well as he does? And do you know as much about the poems of Milton?"

Sam had the grace to flush beneath his heavy, permanent tan. "I deserved that, Pa."

"I'm not insisting you become a schoolmaster, of course. You still have years ahead of you before you need to make a decision. You might take a fancy to medicine or the law—"

"Maybe so, but I don't have a feel for either of them."

"You're too young to judge yet. All I'm trying to say to you, Sam, is that you aren't like the rest of the family—"

"I'm exactly like you!"

"No, you're more like your mother. I've done a great deal of reading, but it doesn't come easy to me, and there are times when it takes me hours to puzzle out the meanings of some of the words. Your ma, now, she's a genuine scholar. And since it doesn't look as though you'll ever amount to much as a farmer, she has other ambitions for you."

The boy was unimpressed.

"What matters is that you develop ambitions for yourself. Every now and again I take off for a few hours to hunt, but I don't come out here into the woods every day."

Sam knew he might be whipped for impertinence, but couldn't resist asking, "If you had a free choice, Pa, wouldn't you spend all your days in the forest?"

"Seeing as I have a family to support and rear, I can't even think about such luxuries." Major Houston was irritated, but was too good-natured to harbor anger for more than a few moments. He glanced up at the sun, yawned and stood. "We've lazed away the morning, youngster. Life won't be worth living for either of us if we go home without a week's supply of meat for the larder."

They climbed down to the ground, and Sam happily followed his father as they set out through the deep woods. They were together, and the boy didn't care if they enjoyed good luck in their hunting. It was enough for him that he was spending the day with the person he loved and admired more than all others.

A raw wind from the mountains to the west whipped across the Virginia hills, gathering leaves from oaks and elms, bending the branches of evergreens and causing most people to hurry to the warmth of their hearths. Horsemen rode at a canter down the Lexington Road, and the few pedestrians pulled their broad-brimmed hats lower on their foreheads, buried their faces in their collars and walked rapidly.

Only Sam Houston dawdled, as he always did on his way home from school. His books, lashed together, were slung over a shoulder, and forgotten. Indifferent to the harsh weather, which caused him no discomfort, he was preoccupied with things that others took for granted. From the crest of a hill he could catch a glimpse of a portion of the Shenandoah Valley, resplendent in its many shades of green. Less than one hundred yards from the road was a natural spring that produced hot water, and although others thought the odor of the water disgusting, Sam amused himself by cooking two tiny eggs he had taken from a bird's nest.

There were other delights, too, that fascinated a boy who knew he would be required to begin his evening's studies as soon as he reached home. Honeysuckle that grew in protected crannies was sweet to the taste, and so were the white shafts of tall grass which he plucked with care, leaving the roots undisturbed. He spent a half-hour or more lying on his stomach and peering down into the waters of a swift-running brook, feeling a sense of satisfaction every time he caught a glimpse of a speckled trout. One of these days, after Pa recovered from the ague that had been troubling him, they would come to the brook for a morning's fishing. No one else, he felt certain, even knew there were fish in a stream located so close to the Lexington Road.

The sun was settling into place behind the haze where the mountains and horizon met by the time Sam finally reached the farm. He was somewhat later than usual, but the yard and fields were deserted, so there was little chance that a brother or sister would report him to their parents. With luck, he could sneak around to the side door and reach his room undetected. Then, if anyone came in, he could pretend he had been studying for an hour.

Moving instinctively from one shade tree to the next, he made his way toward the side door, but stopped short when he saw the familiar figure of his mother in the frame. Undoubtedly she had seen him, too, so he would have to submit to a lecture. He squared his shoulders and stepped into the open.

At first he thought his mother was angry, and braced himself for the infrequent but severe storms she reserved for the occasions when he deserved more than a tongue-lashing. But her expression was unique, bewildering, and the boy became increasingly uneasy. "I'm sorry I'm late, Ma," he said. "I have no excuse."

"Come here, Sam." Elizabeth Houston put her hand on her son's shoulder, and her strong, bony fingers dug into his flesh. "I sent some of the others to look for you, but they couldn't find you." Her voice was hoarse but firm. "Your pa isn't with us any more."

Sam looked at her blankly.

"The good Lord took him this noon, while he was asleep."

All at once the boy's world was destroyed, and he thought he would become ill.

"He was a good man, and the Lord rewarded him. He suffered no pain at the end. There was a smile on his face, as natural a smile as ever you've seen."

Sam started to break free of her grasp. He could think only that he wanted to go to his father.

"No, Sam!" Elizabeth said sharply. "He isn't here."

"Where is he, where is he, Ma?"

"John and David took his body into Lexington to be measured for a box lined with velvet cloth. It isn't fitting that a gentleman who held high office in the Virginia militia be buried in a plain one."

The boy found his voice. "It isn't true, Ma! He's alive!"

The hand on his shoulder continued to hold him. "I've told you the truth."

Horror widened his eyes.

"I know how much you cared for him, and now you must prove you're worthy of him. All of us must bow to death, so accept his passing as he'd want you to, like a man."

He had become too numb to feel anything other than shock. "I should have been here with him."

"You were at school, where you belonged. Duty comes first. Besides, he left us the same way he lived with us, quietly, making no bother."

Sam saw that his mother was dry-eyed, and knew he could not subject her to additional torment by breaking down in her presence.

"When you're able, take one of the horses and ride to the parsonage. We'll be wanting your uncle to deliver the funeral oration—and bury him."

Elizabeth understood her son better than he knew himself. "When you're able," she repeated. "You'll want to think of a way to tell your uncle the news gentle-like."

She released him, pushing him into the house.

Sam stumbled, recovered and made his way blindly toward his own room. Several of his brothers and sisters were in the seldom-used parlor, reading the family Bible together, and the boy thought how strange they looked, wearing their Sunday clothes in midweek. Reaching his own room, he closed the door behind him. Then, very carefully, he reached into the pocket of his linsey-woolsey shirt for the bird's eggs he had hard-boiled in the bubbling spring as a special treat for his father. He placed them on the table of unpainted pine that served as his desk, and looked at them with unseeing eyes.

Gradually the eggs came into focus, and their speckled coloring was so pretty that Sam was outraged. He had no use for the eggs now, and reached out with a fist to smash them. But he could not complete the act, and his hand fell wearily to his side.

Suddenly hot tears scalded his cheeks, and he buried his face in his hands. Nothing would be the same again, ever; no joys would be complete, no triumphs worth winning. He had been cheated, but could appeal to no higher authority for redress. In his anguish he hated God for taking his father from him, then hated himself for his weakness.

Night had fallen by the time he rose and went out to the well for some cold water to wash his swollen face. Never again, he swore, would he weep, and many years would pass before he broke that promise.

More than a decade had passed since Tennessee had been admitted to the Union as the sixteenth state, but she was still a frontier land of virgin forests and rolling hills, swift-flowing rivers and forbidding mountains. Her inhabitants were pioneers, men who cleared their land and built their homes with their own hands, who relied on their rifles to protect them from the Cherokee and the Choctaw, and who banded together with their neighbors to mete out justice when the circuit-riding judges were tardy in appearing at tiny log-cabin courthouses.

The immigrants crossed the mountains and made their way through the deep, silent forests of ash and elm and hickory on trails cut by their predecessors, and the few who had believed they were moving into a civilized land quickly discovered their error. The men and older boys rode in the van, on the flanks and at the rear of the caravans, protecting their families from raids by savages and the bandit outlaws who preyed on the unwary. The women, their daughters and the smaller children rode in carts piled high with their household goods, treasured heirlooms and frying pans, bedsteads and medicines, occasional bolts of cloth to make new clothes and the tools the men would need to carve new homes out of the wilderness.

Sam was too young to ride with the men, but was given a place in the vanguard, nevertheless, when his elders learned that he was the best shot in the company with either rifle or pistol. He accepted the post with a dignity beyond his years, and only occasionally strutted for the benefit of his sisters and the other girls in the party.

The Cumberland Mountain country, the boy discovered, was similar to the Virginia he had left behind, but was wilder, more rugged. In the forests there were stands of yellow poplar and gum, hemlock and chestnut that stretched for miles, and even in the state's few communities the forest often extended to the town line.

Knoxville, the capital, was a collection of cabins, and not even the governor's so-called mansion, the legislature's assembly hall or the courthouse where the justices of the Tennessee Supreme Court sat were made of clapboard. Leaving Knoxville, the Houstons and their traveling companions headed southwest toward a still smaller settlement, Maryville, and it was on this wilderness road that Sam saw his first Cherokee.

He was riding in the vanguard with two of his brothers and several other men when, seemingly out of nowhere, a party of warriors in buckskin appeared directly ahead on the trail. The boy immediately raised his rifle to his shoulder, but one of the men knocked it aside with such force that Sam lost his balance and almost toppled to the ground.

"In these here parts," the hired guide who was conducting the immigrants said roughly, "you never fire at Naturals until you find out if they're in a mean streak." He rode forward, his own rifle laid across the pommel, one hand raised in greeting.

The Indians returned the salutation, and as the guide spoke to them in a guttural language, Sam watched in fascination. The savages were tall, husky men who wore necklaces of colored stones over their buckskin shirts. One, apparently the leader, had a headdress with two eagle feathers emerging from it, and was the only one of the Cherokee who carried a modern rifle. The others were armed with old-fashioned muskets, and carried powder horns slung from their belts.

All but one of the Cherokee ignored the immigrants, and Sam was startled when it occurred to him that the Indian studying him was a boy of approximately his own age, at most a year or two older. He grinned at the savage, then winked, but the young brave returned his gaze with unblinking solemnity.

"There won't be no troubles," the guide shouted over his shoulder. "These here are the advance scouts for a hunting party. They don't want a fight any more'n we do!"

On sudden impulse Sam spurred forward.

The Cherokee immediately raised their firearms, and he found himself facing the muzzles of a half-dozen cocked weapons. Ignoring the threat, as well as the consternation of his own comrades, he reached into his boot-top for his paring knife, and presented it with a flourish to the young Cherokee.

"Maybe," he said, "you can use this."

To his astonishment the Indian boy replied in English. "Lu-li has much use for knife. But Lu-li cannot accept a gift unless he makes a gift." Reaching inside his shirt, the young Cherokee produced a skinning knife with a carved bone handle, which he handed to the youth on horseback.

The ice was broken, and both boys laughed.

The guide stared at them, muttering, "Damn my soul."

"How come you speak English?" Sam asked.

"For two years Lu-li went to the school of the settlers," the young Cherokee replied. "But he likes it better in the forest, with his own people."

"I can't say as how I blame you." Sam sounded envious, but recovered, and held out his hand. "Me, I'm Sam Houston. If you live near Maryville, I reckon we'll meet again."

"Lu-li will watch for his friend." The Indian boy followed his elders into the forest.

The guide turned to the other members of the immigrants' vanguard, who were moving forward. "I been out in these parts twenty years, and I fought in every one o' John Sevier's campaigns against those buzzards. Twice I near got scalped, and I collected me a few scalps o' my own. This here is the first time I ever seen one o' us shake hands with one o' them, or give one of 'em a free gift for no damn reason at all!"

The Houstons moved up on either side of their young brother. "What got into you, Sam?"

"I liked him," the boy said defiantly. "What's so wrong with that? The Bible tells us to love our neighbors, doesn't it?"

The guide heard him and shook his head. "Loving Cherokee is going a mite too far!"

Sam said nothing, but felt great pleasure as he examined the skinning knife. Strange, stylized figures had been carved on the

21

handle, and he wouldn't be satisfied until he knew what they meant.

"The fool boy could have brought on a shooting scrape," one of the men said.

The danger had been slight, Sam thought, saying nothing. He had learned his first great lesson about Indians, and vowed he would remember it. They were like other people: they responded in kind to gestures of friendship, and, he supposed, became hostile when they felt they were threatened.

The men were glowering at him, but he paid no attention to them. If Pa were here, he would approve. He had fought against Indians in the Revolution, to be sure, but he had also accepted the aid of savages in two battles. If Pa had lived, he would have been the first to seek ways to end the wilderness warfare between the settlers and the Cherokee.

Elizabeth Houston paid twenty-five cents an acre for a tract of four hundred and nineteen acres in Baker's Creek Valley, where her late husband had taken an option on a parcel. On one side soared the peaks of the Great Smoky Mountains, and on the other the forest stretched out as far as anyone could see. Her sons built a house of logs for the family on a plateau, a shelf of land that faced the mountains. Less than fifty feet from the house was a spring of cold, pure mountain water, and the widow said the Almighty had directed the family to its new home.

The soil was rich, and the boys went to work in earnest, uprooting trees so they could finish their planting of corn, wheat, oats and vegetables before the hot summer weather came. Only Sam demurred. "Why bother to dig out trees?" he asked. "There's enough game in these forests to give us fresh meat every day of our lives."

"You'll dig up trees with your brothers," Elizabeth told him. "We aim to live on a farm, not in the forest."

Sam was a dutiful son and did his best to obey, but her order made no sense to him. Pa would have felt as he did, that it was senseless to engage in back-breaking work when there was food for the taking in the wilderness. The Cherokee, who ate wild grain when they could and planted corn only when they needed it, had the right idea.

Cutting down trees and uprooting stumps was cruel work, and it was far more pleasant, in the heat of the day, for a boy to seek the shelter of the ash tree that shaded the spring, and to sit there in seclusion, reading of the adventures of Achilles and Menelaus, Hector and Priam. It was interesting, too, to open the cartons of Pa's books that the family had carried all the way from Virginia, and to become absorbed in the stirring pamphlets that Tom Paine had written before and during the Revolution. Then the boy discovered the works of John Locke, and put aside his other reading.

He had found the mainspring of American democracy, and as he lounged beside the spring, enthralled, he began to understand the dream of the men who had founded the United States of America. He was fortunate to have been born in such a land.

He was far less fortunate, however, when his brothers became annoyed with his failure to do his share of the work. They complained to their mother, and Elizabeth retired behind the closed door of her bedchamber to think about the problem. She said nothing the following day before going into Maryville to buy some flour, thread and other necessities, but on her return, while one of the boys took the horses and carriage to the newly built barn, she went straight to the spring.

Sam sat up guiltily, but it was too late for him to hide his book.

His mother took it from him. "Locke's *Two Treatises on Government,*" she said. "Very commendable. I've read no Locke in many years." There was a trace of amusement in Elizabeth's stern manner. "So I don't rightly recall whether he mentions that even the most sovereign of people must earn a living for themselves unless they happen to be very wealthy. Laziness is no excuse for shirking, and the slothful man often starves to death."

Sam knew it would be wrong to evade issues that needed to be settled. "I'm not lazy, Ma, but I hate farm work."

"You've made that very clear."

"There are other things I can do when I'm grown."

"You stand six feet already, and you're still sprouting. This very minute you're taller and huskier than most men, and I won't allow you to spend your time in idleness."

"I've started to develop some ideas, Ma. I'm thinking of becoming a land surveyor, maybe. Or a soldier, like Pa. Or—"

"It's all settled," Elizabeth said grimly. "I found work for you in Maryville today. You're going to be an apprentice in the general store, and they'll give you your board, keep, and wages of one dollar in silver a month."

A life as a storekeeper wasn't appealing, but Sam was in no position to protest. At least he'd see a great many people every day, which he would enjoy. And he owed it to his mother to do his best, even though the work offered him no challenge.

There was nothing duller than weighing tea, coffee, or sugar on Mr. Whitman's scales, measuring cloth by the yard or refusing the demands of haggling housewives who insisted that the prices of ironware be lowered. Never had Sam known such misery. He awakened at dawn to light the cooking fire in the kitchen hearth behind the Whitman store and residence, scrubbed the pine counters of the store with a mixture of yellow soap and hemlock sap, and, after a hasty breakfast, went on duty to wait on customers. Each day was the same: there was an endless procession of frontier dwellers and their wives in and out of the store, all of them seeking bargains, all of them anxious to waste a half-hour in gossip about their neighbors. Not until nightfall, when the store closed, did Sam eat his second meal of the day, and by that time he was so hungry he usually felt ill. After the meal he cleaned and swept the store, tidied the stock and helped Mr. Whitman take inventory.

Only then, after a fourteen or fifteen-hour day, was the boy free to read the philosophy of Locke or the romantic exploits of Homer's heroes. Often, lying on his pallet and holding his book close to the feeble glow of a sputtering candle, he was so tired he fell asleep before he could read a word. Even his dreams of glory and adventure had become garbled, and often he could remember no more than snatches of them. In brief, life had become intolerable.

Gradually an audacious plan formed in his mind, and it seemed so logical and reasonable that he made methodical plans to carry it out. First, on a Sunday visit to his family, he managed to sneak his rifle, the precious weapon his father had left him, out of the house. It was far easier to take the skinning knife he had obtained from the young Indian. Returning to Maryville, he left portions of his meals uneaten, in spite of his ravenous hunger, and gradually built up a small store of such staples as jerked beef and venison, salt fish and parched corn.

At last all was in readiness, and he was prepared to run away. Since it was a serious matter for an apprentice to vanish from the home and workshop of his master, Sam had to proceed with great caution. He was certain a search would be made for him, so it was essential that he gain as much of a head start as possible. His next Sunday holiday would be best for the purpose, he decided, since Mr. Whitman would think he was visiting his family, and the Houstons would believe him in Maryville.

The wait of almost a month was interminable, but at last the weekend arrived. Carefully explaining to his employer that he intended to go home before dawn on Sunday morning, Sam actually left on Saturday night, creeping out of the shed behind the store. The night was dark, the rutted mud roads of Maryville were deserted, and few lamps or candles were burning in the homes of the little town's residents. Everything seemed to favor the boy's bold enterprise.

He made his way as rapidly as he could to the forest beyond the town, then slowed his pace somewhat as he headed due west. At least twenty-four hours would pass before anyone knew he was missing, so he would not be forced to hurry, but could not afford to dawdle, either. Few Tennessee settlers ventured into the wilderness after dark, but Sam did not feel particularly concerned. Any animals he might encounter, including bobcats, would be more afraid of him than he was of them, and would not attack him unless cornered. As for any Indians he might encounter, he had no fear of them, either. They had no reason to harm him, any more than he wanted to hurt them, and felt positive they would not molest him.

Wishing he knew how to cover his tracks, he spent the better part of the night walking. A little before dawn he came to a small stream, and sat down to his first meal of the food he had saved. Then, aware that it would be unwise to become too careless, he made a thorough search for a secure resting place, and at last found a bramble-protected hollow behind a huge boulder. There he slept for several hours, and became panicky, after awakening, when he saw that the sun was high overhead.

He was tempted to resume his journey immediately, but remembered his father had told him that men became ill when they ate on the march. So he forced himself to remain seated while he quickly consumed a light breakfast of parched corn and pickled trout, and then started to make up for lost time. The farther west he traveled, the deeper and more impenetrable the forest seemed to become, but the boy was enthralled. Trees fifty to sixty feet in height were commonplace, and he had never seen such magnificent stands of poplar and oak. Hickory and pine, spruce and birch and hemlock were everywhere, too, and he wished he had time to roast the chestnuts he saw growing in abundance.

By afternoon he began to feel apprehensive, wondering if either Mr. Whitman or his family had as yet realized he had run away. But the forest soothed him, and in some inexplicable way he felt completely at home in it. He was reminded of his long walks with his father in the far more civilized woods of Virginia, and finally realized he loved the wilderness because it reminded him of the happiest period of his life.

In midafternoon he came to a mighty river, a broad, swift-flowing stream of deep, clear blue that churned over rocks, and knew he had come to the Tennessee. He was drawing near to his destination, but an obstacle he had not anticipated now confronted him. In order to reach his goal he had to cross the river, which was too wide and powerful to swim, and he had no boat. Under the circumstances, he decided, he would have to make one.

He found a fallen tree about a foot in diameter at the base, and after hacking off the branches with the skinning knife, he managed, with great difficulty, to haul it down to the river's edge. Fastening his pack more tightly to his back and strapping his rifle across his shoulder blades so it would not become wet, he pushed the log into the water, intending to jump onto it and straddle it.

Unfortunately, it promptly sank. Chagrined, the boy realized belatedly that his own stupidity was responsible. The tree had soaked up ground water, which he should have realized immediately when he had found it so heavy. He was tired, but knew he had to persevere, and cut down several saplings, which he lashed together with vines. The raft was small but fairly sturdy, and he pushed off on it, hoping for the best.

The next thirty minutes were the most terrifying Sam had ever spent. Although he had been familiar with forests all of his life, he knew virtually nothing about boats, as he became increasingly aware with each passing moment. The raft shot downstream, unguided, and when, fighting his panic, he unstrapped his rifle and tried to use the butt as a paddle, he almost fell overboard.

Then the little craft became wedged in some rocks, and almost came apart in the foaming, turbulent water. Freeing himself with great difficulty, and becoming drenched in the process, Sam resumed his wild ride, certain that each moment was his last. The raft swept around a great bend, still out of control, and shot toward the western bank. For an instant the boy's hopes flared, but a submerged rock cut through the sodden vines, the raft disintegrated and Sam was dumped into the cold waters of the Tennessee.

The shore was only thirty yards away, and he swam for his life, gripping his rifle in his right hand. Encumbered by it and by the pack strapped to his back, his progress was tantalizingly slow, but at last he reached the shallows and was able to stand. Exhausted and gasping for breath, he continued to fight the current as he waded ashore, his mud and water-filled boots making it a torture to lift one foot, then the other.

At last Sam reached the sanctuary of dry land, and threw himself headlong onto the grassy bank. For a long time he lay there, his mind dazed and his body aching, realizing he had narrowly escaped death and that it would be foolhardy to attempt another crossing of the river until he learned to navigate it in a safer, more substantial boat.

Suddenly he became aware of slight sounds directly above him, and rolling onto his side, saw three tall Indian warriors in loincloths. Two held skinning knives close to him, and the third was brandishing a pistol. Too weak to assure them he was a friend, Sam instinctively reached for his rifle.

One of the braves knocked it from his grasp, and he knew he had been foolish. Not only had his gesture been a sign of hostile intentions, but the weapon was wet and, therefore, useless.

The warriors spoke to each other rapidly in their guttural tongue, and the helpless Sam found his ankles and wrists being fastened to a pole. Trussed and unable to defend himself, he was subjected to the final indignity of being hoisted into the air and carried off through the wilderness like the carcass of an animal. Unable to rectify the damage, he finally found his voice and called out hoarsely, but the Indians paid no attention to him. Perhaps the settlers had been right, after all, when they had insisted that the savages were dangerous, but he was learning the ultimate lesson too late, and fully expected to pay for his error with his life.

The Cherokee village was hidden in the remote forest, guarded day and night by sentries who maintained a silent, incessant patrol. Only a short distance from the community there was no indication that such a place existed, but, after emerging into a clearing, it was astonishing to find more than two thousand people living, working, and playing. The village was located on the shores of a small, stream-fed lake, which it surrounded.

On one side were the longhouses of the young warriors, and opposite them, those of the unmarried maidens. These buildings were of simple but sturdy design, and had been constructed by stretching animal skins taut between trimmed saplings that served as poles. The private dwellings of the married warriors and their families were even more substantial, and were made of saplings and somewhat larger trees lashed together in conical shape, with animal skins used as door flaps. Some of the larger huts obviously belonged to the leaders of the nation and the elders, who were treated with great respect by the others.

Cooking was done in stone-lined pits located in the open; there were several near each of the longhouses, and every private dwelling boasted its own. Women were at work in cornfields and vegetable patches located beyond the buildings, but few others were busy. Several elderly squaws were smoking haunches of venison and bear over low hickory fires, and a few young girls whose deerskin dresses were ornamented with brilliantly dyed porcupine quills were carrying buckets of water from the brook that ran into the lake.

Several naked boys were swimming and cavorting in the water, but their shouts and laughter did not disturb a grizzled elder, wrapped in a blanket, who was dozing in the sun as he sat propped against the base of a small tree near the water's edge. Nearby a group of muscular braves threw axes at targets in an attempt to improve their aim, and they, too, paid no attention to the noise made by the children.

The whole town seemed to come alive when Sam, after twenty-four hours of captivity in a hut, was led into the open. His clothes had been taken from him the previous day, his hands were bound behind his back and another leather thong tied around his neck served as a leash. He expected to be put to death in a public ceremony, and perhaps tortured first, but his shame was so great that he didn't care what became of him.

Unable to prevent his captors from parading him through the town, he tried in vain to ignore the warriors and squaws who stared at him. Barking dogs surrounded him, snapping at his heels and legs, and he suffered his worst humiliation when he was marched past the longhouse of the unmarried girls, who gathered in front of the building, giggling.

To his surprise, however, no one beat at him with sticks or threw rocks at him, the treatment allegedly accorded captives. So he surmised that a special, perhaps far worse fate was in store for him. His guards, after leading him around the lake, escorted

29

him to one of the larger houses, and the entrance was so low that he had to stoop as he squeezed past the flap.

Inside, sitting cross-legged on a mat of pine boughs near an open window, was a mature, solidly built warrior. Sam's first impression was that the warrior was ferocious; there were streaks of green and yellow paint on his high cheekbones, and at the crown of his stiff scalplock he wore five white eagle feathers. His eyes were unexpectedly gentle when he glanced at the boy, however, and a gleam of humor appeared in them as he said something to the braves who stood close to their captive.

One of the warriors reluctantly drew his knife and cut Sam's bonds.

The older man spoke again, and the guards withdrew, obviously against their better judgment.

"Oo-loo-te-ka has told them," the man said in accented but fluent English, "that the young warrior who brings books through the forest means no harm to the sachem of the Cherokee."

In the far corner of the hut Sam saw his belongings heaped in neat piles. His muddy clothes had been washed, and, as nearly as he could judge, only his boots had been ruined. His rifle and knife were there, as was his pouch of bullets, although his gunpowder, rendered useless when he had been drenched in the river, had vanished. His precious books, to which the Indian had referred, apparently had been drying in the sun, although several were still damp. Nevertheless, the care that had been taken to preserve his property was encouraging, and Sam dared to hope, for the first time, that he might be allowed to survive.

"You are Houston, as it is written in these books?"

Sam found his voice. "Yes, sir," he said.

"Some of the elders and warriors of the Cherokee think the men-who-have-crossed-the-mountains sent Houston to spy on our people. But Oo-loo-te-ka, sachem of the Cherokee, does not think this. Houston will tell Oo-loo-te-ka why he has come to this land."

Under the circumstances, Sam's romantic notion seemed absurd, but he forced himself to reply honestly. "I hate storekeeping as much as working on the farm with my brothers. I came here to live with the Cherokee—if you'll have me."

The Indian's roar of laughter filled the hut. "It is so! It is as Oo-loo-te-ka thought." Reaching behind him, he brought forth a pair of buckskin trousers, which he handed to the boy. "The clothes of Houston are weak after their bath in the river-of-white-water."

Never had Sam felt so grateful, and stammered his thanks as he donned the trousers.

"Does Houston know the games of young braves?"

"I reckon nobody can beat me at wrestling or in a free-for-all!"

"The young brave must prove his strength and skill before he boasts," the chief of the Cherokee said in quiet reproval.

The boy knew he deserved the reprimand, and felt abashed.

"Does Houston use the firestick?"

"Yes, sir," Sam muttered.

Oo-loo-te-ka approved of his reticence. "In three suns," he said, "the young will show their skills. Houston will take his place with the others. If he is strong and clever, he will become the son of Oo-loo-te-ka. Then Oo-loo-te-ka will teach him the ways of the Cherokee."

Sam was dazed by his sudden good fortune. The offer, made so soon after he had expected torture and death, exceeded the desperate dreams that had sustained him during the long, dreary weeks of his apprenticeship in Maryville.

"It is the wish of Oo-loo-te-ka that Houston teach his other sons to read the words of the men-who-have-crossed-the-mountains."

"I've never been a schoolmaster, but I'll sure try," the boy said, and grinned. He realized he was being given a rare opportunity, that by teaching Cherokee and settler to speak one another's language, much of the tension that was ever-present on the frontier would be reduced.

"Houston will sleep in the lodge of the young braves. But he will eat at the fire of Oo-loo-te-ka and his sons. The sachem is not too old to learn more of the tongue of the strangers."

The chief of the Cherokee appeared to be wise as well as ambitious for his sons, Sam thought. He himself, of course, would

31

be learning the language of the Indians while he was teaching the sachem and his sons English, and the prospect delighted him. Pa, if he knew, would be very pleased.

Oo-loo-te-ka fell silent, and was lost in thought.

Sam was afraid to interrupt him.

Finally the man raised his head. "Houston has brothers in the land of the men-who-have-crossed-the-mountains, the land that once was the hunting grounds of the Cherokee."

Apparently the sachem was thinking of possible complications, and Sam could only nod, afraid to admit he had five healthy, stalwart brothers.

"They will come to the land of the Cherokee. They will bring many other men with firesticks."

"Nobody cares enough about me to start a war," Sam protested.

Oo-loo-te-ka ignored the interruption. "When the brothers of Houston come, Houston will go alone through the forest to meet them. If he wishes to leave the Cherokee, he will go. If he wishes to stay with his new people, he will tell this to his brothers-from-across-the-mountains. Then they will go back to their own lodges, and will not fight the Cherokee."

Sam realized he was being asked to agree to the terms. "I'll do just as you say," he promised, "and you can bet your last dollar that I'll stay right here!"

Sam moved swiftly through the forest, his moccasins making no sound on the carpet of grass and underbrush. His tan was deeper, his dark brown hair was sun-streaked and, still taller than he had been when he had joined the Cherokee, his lean frame had filled out. He trotted with the self-confidence of one completely at home in the wilderness, and even though he was intent on reaching his destination, he was aware of every faint sound that indicated a small animal or bird was nearby. Before he had made his home with the Indians he had believed that the forest was silent, but he knew better now, as he did about so many things. When one had been taught how to listen, the wilderness was alive, its rhythms ever-changing. And it amused him that he left no tracks in the grass, having learned to step lightly on the balls of his feet, which he could do for long hours at a stretch without tiring.

After an hour's jog he heard the low murmur of voices in the distance, and slowed to a walk before coming to a clearing. Several tents had been erected, he saw, and seven or eight settlers armed with rifles were standing guard. Glad he had taken the advice of Oo-loo-te-ka and left his own firearms in the town of the Cherokee, he stepped into the open.

Someone shouted a warning, and the rifles were leveled at the boy.

Sam stood still, his arms at his sides.

One of his brothers was the first to recognize him, but he waited for an invitation before coming forward.

Then someone emerged from a tent, and Sam was startled to see his mother. It had not occurred to him that she might make the long, difficult journey to the land of the Cherokee west of the Tennessee River.

She started toward him, but one of the men tried to halt her. "Wait, Mrs. Houston! The woods may be filled with Naturals."

Elizabeth Houston ignored the warning and continued her slow, dignified walk toward the boy.

"I'm alone," Sam called, "and I give you my word that nobody is going to harm any of you, least of all my mother." The suspicions of the settlers were too ridiculous to be treated seriously.

The woman halted to look up at the boy who now towered above her. "You've grown again," she said. "And you look healthy."

He stooped to kiss her, and she allowed herself to be embraced. "I've missed you, Ma." He was surprised by the huskiness of his own voice. "Did you get the letter I sent to you so you wouldn't worry about me?"

"It was under the door sill one morning, so we guessed that one of your Indian friends delivered it."

He nodded, wanting to tell her that Oo-loo-te-ka had dispatched a special courier with the message, but realizing he would first have to identify the sachem. There was so much about his new life that his mother did not know.

"I had to see you for myself, to make sure you aren't being held a prisoner."

"I've never been this free, Ma," the boy said truthfully. "And although I thought that maybe somebody would come looking for me, I sure didn't expect to see you. Was your journey wearing?"

"I didn't mind it, since I made it for a purpose." Elizabeth scrutinized her son carefully. "Do you take baths, Sam?"

Her maternal concern broke his tension, and he grinned. "I swim every day, Ma, and I scrub with pine needles until I'm raw."

The members of Elizabeth's escort, standing at a distance, were surprised by the boy's laughter. They had conceived of their errand as grim, and were annoyed by his flippancy.

But his mother seemed to understand, and her eyes softened. "Why did you run away?"

"I—I'm not sure. The more I think about it, the less I understand my reasons. All I know is that I had to do it."

"You're happy with the Naturals?"

"More than I've ever been—since Pa died. Except for not seeing you."

Again she inspected him. "They've turned you into a savage."

"No, they're civilized, but not in our way. Besides, I read all the time. I can make my own translation of the *Iliad* from Greek into English now."

She tried to hide her reaction, but it was obvious that she was impressed.

"I've been teaching my Cherokee brothers English, and I do it by pretending I'm making speeches. After I've spent another six months with them, I'll be an orator, Ma."

"What good will oratory do you in making a living, boy?"

"I've been thinking about that, too. Until I came to the land of the Cherokee, all I knew was what I didn't want. Now I'm beginning to get all kinds of ideas, Ma. Maybe I'll be a schoolmaster some day, like you wanted me to be. I'm not sure yet, but I'm able to sort out things in my own mind."

She realized he was becoming a man, and her eyes indicated her reluctant approval.

34

"I don't aim to spend the rest of my days with the Cherokee, if that's what you fear. But only good can come of my knowing them, and being accepted by them. Tennessee is growing fast, and it won't be long before settlers start pushing across the big river. Then there'll be a war for certain, unless somebody can step in as a kind of judge."

"You fancy yourself, youngster."

"Not right off, Ma. But some day, maybe."

"When do you plan to come home?" Elizabeth demanded.

"I don't rightly know, but I'd like to visit you, if you'll let me."

"My door has never been closed to you, nor will it be."

The boy blinked rapidly, averting his face until he regained his self-control.

"Sam, I knew you'd joined the Naturals of your own free will, just as you said in your letter to me. There are some who think you'll be a chief of the Cherokee in time to come, but most believe I ought to send you to a madhouse. One or two in Maryville are convinced you'll be governor of the state, but they're none too sane themselves. Whatever may be, I've got to let you live your own life, even though I've never known anyone to take on so peculiar."

The boy tried to express his gratitude, but his mother silenced him.

"I came here for just one purpose, to take you home with me, no matter how hard you fought me."

"No, Ma!"

"But that would do no good. You'd probably run away again."

He could not deny it.

"I've got to keep reminding myself that you're not like the rest of the family. You like to think you take after your father, but you don't, Sam. He was a dreamer, too, but you're determined to make your dreams real. So be it. Do you still believe in the Almighty?"

"Of course, Ma!"

"You haven't bowed down before heathen idols." She made a flat statement, in relief, rather than ask a question. "Then you'll

35

be able to accept the Lord's justice meekly. You've grown too big for me to whip you, Sam, but the Almighty will chastise you for your transgressions. Live as you please, but be prepared to pay the penalties, and while you're about it, pray for His mercy!"

TWO

1813–18

A bronzed physical giant of eighteen returned to the eastern Tennessee settlements after spending three years with the Cherokee. Often silent and wooden-faced, frequently elusive in his manner and evasive in answering questions about his life in the wilderness, Sam Houston apparently had adopted many of the Indian's characteristics.

"He's changed," his mother said, "but I don't rightly know whether it's for better or worse."

She soon discovered he had new energies and an inner drive that had been lacking when he had vanished into the forests. Owning nothing but the buckskins on his back, he borrowed money for a wardrobe and other necessities, and taught school for several months in order to pay off his debts, which he did, promptly and to the penny. Then, to the astonishment of his mother and other relatives, he returned to school himself, as a student. But this new role was short-lived.

The United States again had gone to war against the nation from whom she had won her independence, Great Britain. In the cities and towns of the seaboard states men flocked to the colors to ward off a new invasion of Redcoats. And in the frontier lands west of the mountains, the Indian nations gladly accepted English gold and muskets, rum and ammunition, and went on the warpath against the settlers who were encroaching on their hunting grounds. The fierce Miami of the Ohio Valley prepared for a major conflict, and in the vast Alabama Territory, south of Tennessee, the disciplined, proud Creek nation prepared for its greatest conflict. Only the Cherokee were still quiet, and no one except a confident Sam Houston dared to predict that they would not join the other tribes.

The Regular Army and the state militias entered a lively competition for the services of volunteers, and the need was so great that a recruiting party of Regulars, including speechmaking sergeants, a fife and drum corps and a drill team, penetrated the interior of Tennessee as far as Maryville.

Sam, en route home after school, listened to the fiery, patriotic addresses of the recruiting sergeants, and immediately enlisted, to the dismay of his brothers and their friends, all of whom had become men of substance in the district.

"You're really mad," they told him. "An educated gentleman shouldn't go into service unless he holds a commission."

Sam delivered his first oration. "You're fools to look down on the common ranks," he said. "Who are you to hold yourselves so high that you despise the ordinary soldier? My father, who was a military genius of his day, began his career as a private, and rose through the ranks to the high post of major. If I'm able, I shall emulate him.

"But if I should be less fortunate and display too little talent, I shall nonetheless serve with dignity. I would much sooner honor the ranks than disgrace an appointment as an officer. I do not qualify for a commission, but I shall, I promise you. You don't know me now, but in time to come you shall hear of me!"

Leaving them with nothing to say in reply, he went home to break the news to his mother.

Elizabeth, sitting in a rocking chair near her parlor hearth, heard him in silence. Then she rose, stiffly, and disappeared into her bedchamber for a moment. "Here, boy," she said, "is your father's favorite rifle. Take it, and never disgrace it."

Sam accepted the familiar weapon and fondled it.

"Remember," Elizabeth said sternly, "that I would rather see all of my sons fill one honorable grave than that one of them should turn his back to save his life."

She was magnificent, Sam thought, and was proud to be her son.

"Remember, too," she continued, "that while my door is always open to brave men, it is shut for all time to cowards."

"I won't forget, Ma."

Elizabeth opened the leather purse she carried on her belt, and searched in it. "I know how highly you think of your Pa, and I want you to have something he gave me many years ago, long before you were born. I've always intended to give it to you, Sam, but I made up my mind that you shouldn't have it until you earned it. You'll earn it now." She held out her hand, a ring of plain gold on the palm.

Sam took it from her, and saw something engraved on the inside of the band. He examined the inscription more closely, and saw the single word, *Honor*.

His mother slipped the ring onto the little finger of his left hand.

He squared his shoulders. "I'll remember what's written there, Ma. And this ring won't come off my hand as long as I live."

The United States 7th Infantry trained at a camp outside Knoxville, and there, in the ankle-deep mud, Sam Houston learned the rudiments of close-order drill and the manual of arms. He became so adept that he was soon promoted to corporal, then to sergeant. His skill, combined with his zeal and sense of discipline, called him to the attention of his regimental and battalion commanders. When they discovered that, in addition to his other assets, he was literate, he was made an ensign, the lowest rank of commissioned officer. He had taken the first major step toward the fulfillment of his boast to his brothers and their friends that they would hear of him.

While Sam was learning his profession as a soldier and advancing in rank, catastrophe threatened the United States in the Alabama Territory. Thousands of Creek warriors went into the field, equipped with British arms, and instituted a reign of terror, burning and looting villages, and murdering settlers. A force commanded by Major General Andrew Jackson of Nashville was sent to contain and destroy the Indians, but it enjoyed little success.

Jackson's corps was made up, in the main, of Tennessee militiamen who had enlisted for short periods. Plagued by a lack of food, ammunition, and other supplies, the discouraged troops had no will to fight, and many departed for their homes. But Jackson refused to admit that any difficulties were insurmountable, and attacked the enemy repeatedly.

The Creek withdrew slowly, and their main body of approximately two thousand men took up their defenses in a strong log fort located on a peninsula known as the Horseshoe Bend of the Tallapoosa River. There, in a position they believed impregnable, they prepared for a battle to the death.

Jackson's militia infantry units were undependable, and as he could rely only on the cavalry commanded by his friend, Brigadier General John Coffee, he asked the Regular Army for reinforcements. The 39th Infantry Regiment was assigned to him, and, since it was undermanned, officers and men were taken from other units to bring it up to full strength. Among those transferred was Ensign Sam Houston.

The regimental commander and a small advance detail having already left to join the corps in the field, the bulk of the unit left Tennessee in mid-January 1814 under the command of Lieutenant Colonel Thomas Hart Benton, a square-jawed soldier-lawyer who was known as the Army's strictest disciplinarian. Ensign Houston won his esteem on the march by insisting that all of Benton's orders be obeyed instantly and without question.

On the afternoon of February 3, the regiment reached the bivouac of the corps and set up its tents in a clearing adjacent to that of an unruly battalion of Tennessee militia. A few hours later, as the 39th was preparing its supper from its own meager store of supplies, Sam caught his first glimpse of General Jackson.

Had the corps commander not been wearing the epaulets of a major general on the shoulders of his shabby uniform, Sam would have mistaken him for a living scarecrow. Ill for many weeks,

Jackson hobbled painfully as he walked from unit to unit, his skin a sickly white, his red-brown hair shaggy. Neither his bearing nor his shuffling gait were military, and his behavior did not remotely resemble that of a senior officer as he strolled past the campfires of the militiamen and called various soldiers by their Christian names. Sam noted, however, that the spirits of the militia troops improved immeasurably by the time the corps commander had completed his leisurely tour.

Suddenly General Jackson turned in the direction of the 39th's camp, and, as Colonel Benton hastened to join him, Sam called his platoon to attention. He had only a short time to make his men presentable, and walked swiftly down the line, trying to utilize every minute. "You, Bailey," he said, "tighten your crosswebbing. Hardy, there's a smudge of dirt on your bayonet. Allison, straighten the plume on your helmet."

An indulgent chuckle sounded behind him. "This is right nice. I haven't seen a dress parade in a year."

Sam turned, his face growing hot as he saluted stiffly.

"General," Colonel Benton said, "permit me to present Ensign Houston, acting commander of the 3rd Platoon, Company B."

"Do your men always use spit-and-polish in the field, Houston?" Jackson asked amiably.

"Yes, sir. Regulations require it."

The commander-in-chief exchanged an amused smile with Colonel Benton. "Let's hope," he said, "they can fight, too."

"Show us the enemy, sir," Sam replied brashly, "and we'll show you what we can do." He could feel the faint, approving stir of the troops behind him.

Andrew Jackson scratched his long jaw and studied the young officer closely.

The General's pale blue eyes were so piercing they made a man uncomfortable, Sam thought, but he managed to meet his superior's steady gaze.

"Is he a talker, Tom, or does he give you the results you want?" Jackson asked.

"He came up through the ranks. He's from Maryville."

Andrew Jackson's lined face was creased by a broad grin. "A

41

Tennessee boy! Why in hell didn't you say so, Tom?" He extended his hand to Sam. "I'll guarantee you all the fighting you can stomach, Houston. The rest will be up to you, and to these lads." Jackson limped off toward the bivouac area of another platoon.

Sam put his men at ease, and a half-hour later, while eating his supper, he continued to feel a glow of excitement and satisfaction. He had read of great leaders whose subordinates would gladly die for them, but, until today, he had never met one. He couldn't analyze the General's appeal, but knew he would be willing to make any sacrifice that Jackson demanded of him.

Two companies of Cherokee scouts joined the corps, but no other reinforcements appeared, nor did badly needed supply wagons, in spite of the War Department's repeated promises. Andrew Jackson waited for almost two months, fretting. Then, knowing the Creek were strengthening themselves at Horseshoe Bend and would be impossible to dislodge if he tarried much longer, he decided to risk everything in a single, climactic battle.

On the morning of March 27, after a rapid march through the wilderness, the corps reached Horseshoe Bend and saw the high walls of the log fort across the waters of the Tallapoosa. The commander-in-chief immediately sent John Coffee with his cavalry and the friendly Indians across the river at a ford two miles to the south, and the horsemen formed a loose ring around the bastion to prevent a major escape breakthrough. Meanwhile the main body moved into position opposite the bend, on the north side, and Jackson's artillery began to pound the fort.

The cannon opened their fire at ten o'clock in the morning and roared steadily. Sam, watching the bombardment from his place in the infantry ranks near the shoreline, became increasingly impatient. Even after three hours of unrelieved shelling, as nearly as he could judge, no appreciable damage had been done. The huge logs of soft wood absorbed the iron shot, and, if anything, actually made the fort stronger. Surely, he thought, Jackson realized he was wasting the day!

Suddenly, a little after one in the afternoon, there was a commotion a short distance from the fort, and the infantrymen saw that the Cherokee and a company of scouts had found scores of canoes and other small craft hidden in the high reeds. It was obvious that the Creek had intended to use these boats to make their escape in the event that the battle went against them.

Before a force could be sent from the fort to retrieve the craft, General Coffee took swift action. Sending about half of the armada across the river to transport the foot soldiers to the base of the fort, he burned the rest of the canoes. A column of black, acrid smoke rose high into the air, and Sam settled his helmet more firmly on his head. Now, he told himself, the infantry would be sent into battle.

But the chivalrous Andrew Jackson was not yet ready to make his assault. First he sent a courier to the Creek under a flag of truce, offering to permit all women and children to leave. His courteous gesture was accepted, but the defenders were in no hurry, and another hour passed before the last of the noncombatants departed and the gates of the fort again were closed.

A number of officers were clustered around General Jackson, who sat on his horse at the crest of a small hill a short distance to the rear, and Sam watched them anxiously as they talked. Then they parted, and he knew from the expression on the face of Colonel Benton that the regiment would be given its fair share of action. His guess was confirmed when the word was passed down the line, "The 39th will lead the attack!"

Sam raced at the head of his platoon in an orderly rush to the boats.

Senior officers swam their horses across the Tallapoosa to the spit of land that General Coffee had taken previously, their juniors and the troops riding in the canoes and other craft. Once the landing was completed, the order of battle was given: the 39th would act as the vanguard, followed by the most experienced of the militia units, a brigade from Tennessee.

"Prepare to attack!" Colonel Benton ordered.

Sam discovered he was shaking, but his voice was firm as he called to his men, "Load your rifles. Check your ammunition. Steady, boys."

During the pause that followed, he thought he might become ill, and wiped a film of cold perspiration from his forehead.

Then a bugle blared, Benton pointed his sword in the direction of the fort, and Sam forgot his fear as he ran forward.

The first obstacle to be overcome was an outer breastworks of logs and earth, about eight feet high, that formed a ring around the fort itself. Sam headed toward it at a dead run, urging his men to keep pace with him. He could see one officer, a major, a few feet ahead of him, who managed to reach the top of the breastworks before a bullet caught him between the eyes and sent him toppling backward onto the ground.

Trying not to think about the major, Sam pulled himself up onto the barricade, scrambling and slipping, then getting another foothold and hauling himself higher. The defenders were firing muskets and their more primitive, traditional weapons from the parapets of the main fort, and Sam realized he and his comrades made perfect targets. Bullets and arrows sang past him, and a spear, badly aimed, passed high over his head. At last he stood erect on the top of the breastworks, waving his sword as he encouraged his men. "Come on, boys! The fort is ours!"

Not until much later did he learn that he was the first to climb the breastworks and that, as a consequence, scores of Creek warriors directed their fire at him.

A savage pain shot through his left thigh, and he lost his balance. Clutching in vain at the rough logs of the breastworks, he half-fell, half-slid to the ground below, where the men of the 39th were huddling in an attempt to avoid the enemy fire. Staring dully at his thigh, Sam realized that a barbed arrow was imbedded in his flesh.

"Tear it out, sir!" he called to a lieutenant who was only a few feet from him.

The officer crawled to him and tugged at the shaft, but it would not move.

There was only one thought in Sam's mind. The attack had been halted, and he wanted to lead his men across the barrier. Impatient and angry, he took a firm grip on his sword, intending to cut out the arrow himself.

At that moment the lieutenant worked it free, and, as he removed it, blood spurted from the wound.

Sam felt faint, and was unable to protest as two men hauled him to the rear, dragging him on the rough ground until they were out of range of enemy fire, then standing and carrying him. He was the first to have been wounded in the assault, and a number of surgeons were available to help him. One stopped the flow of blood, and was dressing the wound, when Sam heard a vaguely familiar voice above him.

"You tried hard, lad," General Jackson said. "There aren't many who show that kind of courage."

Sam tried not to wince as the surgeon wrapped the bandage more tightly around his thigh. "I intend to do better as soon as the doctor here is finished, sir. We need to get the attack started again!"

Jackson raised a bushy eyebrow, then turned to the surgeon. "Will he be fit for more combat today?"

"No, General! His injury isn't serious, but he's lost a goodly quantity of blood, and ought to spend at least a week at rest on his pallet."

The indignant Sam raised himself on one elbow. "You seem to forget we're fighting a battle! I have my duty to perform, and nobody is going to stop me from—"

"You'll do what you're told," Jackson said.

"But, sir—"

"You've done your share of fighting for the day, Houston. You'll go off to the rear, and you'll stay there. That's an order, lad, and you'll obey it!" The commander-in-chief limped away.

Sam remained silent, and when the surgeon had completed his work, two soldiers moved the wounded young officer farther to the rear. The attack was being resumed, and the sound of rifle and musket fire crackled a few hundred yards away. The mere thought of missing the action was unbearable, and Sam, alone now, stood and tried resting his weight on his injured leg. It throbbed, but he found the pain bearable, so he picked up his rifle and sword, which had been placed on the ground beside him, and started forward, making a wide detour around the area in which the surgeons were at work.

The troops of the 39th were storming the breastworks again, so he increased his pace, hobbling, and soon caught up with his company. Pushing forward through the ranks, he found his own platoon, and put the ache out of his mind. "This time we'll take them, boys!" he shouted, waving his sword.

Several of the men hoisted him onto the top of the breastworks, where they joined him. Other Regulars were swarming over the obstacle, too, so Sam safely lowered himself to the ground inside the breastworks, and was one of the leaders of the rush to the main wall of the fort.

The Indians were maintaining a steady fire, but their marksmanship was inaccurate, and the soldiers found it relatively easy to hoist their scaling ladders. A corporal helped Sam climb to the top, and when he reached the parapet he found a score of individual fights in progress. Still rallying his men, he continued to shout encouragement to them as he fired his rifle point-blank at a warrior, then reloaded and fired again.

The savages apparently realized that he was a man whose aim was too accurate, and several of them rushed him. His wounded leg made it difficult for him to move quickly, and the platform was so narrow that his problem was compounded. Unable to reload again, he grasped the long rifle by its muzzle and, using it as a club, struck repeatedly at the braves who were trying to maneuver him into a corner.

He struck one a resounding blow on the side of the head, and the man dropped to the ground thirty feet below. But the others continued to edge toward him, one jabbing at him with a spear, the others holding knives as they waited for the opportune moment to pounce on him.

Dropping his rifle to the platform, he slashed at the spear with his sword, and after several attempts managed to slice off the stone tip. But his preoccupation enabled the other Creek to work still closer to him, and one was about to pounce on him from the side when an infantry soldier's rifle shot felled him. Sam leaped at his remaining foe, and although the jolt sent hot flames of pain

46

through his leg, he managed to skewer the savage with the point of his sword.

He had a brief respite now, and was elated when he saw the Regulars, followed by the troops of the Tennessee militia brigade, spreading out through the interior of the fort. Those of the warriors who tried to make a stand were slaughtered, and the others fled from the compound, heading in the direction of a ravine behind the fort. For all practical purposes the battle appeared to be at an end, and the troops began to cheer.

But their joy was short-lived. Colonel Benton, his uniform blackened by gunpowder, the plume on his helmet bedraggled, mustered the men of the 39th in the inner compound of the fort, where the stench of death was overwhelming. "Boys," he said grimly, "our work isn't done. Several hundred of the Creek—we don't know how many—have holed up in a reserve fort back yonder at the ravine. We've got to force them to surrender—or kill every last one of them."

The regiment marched out of the fort, then halted as they saw the cleverly constructed bastion where the Indians had chosen to make their last, desperate stand. A heavy log roof had been built over a portion of the ravine, and walls a few feet above the lip of the ravine had been added as well. The savages had almost perfect cover, and could fire with impunity at any foes who tried to rush them.

There was no alternative, however. The bugles sounded, and the companies of the 39th Infantry Regiment moved forward at a trot.

Again Sam's platoon was one of the units in the lead, and again he urged his men to maintain their pace without faltering. The braves opened a deadly fire, and were so well protected that it was almost impossible to cripple them in return, but the Regulars continued to move toward them, ignoring their own danger.

Sam, repeatedly waving his men forward with his sword, was no more than ten yards from the enemy, and knew that if he could reach the Indians' stronghold, it would be easy to set fire to the roof. Suddenly, however, he felt two violent thrusts against his right shoulder that spun him around and sent him sprawling onto the ground.

The shock was so great that he was numbed, and felt no pain. But, as he reached with his left hand to feel his shoulder, he realized it had been shattered. Dismayed but unable to think clearly, he fell back onto the ground, and the sky spun dizzily above him. Steady rifle fire was being maintained by both sides, and the screams of the dying and wounded seemed to fill his head. Then, slowly, he lost consciousness, his day's work at last completed.

The blankets made a softer bed than any Sam had known in many months, and when he awakened he thought he was in his own bed, at home. Then the steady, unyielding pain in his shoulder reminded him that he had suffered an injury, and he reached for the spot with his free hand. Surprised to find it bandaged, he opened his eyes.

"I told you I thought he'd regain consciousness, sir," a voice said. "Ensign Houston appears to be indestructible."

Sam saw a surgeon bending over him. Turning his head slightly, he was startled to find General Jackson and Colonel Benton squatting beside him.

"Don't move, lad," Benton said. "They've taken two bullets from your right shoulder, while a third penetrated so far you'll carry it for the rest of your life. You're lucky to be here, Houston. There aren't many who could have pulled through."

"What happened at the ravine?" Sam asked in a weak, hoarse voice.

"We were repulsed three times," Benton replied, "and our losses were so heavy we finally had to burn down the fort with flaming arrows. Our Cherokee did the deed for us."

Sam was pleased that his Indian brothers had played a significant part in the engagement.

"The battle is over," Benton continued. "We won a complete victory, and the few Creek warriors who lived have been scattered. The Alabama Territory will be at peace now."

In spite of his intense pain, Sam grinned.

"Don't move!" the surgeon told him. "You'll have to hold yourself as still as you possibly can, and for a long, long time, to give your bones a chance to mend."

For the first time Sam thought of himself. "Will I be whole again?"

The others were silent, until General Jackson said curtly, "Tell him the truth."

"We don't know," the surgeon declared. "You may regain use of your shoulder and arm, but you may not. If you do what you're told, you'll have a fair chance of recovery."

"Ensign Houston isn't one who does what he's told." Andrew Jackson sounded severe. "I wonder if you realize you could be court-martialed for disobeying a military command given to you by your commander-in-chief. I told you not to go back into the fight, but you deliberately defied my order."

Sam wanted to justify what he had done, but thought it just as well that he lacked the strength. He was a professional soldier, and there was no excuse he could offer.

Jackson stared at him solemnly. "What do you suppose would happen to my corps if all my officers behaved as you have?"

Sam didn't know what to say.

"He's not too ill to speak, is he, Doctor?" The General raised his voice, and several other wounded men in the clearing looked uncomfortable.

"No, sir," the surgeon replied, "but I must urge you to use caution. He's just beginning his convalescence, and—"

"By the Eternal, young man, you'd think I'd never suffered a wound myself. I'll thank you to let me be the judge of how much a man who is ill can tolerate!"

The surgeon coughed nervously, then suddenly discovered that another patient required his attention.

"Now, Houston!" Jackson pointed a long, bony finger at the young officer on the pallet. "Answer my question!"

Sam opened his mouth, but was unable to make a sound.

"Very well, I'll tell you what would happen if all my officers had disobeyed me as you did! We'd have won the battle in half the time it took us, by the Eternal!"

Colonel Benton roared with laughter.

The best Sam could manage was a weak grin.

"You put me in a strange position, Houston." Jackson's face remained grave, but he allowed a trace of humor to show in his eyes. "If I rewarded every man who disobeyed me, I wouldn't have a military corps. No, sir, we'd be reduced to mutinous bedlam! On the other hand, I've commended your battle conduct in a special report I've sent to Secretary of War Monroe, and I've asked him to call it to the attention of President Madison. I'll be damned and will blister in Hades for the next five thousand years if I've ever seen such heroism. You may lack good sense, Houston, but you have courage!"

Sam glanced at the gold ring his mother had given him, and knew she would be pleased that he had conducted himself honorably.

"What's more," the General said, not bothering to lower his grating voice, "I've directed Colonel Benton to issue orders promoting you to the rank of third lieutenant. Give him the papers, Tom!"

Benton put a parchment scroll into Sam's left hand. "Congratulations, Lieutenant Houston," he said. "But I urge you to be a bit more careful in the way you work for your next promotion."

Sam stood at the edge of the forest that still covered fifty acres of his mother's property, and wiped his brow. The sun was hot, the air was humid and he wanted to return home to rest, but another hour's work remained to be done. He had set himself the task of chopping down four oaks in a day, and was determined not to stop until dusk. Stooping, he picked up the ax he had dropped to the ground and, using only his right hand, chipped at the wood.

His convalescence had been slow at first, and when he had arrived at the farm after his long journey from the Alabama Territory wilderness he had not cared whether he lived or died. But his mother's nursing had worked miracles, and in less than a month he regained most of the weight he had lost. Thanks to his strong constitution, his wound healed rapidly, but his right arm was useless, and he needed all of his strength to raise it a few inches.

Maryville's two physicians told him he would be crippled for life, and another physician, summoned from Nashville at the insistence of Sam's older brothers, agreed with the diagnosis, adding that he believed the bullet still lodged in the patient's body had irreparably injured his lungs, too.

Sam flatly refused to accept the verdict. "Before the end of the summer," he said, "my arm will be as sound as it ever was. I don't propose to be retired from the Army as a third lieutenant."

His brothers had humored him, but Elizabeth Houston had faith in him. "I know now what sets you apart from the others," she told him. "When you put your mind to something, you do it."

Day by day, week by week, he had doggedly set himself the goal of proving her right. It had been frustrating, maddening, to teach himself to use his fingers again, to spend hours picking up wood chips, then horseshoes, and finally such heavy objects as an iron kettle. Then, gradually, he had exercised his arm, and at last the pains in his shoulder and chest had disappeared.

Now, in the final stages of his rehabilitation program, he forced himself to labor unsparingly from dawn until sundown six days each week. Only his respect for his mother prevented him from exercising on the Sabbath as well. He could do as much with his arm as could many normal, healthy men, but was not yet satisfied. He was Sam Houston, endowed with great physical prowess, and he would not be content until all his strength was restored.

The ax bit deep into the oak, and Sam withdrew it, then struck again, and yet again.

On the day before Christmas, 1814, representatives of the United States and Great Britain signed a treaty at Ghent, Belgium, bringing the War of 1812 to an end. But, before word of the agreement reached the New World, General Andrew Jackson inflicted a severe defeat on a strong Redcoat force, the conquerors of Napoleon, at New Orleans, in a two-week battle that ended in January 1815. The American people saluted their new, great hero, and Jackson responded by saying, "My men win my victories. Remember and honor them, as I aim to do."

He soon proved he was as good as his word. Sam Houston had applied to the Secretary of War for a return to duty, but in the flush of triumph his request was either forgotten or ignored. Anxious to resume his career, he sent a personal letter to Jackson, and within two weeks orders were issued. Sam was promoted to the rank of second lieutenant and was directed to proceed to New Orleans to join the country's elite regiment of Regulars, the 1st Infantry.

Garrison duty in peacetime proved dull, however, and life became lethargic after Jackson, now the commander of the Army's Southern Department, moved his own headquarters to Nashville. Sam, who was almost completely restored to good health, was bored, and volunteered to act as a convoy escort when several companies of troops were transferred to New York. If nothing else, he thought, he would see a part of the country he did not know, and at the government's expense.

The journey was made by ship, and when a storm blew up in the Gulf of Mexico forty-eight hours after the voyage began, Lieutenant Houston learned he was not destined for the life of a sailor. Seasickness sent him to his bed, and he remained there for several days, until the storm subsided.

The rest of the voyage was uneventful, and at last the troop transport dropped anchor in New York's East River. The city had just become the largest in the United States, her population having leaped past those of Philadelphia and Boston during the war years. And Sam, who had thought of himself as sophisticated after his stay in New Orleans, was stunned by the bustle and cosmopolitan atmosphere of New York. There were eight theaters and four lecture halls in the town, all of them playing to large crowds, three public gardens were filled with strollers from the time their gates were opened at noon until they were closed again at nine in the evening, and in the vicinity of the Battery, at the southern tip of Manhattan Island, the visitor counted sixteen different taverns and inns, at least half of which charged prices that a man earning a second lieutenant's wages could not afford to pay.

Ships from many lands rode at their berths in the Hudson and East Rivers, and it was common to hear seamen speaking foreign tongues. New Yorkers themselves, however, sounded remarkably like Englishmen, perhaps because of the city's long occupation by Redcoat troops during the Revolution.

The carriages of the wealthy were drawn by teams of four superbly matched horses, and most boasted lackeyed footmen as well as coachmen on the boxes. The young officer from Tennessee gaped at the expensive boots of kidskin and the silver spurs worn by horsemen who cantered recklessly through the busy streets on blooded stallions, and for the first time in his life he saw people actually wearing cloaks of otter, beaver, and fox, furs that the trappers of the frontier regularly sent off to the seaboard.

The houses and shops of red brick or gray fieldstone were substantial, and few buildings were only one story high. New Yorkers crowded close together, and, since real estate prices were exorbitant, it was common to see private dwellings, manufacturing establishments, and shops of five or six floors. Sam wanted to take his mother and sisters souvenirs, but the prices of merchandise, from bolts of cloth to smokeless tapers imported from France, were staggering.

Fortunately, his quarters cost him nothing. He was housed in the officers' building at Fort Washington, an old, walled compound that had been known as Fort George before the Revolution. He had virtually no duties to perform while awaiting orders sending him on to his next permanent assignment, and spent the better part of his time wandering through the town, sometimes looking at the wares in shop windows, sometimes watching the unloading of foreign ships.

It did not take him long to discover that the young women of New York were infinitely bolder than the circumspect young ladies of Tennessee and the relatively modest girls of New Orleans. Even the wealthy made no attempt to disguise their interest in the tanned, uniformed giant, and Sam found it impossible to walk more than a city square or two without becoming engaged in a lively flirtation. He enjoyed himself, but, as the days passed, began to want a more substantial relationship.

One afternoon, while dining at the Twin Masts, a Broad Street tavern frequented by the officers of visiting merchant ships, he was fascinated by the proximity of two separate groups of young women, who were unescorted. Unlike the harlots of any town, who were instantly recognizable, these girls were circumspect in appearance, dress and manner. Although it was inconceivable that ladies would go without gentlemen to the Andrew Jackson Inn in New Orleans, or to Tennessee's most fashionable gathering place, the Nashville Inn, New Yorkers obviously lived according to freer standards of their own.

One young woman in particular, a willowy brunette whose hair was piled high on her head, interested Sam, and, as he opened and ate the platter of oysters that was his first course, he could not resist staring at her. She was conscious of him, too, and when their eyes met, neither looked away. The other members of the girl's party seemed conscious of what was happening, but, discreetly minding their own business, showed no signs of disapproval.

Sam wondered if he might persuade her to join him for the meal, and finally decided that the worst he could suffer would be a cold rebuff. So he wrote her a short note, and she seemed neither offended nor surprised when she unfolded the small square of paper. Smiling faintly, she nodded, and after waiting a few moments, said something to her companions as she rose.

Sam jumped to his feet, and held a chair for her. "I'm honored, ma'am. Lieutenant Houston, recently of the 1st Infantry, at your service."

"I'm Lisbeth Lucy." Her voice, faintly husky, was well-modulated.

He ordered her a platter of oysters, too, and knowing nothing of wines, left the choice to her. Both of them felt conspicuous at a table in the open, so near to her friends, and the proprietor cooperated by moving them to a booth at the rear of the taproom. There, over bass stuffed with mushrooms, beef and kidney pies, roasted goose and fruit tarts, they engaged in a lively conversation. Sam discovered he had been craving feminine companionship, and even while eating a hearty meal, talked incessantly.

The wine disappeared, and Lisbeth suggested a bottle of another type, which he found equally pleasing. Expanding under the influence of someone who was warm and sympathetic, he heard himself telling her of his wounds and his subsequent struggle to regain his health.

"You don't look like an invalid, sir," she said.

"I assure you, I'm not. I could beat any man in this town in a free-for-all, but that isn't saying much. Most city people always look sickly, not including young ladies, of course." Their meal was finished, and the combination of the girl's close attention, the rich food and the abundant quantities of good wine gave him the most pleasant glow he could recall feeling. Lisbeth was someone he would see again during his stay in New York, and he called for two glasses of brandywine to cement their friendship.

Lisbeth took care to sip only small quantities of the potent drink as she asked Sam about life in New Orleans. He found her interest flattering, and delivered a long monologue on the unique qualities of the capital of the Louisiana Territory. It occurred to him that he was becoming increasingly thick-tongued, occasionally stumbling over a word, but he did not feel intoxicated and paid little heed to the slips until he discovered himself becoming drowsy.

He made an effort to remain awake, horrified at the girl's reaction if he dozed, but found it impossible to keep his eyes open. At last, unable to struggle any longer, he slumped in his chair and fell into a deep sleep.

When the sound of voices in the distance awakened him, he was alone at the table. A violent headache tore at his temples, his hands trembled as he pushed himself away from the table, and he could not focus clearly. His step faltering, he went into the corridor outside the booth, and saw that the table occupied by Lisbeth's friends now held another party. Gradually it dawned on him that oil lamps were lighted in the taproom, and that, apparently, a number of hours had passed since he and his companion had eaten. He reached for his gold watch, but it was missing.

Half-collapsing into his chair in the booth again, he made a systematic search through his pockets. Not only was his watch gone, but so was his purse, with the month's pay he had just received twenty-four hours earlier. In fact, even the gold tassel that ornamented the dress scabbard that held his sword had been cut away.

Only one glass still sat on the table, his own. There was literally no sign that the girl who had called herself Lisbeth Lucy had ever spent time with him. A sudden suspicion impelled him to reach for the empty glass, and when he sniffed it he smelled a strange, pungent odor. Angry in spite of feeling so ill, he summoned the proprietor.

The man, a leather apron over his shirt and trousers, beamed as he came to the table.

"I was drugged and robbed by the girl who joined me for dinner," Sam said hoarsely.

The man's attitude changed at once, and his eyes became hard. "That's a serious accusation, Lieutenant. Can you prove it?"

"I dropped off to sleep here—"

"That's not surprising. You drank a great deal of wine and liquor."

"And when I woke up, my money and watch were gone. So was the girl."

"I don't recall seeing you dine with a lady."

Sam's temples pounded still harder. "When I was wounded, I lived for days on laudanum the surgeons gave me to ease the pain. I'd know the smell anywhere. Here."

The proprietor accepted the glass that the young officer thrust into his hand, held it to his nose for a moment, and then deposited it on a tray being carried to the kitchen by a barmaid. "You're either dreaming or trying to cause trouble."

"Give me that glass! It's my only proof—"

"Lieutenant, I've seen your kind all too often. You think you'll win people's sympathies because you're a veteran of the war, and that the police will listen to you because this is a big town where strangers occasionally stumble. But I've dealt too often with men like you."

Sam hauled himself to his feet, feeling the urge to smash a fist into the man's face. But that, he realized, would do no more than cause him additional trouble. He literally could not prove he had been drugged and robbed, and if he became involved in a fight, he would be hauled before a court-martial board for conduct unbecoming an officer and gentleman.

"Pay your bill," the proprietor said, "and get out."

Sam almost choked. "I've already told you, every penny I have to my name was taken."

The man looked at him with contempt. "I see. You tell a pretty story to avoid paying for your meal." He shook his head. "I ought to report you to the commandant of Fort Washington."

"If you want to start a ruckus, I'll see it through to the end." Sam knew his own position was weak, but refused to be bullied or frightened.

"I ought to prosecute you until your insignia are stripped from you. But I'm willing to forgive a man who fought for his country. I'm not wealthy, but I can pay for your meal. All I'm telling you, Lieutenant, is this. Don't come near my tavern again, and don't spread false stories about us. I run a respectable eating and drinking house, and I'll ruin anyone who tries to hurt my good name."

Sam found it difficult to place one foot before the other, but he walked with as much dignity as he could muster. Retrieving his helmet from a stand near the entrance, he made his way out into Broad Street, where the fresh air helped revive him.

Undoubtedly the owner of the tavern and the girl had been working together, and between them had been very clever. Complaints to either the police or his own military superiors would only reveal him as naïve and foolish, and he would not be able to offer any substantiation of his charges. So, under the circumstances, he would be wise to accept his losses and keep quiet.

His head was groggy, his feet dragging, as he started toward Fort Washington. He was disgraced, but the fault was his own; he could blame no one else for his gullibility. It was useless, too, to damn New York, and he was willing to admit he was too ingenious to cope with the sophistication of a big city. But some day he would return, after earning the respect of the town's people, and would hold his head high. Until then, he would remember the most humiliating lesson of his life.

Major General Andrew Jackson carried his hatred of formality to its logical conclusion by refusing to occupy the office space in Nashville provided him by the Federal government and, instead, making his personal headquarters in the new Nashville Inn. There, with venison and beef, whisky and beer readily at hand for visitors, he conducted the business of the Army's Southern Department, chatted with friends who urged him to enter politics, and took the initiative in solving problems too difficult and complex for the timid or unresourceful to resolve.

It was in the undecorated back tavern of the Inn that Lieutenant Sam Houston found him, eating a meal of bear bacon and roasted eggs, which he was washing down with a tumbler of watered wine. In spite of the relaxed surroundings, however, Sam stood stiffly at attention and saluted.

"Lieutenant Houston at report, sir."

"Well, now. You made good travel time from New York, lad." Jackson grinned at the younger man.

"My orders directed me to report to you at my earliest convenience, General."

"So you didn't even take the time to wipe the dust from your boots. I like that." Jackson waved him to a seat and ordered some food for him. "Houston, I happened to learn recently that you spent several years with the Cherokee and were adopted into their tribe. So I think you're just the right man to perform a confidential mission for me."

"I'm willing, sir, provided it won't be harmful to the Cherokee."

"It's the only way I know to save them from fighting a war they can't win."

Sam hoped he would not be forced to test conflicting loyalties.

"Tennessee is expanding fast these days, Houston. It won't be long before all the land this side of the Mississippi River is settled, and the Cherokee are unhappy about it."

"I can't rightly blame them, General. According to the terms of their treaty with the United States, they were promised they could keep the territory they now hold."

Andrew Jackson speared a chunk of bacon on the point of his

knife. "It was a treaty that shouldn't have been made. Nothing on this earth can stop the westward push of the American people. If the Cherokee are sensible, they'll accept the offer of new territory west of the Mississippi, a much larger grant than they're being asked to give up."

"Nobody likes to be deprived of his home, sir." Sam shook his head. "It's a nasty problem."

"It's worse than you realize, Houston. Some of the minor Cherokee chiefs have already signed an agreement ceding about one million, three hundred thousand acres to the United States in return for a new grant across the Mississippi."

"How were they persuaded to sign?" Sam demanded.

"I asked Secretary of War Calhoun the same question, but his answer was evasive." Jackson became thoughtful as he chewed his meat. "I have me a hunch they were bribed."

"I'd be willing to bet on it, General," Sam declared emphatically.

"The two main sachems of the Cherokee, Oo-loo-te-ka and his brother, Tah-lhon-tusky, won't even consider accepting the new agreement. They say the United States has broken its word to them too many times."

"And so we have, sir. We've sent rascals and thieves to them as our agents—"

"Exactly so. That's why I propose to send someone they trust to deal with them in this situation. You, Houston."

Sam's meal arrived at the table, and he began to eat his roasted eggs with his fingers. Not even the gravest of problems interfered with his appetite. "Hold on, General. Maybe you've never heard that Oo-loo-te-ka adopted me as his foster-son when I was a boy. I could no more lie to him or cheat him than I could my own father."

"I wouldn't ask you to do either." Jackson rarely tolerated insubordination, but admired Sam's candor. "I've found a way to solve this problem, and while it isn't perfect, I'll grant you, it's the best that can be done. The Cherokee have a long list of grievances against us. Legitimate grievances. You could make them

59

promises, and so could I, but neither your word nor mine would mean a thing without the support of Washington City."

"That's been the difficulty ever since we started dealing with the Cherokee when they lived on the seaboard, sir."

Jackson was conscious of the younger man's appetite, and moved several thick strips of bacon from his own plate to Sam's. "The sachems trust you."

"Yes, sir." Sam was wary, but continued to eat ravenously.

"Persuade them to go to Washington City. Escort them there yourself. I'll provide you with the best boats for river travel, horses and food supplies—whatever you need. But before they start their journey, get a full list of their grievances, and send it along to me in writing. I'll forward it to Secretary Calhoun, and I'll guarantee that he'll receive the sachems. When he gives them his personal promise to right the wrongs—in President Monroe's name and the War Department's—it won't be the same as some swindling little politician making them cheap promises that won't be kept. The Secretary of War will be obliged to keep his word, and to prove it. When the sachems see he means what he says, it should be easier to persuade them to give up their present territory for lands across the Mississippi."

Sam ate a thick, dripping chunk of bacon. "My God, I sympathize with them, General."

"So do I. Their alternative is mighty harsh."

Sam reached for his mug of ale. "If they insist on holding on to their present land, settlers will soon begin encroaching on it. There will be fights, and murders, and scalpings. And then there will be a cry for the Army to step in."

"We'll be ordered to intervene." Jackson's thin forefinger tapped a metal button on the front of the younger man's tunic. "You and I, Houston, will be bound by our oaths as officers to drive them out. That's why I want a peaceful solution now, with no bloodshed, and at the same time I'd like to protect the Cherokee as best I can. I haven't forgotten the help they gave me in the Creek campaign. Well, Houston?"

Sam remained silent for a moment. "It seems best for the Cherokee as well as for us, General. I'll do it."

Washington City was a town of sharp contrasts. Its streets were rutted dirt roads that oozed mud when it rained, its buildings were shabby wooden structures and most of the amenities of civilization were in short supply. In fact, even paint was so scarce that the Executive Mansion, the home and office of the President, had been coated with whitewash to hide the scars inflicted by the British when they had tried to burn it down during the War of 1812.

At the same time, however, this busy town was the most cosmopolitan metropolis in the country. The United States had won the diplomatic recognition of fourteen nations, and the legation heads, their wives and staffs were the acknowledged social leaders. Even President James Monroe, who had himself spent a number of years as the American representative in London, Paris, and Madrid, wore satin waistcoats, long tailcoats and high collars, all the mark of the diplomats. The ladies copied the most recent European styles, and the dining rooms of the new hotels presented their guests with menus written in French, to the secret annoyance of Congressmen from rural districts.

First Lieutenant of Infantry Sam Houston, recently promoted, created a mild sensation in the town when he and his Cherokee brethren arrived for their meeting with Secretary Calhoun. All, Sam included, wore breechcloths and moccasins, eagle feathers adorned their hair and they wrapped themselves in coarse blankets embroidered with dyed porcupine quills. Congress had just started a new session, so the town was crowded, and the Cherokee calmly pitched tents in a vacant lot only a stone's throw from the two-story wooden War Department building. Sam, of course, elected to live with the Cherokee during their stay.

The grievances presented by Oo-loo-te-ka and Tah-lhon-tusky were examined in detail by civilian and military officials of the War Department in a series of meetings that dragged on for three weeks. Sam, acting as the interpreter for the Cherokee, actually became their spokesman, and presented their case with such vigor that all of their demands were met. They, thanks to his persuasion, agreed in return to move their nation to a site west of the Mississippi River.

By March 1 all of the details had been settled, and it remained only for the Secretary of War to meet with the sachems and sign the agreement in their presence. Promptly at eight o'clock in the morning the group was ushered into his office, and two aides provided chairs for the visitors while the unsmiling Secretary stiffly shook the hand of each Cherokee.

When John C. Calhoun elected to be charming, no man in Washington City exercised greater magnetism, but it was commonly believed that he was opposed to the policy of granting concessions to the Cherokee, a stand which President Monroe had adopted at the instigation of General Jackson. But Calhoun was too wise to oppose his superior or make any other move that might jeopardize his chances of winning still higher office. A South Carolinian who had been educated at Yale, his career had been meteoric: sent to the House of Representatives by his constituents in 1811 while still in his twenties, he was now only thirty-six, and had already spent almost a year in one of the key posts in Monroe's Cabinet.

A square-jawed, stocky man whose political opponents claimed he lacked a sense of humor, he sat down behind his desk and began to read a long statement emphasizing the debt of the Cherokee to the United States.

"Mr. Secretary," Sam interrupted, "if you don't mind, sir, I'd like to translate your speech to the sachems as you go along."

Calhoun raised an eyebrow and nodded curtly, but the change in his tempo was imperceptible.

It was just as well, Sam thought, that he was reading very rapidly. Oo-loo-te-ka and the others had only a limited command of English, and therefore undoubtedly missed some of the more patronizing nuances. It was best to eliminate them from the translation.

At last Calhoun was done, and an aide dipped a quill pen into a jar of ink, then handed it to him with a flourish. He signed seven copies of the agreement, the sachems did the same, and each was presented with one. Then Calhoun circled the room, shaking hands again, and the ceremony was ended.

Sam breathed a silent sigh of relief. The new treaty represented the most significant accomplishment of his life, one that won the Cherokee all that was attainable for them, while guaranteeing them justice, and at the same time giving the United States major benefits without the need to fight a costly and bloody war.

The aides started to guide the visitors out of the office.

"Houston," Calhoun called, "I'll be obliged if you'll stay behind for a moment."

Sam was pleased. Although he hadn't expected praise, he had hoped he might be given an official commendation for his work, and perhaps, if he was lucky, another promotion in rank. He knew General Jackson would be delighted with the results of the Cherokee sachems' visit to Washington City, and it was good to realize that the Secretary of War, on behalf of President Monroe, was also aware of what he had done.

Calhoun returned to his seat, but did not offer the young officer a chair. "As I understand it, Houston, you hold the rank of a first lieutenant, and are on active duty in the Army."

"Yes, sir."

"Then I demand to know why you've disgraced the entire military establishment of this nation by appearing in outlandish masquerade—and living in a tent like a savage!"

For an instant Sam was too shocked to reply, but he recovered swiftly. "The advantages seemed obvious, Mr. Secretary." He took great care not to let Calhoun see that he was angry. "I was adopted by the Cherokee years ago, and they think of me as one of their own. By dressing as they do, and living with them, they accepted me as a Cherokee, not a representative of the United States. They listened to my advice, as the treaty proves."

"That's no excuse," Calhoun replied. "The whole town has been laughing ever since you arrived here."

"Out in Tennessee, Mr. Secretary, we believe there's more than one way to skin a bear." Sam's self-control began to slip, and his voice became louder. "Let the people who don't understand Indians laugh all they please. They'll stop soon enough when the details of the treaty are published. All of western Tennessee has been ceded to the United States without the loss of a single life or the need to fire one shot!"

63

"I find it difficult to believe the same goal couldn't have been reached without excessive theatrics that hold the Army up to ridicule!"

"In my best judgment it was necessary," Sam retorted. "And the results speak for themselves! What's more, sir, I find it no disgrace to wear the robes of the Cherokee!"

Calhoun looked him up and down slowly, with open contempt. "I've had my doubts about you ever since you came to Washington City, Houston. You may as well know that I've had official inquiries made into your background. There's been a lively smuggling trade of stolen slaves going on through the Cherokee territory, and I had an idea you might be one of the parties responsible."

Sam was so outraged he became inarticulate.

"So far, I must admit, I've found no evidence against you. But I warn you that if and when I do, you'll be prosecuted."

"Any time you want to bring me to trial as a thief, Mr. Secretary, I'll welcome the opportunity to prove my complete innocence." Sam had to remind himself that, as an Army officer, he could be court-martialed and sentenced to a long prison term if he struck the Secretary of War.

"I'm not calling you guilty, Houston. I'm merely pointing out that I wouldn't be surprised if you were. I expect my officers to conduct themselves as gentlemen."

Sam took a step closer to the desk, his fists clenched. "You've never served in the field, have you, Mr. Secretary?"

"I fail to see the connection with—"

"In battle, men don't behave as they do on a drill field, or when parading in full-dress uniform for the Secretary of War. If you'll take the trouble to look up my record, I think you'll find it honorable."

"I can find nothing wrong with your military record, although I sometimes feel that General Jackson is rather extravagant in the praise of his favorites."

Sam was as hurt as he was furious.

Calhoun smiled coldly. "I shall expect you to appear in full uniform no later than this noon, Houston. And, for however long the Cherokee sachems may remain in Washington City, you'll move out of their tents and find lodgings appropriate for an Army officer."

"Are there any other orders, sir?" Sam's voice was almost inaudible.

"Not at present." Calhoun dismissed him with a nod and turned to a sheaf of papers on his desk.

Scarcely able to prevent himself from leaping at the man, Sam saluted smartly, executed an about-face and walked out of the office.

Washington City,
March 1, 1818.

To the Secretary of War.
Sir:
You will please accept this as my resignation from the United States Army, to take effect on this date.

I am, sir,
Your Obt Servt

Sam Houston
1st Lieut., 1st Infy.

THREE

1819–28

"Everybody in Tennessee needs a lawyer these days," Andrew
Jackson said. "Conflicting land claims alone can keep a man busy
for the rest of his days, but if you have your heart set on more
important work, the law is the best ladder I know to help you
climb higher. I'll grant you I'm prejudiced, because that's how I
got my own start. But if it worked for me, it will for you, too."

Sam Houston followed his former commander's advice, and took
up the study of the law in the Nashville offices of Judge James
Trimble, and applied himself so diligently to his work that he
completed his course and passed the state bar examination in six
months instead of the usual two years. Almost immediately thereafter he discovered that, as a friend and protégé of Jackson, he
had more than enough work to keep him occupied.

The influence of Andrew Jackson was omnipresent, and Sam
found himself a member of a small group of the General's ad-
mirers who gathered at the Hermitage, the Jackson plantation
outside Nashville, for dinners and wide-ranging conversations.
Sam soon became friendly with another young attorney, James
K. Polk, and both were willing to accept any plans the General
had in mind for them.

"Jamie," Jackson said, "you need experience in the Legislature.

Sam, it'd do you some good to become prosecuting attorney for the Nashville district." The General's support was all that either young man needed, and both were elected.

Jackson, who always remembered his friends, never forgot his opponents, either. "It's been niggling away at me," he told Sam, "that Secretary of War Calhoun doesn't know a competent officer when he sees one. Tennessee will have to teach him that we know better."

Governor Joseph McMinn was pleased to appoint Sam Houston adjutant general of the Tennessee militia, with the rank of colonel. Sam immediately began spending his evenings and weekends helping to reorganize the militia, and threw himself into the work with such fervor that, only a year later, his fellow officers elected him commander-in-chief of the militia, a post that automatically carried with it the rank of major general.

"I always knew you'd become the most successful of my sons," Elizabeth Houston wrote from her farm. *"May the good Lord continue to bless and keep you."*

In 1822, as President Monroe's second term began to draw toward its close, men all over the United States started to think in terms of his replacement. John Quincy Adams of Massachusetts, son of the second President, was New England's choice, but other parts of the country were far from united in their selection of candidates. Former Speaker of the House of Representatives, Henry Clay of Kentucky, who had retired from Congress for a few years to improve his personal finances, made no secret of his ambitions, and neither did Senator William Crawford of Georgia. Then the friends of Secretary of War Calhoun tentatively threw his hat into the ring.

Sam Houston was erroneously quoted by the Nashville press as saying he would shoot Calhoun rather than see him become President. *"What I said,"* he wrote in a letter to the *Banner,* *"is that I'd be tempted to shoot any citizen of this state so disloyal to our own General Jackson that he would offer his support to someone of Calhoun's obvious inferior talents. No man deserves the Presidency more than Old Hickory, and the people of this nation will be deprived of his leadership only if he himself decides he prefers to enjoy the fruits of the retirement he has earned.*

"Then, but not until that day, would Tennessee consider the merits of our neighbor, Henry Clay, or of Georgia's distinguished Senator Crawford. Of Mr. Adams we know little, of Mr. Martin Van Buren of New York, less, and of Mr. Calhoun, alas, too much."

A number of Jackson's friends were given the credit, which each gladly accepted, for being the first to suggest the name of the General for the presidency. Congressman Felix Grundy, Major William H. Eaton of Nashville, and Governor McMinn's successor, William Carroll, engaged in a lively if friendly dispute, each of them modestly accepting the role in letters to the newspapers which continued to advocate Jackson's candidacy.

"There are only two people in the state who don't like the idea," Old Hickory told Sam as they rode around the grounds of the Hermitage on a leisurely tour of inspection. "Mrs. Jackson wants to stay right here, and so do I."

"I'm afraid you'll be disappointed, sir," Sam told him. "Jamie and I have been working—informally, of course—to answer letters from all parts of the country, and the people are demanding you as President."

"George Washington is the only President we've ever had who was forced by public opinion to take a post he didn't want. All the others actively sought the place, while pretending to be as modest as Washington. I don't believe there will ever be a loud enough clamor for someone who doesn't want to be President to elect him in spite of himself."

"I'm afraid you're in for a surprise, General." Sam reached into his waistcoat pocket for a *segaro*.

"You and Jamie—and Felix and Billy Carroll and all the rest— are whipping up spontaneous enthusiasm for me, eh?"

"You're the obvious choice, sir, and people know it!" It was difficult to light the *segaro* with a tinderbox and flint while riding across broken ground, but Sam accomplished the feat.

"Most of the boys," Jackson said, reaching down with his sword

68

to cut at some tall weeds, "have ambitions of their own, and hope to ride to power on my coattails. Not that I blame them. That's the nature of human animals. Even Jamie Polk, who's the most self-effacing man I've ever known, has his dreams." Jackson straightened in the saddle and pointed his sword at his companion. "What do you want, Sam?"

"General, I already have more than I ever thought would be coming my way. When I retire from the prosecutor's office this year I'll need a partner or two to help me with the law business being offered to me. Every time I look at the gold epaulets on my uniform I think I'm mighty fortunate. Not every man who enlists as a private becomes a major general. What more could I ask?"

"Mrs. Jackson says it's time you find yourself a wife and settle down."

Sam shrugged. "I haven't met anybody I care for that much."

"The ladies make too much of a fuss over you. They spoil you, and that's the truth."

Sam grinned amiably.

"Sometimes I wonder if you wouldn't be just as happy living in the wilderness of the Arkansas country with your Cherokee friends."

Sam's grin faded. "I've often been tempted, General, especially on days when nothing goes right and I'm too busy to drop over to the Nashville Inn for a bite of cold meal and a little mug of ale. But I'm fooling myself. I've become accustomed to rich living, and I wouldn't enjoy giving it up."

Jackson rubbed his long jaw. "I'd have sworn it isn't a fortune you want. Aside from that beaver hat and silk waistcoat that cost you a pretty sum, you live quietly enough at the Inn—"

"I have a roof over my head, plenty to eat—when there's time to eat it—and good friends. What more can a man ask, sir?"

"That depends on the man," Jackson said dryly. "The prosecutor's office hasn't given you a thirst for political power, eh?"

Sam shook his head, wondering why Old Hickory was examining him so closely. "Jamie is the only professional politician I know who isn't greedy. I'm afraid I take after you, General. I don't have much use for the breed."

Andrew Jackson roared with laughter, slapping his thigh. "I knew I could rely on you! One of these years you'll discover that political power is a stronger and better-tasting drink than whisky, and when that happens, you won't rest until you become President yourself. Until then, you're the only man I can trust completely."

"I'm honored, General, but—"

"Wait until you hear what I want of you, boy. I'm doing you no favor, exposing you to temptation." Sobering, Jackson sheathed his sword. "I think you're wrong when you say there's a real demand for me as President, but I believe you're sincere. That's why I want you in Washington City, where you can act as a scout for me. I can form most of my opinions of the political weather from here, but I need someone who can read the winds in Washington for me."

Sam was startled, and wanted to think carefully before replying.

"If I thought the people really wanted me, I could no more refuse the presidency than I could have given up my Army command when I was ill. A man's first duty is his obligation to his country."

"Well, General, if you think it'd be helpful to you, I can arrange to visit Washington City for a few weeks later in the year." Sam puffed on his *segaro*, and a cloud of tobacco smoke hid his face. "But there are men—Felix, for example—who know the town better than I do."

"I know what Felix will tell me. You'll be honest. And you'll learn the ways of Washington City mighty fast when you're a member of the House as Representative from Nashville."

"I can think of ten men who have a better right to sit in Congress." Sam hesitated for a moment, and seemed embarrassed. "Besides, I have obligations to the Dramatic Club. I've promised them I'll play the leading role in Home's *Douglas* this season, and I've accepted a part in another play, too, *Point of Honor*. I realize it's foolish, maybe, to mention such frivolity in the same breath with the presidency, but I've given the Dramatic Club my word."

"When a man gives his word, he must keep it." Andrew Jackson was unsmiling. "You needn't begin your campaign for Congress until the Dramatic Club's season ends. Then, if you will, you can do your play-acting on a far bigger stage."

"All right, sir. If you want me to run for the House, I'll do it."

Rachel Jackson, making one of her rare public appearances, sat beside her husband in the box at the Nashville Theatre, and was so absorbed in the performance of John Home's popular romantic verse tragedy, *Douglas*, that her painful shyness evaporated. She joined in the thunderous applause as the final curtain descended on the play, and when she stood to applaud the players, the rest of the audience rose, too.

The curtain went up again, and the entertainment-starved gentry of Nashville cheered as the amateur actors came onto the stage, one by one, to smile at their friends and bow. The roars became louder and more insistent as the men and women who had portrayed the leading roles appeared, and the applause became deafening when a kilted Sam Houston, looking like a giant from the moors of Scotland, strode briskly to the center of the stage, bowed once and then motioned his fellow players forward.

Rachel Jackson squeezed her husband's arm, and the General bent down to listen to her. "Sam could have become famous as a play-actor," she murmured.

Old Hickory smiled benignly. "Whether he knows it or not, he's always giving a performance." He caught the eye of John Eaton, the director of the play, who was standing in the wings, and gestured briskly.

"Whatever are you up to, Mr. Jackson?" his alarmed wife wanted to know.

"Don't you fret, ma'am." Old Hickory leaned toward the stage to shake the hand of Eaton, who came forward to greet him.

The attention of the audience was transferred to Tennessee's first citizen, and he was given an ovation, in which the players joined.

"Can you quiet them, John?" he demanded. "I'd like to say something."

Eaton tried, but the audience was applauding rhythmically now. "I'm afraid you'll have to do it yourself, General."

Andrew Jackson turned, glowered, and when he raised a hand the crowd obediently fell silent. "I'm not one for making public speeches," he said, "so this will be brief. We've all had a splendid evening, thanks to Major Eaton and these generous ladies and gentlemen, who have worked so hard for us. General Houston, your servant, sir. Your performance was grand!"

The audience applauded again.

Old Hickory waited for quiet. "I reckon this is as good a time as any, and better than most, to let you in on a secret. General Houston's friends have persuaded him to become a candidate for the United States Congress from the 9th District."

The unexpected announcement caught Sam by surprise, but he struck as dignified a pose as he could in his theatrical costume.

"This is a night for pure pleasure, not the serious business of governing our beloved land," Andrew Jackson continued. "But with so many good friends gathered here, I wanted to take this opportunity to tell you that I intend to cast my vote for Sam Houston, and I hope you will, too."

The endorsement of Andrew Jackson was the only support Sam needed. He campaigned actively, although unnecessarily, facing only token opposition, and was elected to Congress by the biggest vote ever recorded in Tennessee's 9th District.

"I'll look after your interests, General," he told Jackson on the day of his departure.

"I know you will, boy. But I want you to be your own man in Congress, not mine."

"I'll stand on my own feet, sir, never fear." Sam smiled faintly. "And while I'm at it, I'll find occasion to show Mr. Calhoun I haven't forgotten his insult to a poor lieutenant."

The new member of the House traveled to Washington City with his colleagues from Tennessee, who were so insistent in their use of his military title that everyone with whom he dealt also called him General Houston. He took quarters in one of the town's newer inns, Brown's Hotel, although somewhat less expensive lodgings were available.

"I wouldn't think of staying anywhere else," he told Felix Grundy. "You've heard the story of my visit here with the Cherokee?"

"Heard it? Hell, Sam, I was right here at the time!"

"Then maybe you'll recall we pitched our tents on the very ground where Brown's has been built. So I wouldn't live anywhere else in Washington City, ever, not if my life depended on it!"

Ensconced in the quarters he considered appropriate, the new member of the House showed his accustomed vigor in learning the responsibilities of his position. He was assiduous in looking after the interests of his constituents, and when Henry Clay returned to the House as Speaker, Sam managed to obtain from him an appointment to the Military Affairs Committee. Less than twenty-four hours later he sent a brief letter to Secretary of War Calhoun.

"At your convenience, sir," he wrote, *"I will be grateful for the privilege of examining such War Department ledgers as pertain to the expenses incurred by the civilian members of the Department, the Secretary, his staff & etc. As a former officer in the Regular Military establishment I know only too well that commissioned officers must exert unceasing effort to obtain reimbursement for expenses they may incur while attending the business of their government. Subsequently, when serving as commander-in-chief of the Tennessee Division, it has come to my attention that those who most frequently abuse and offend the public purse are those civilian supernumeraries who attach themselves to the Military. It is my duty, as a member of the Military Affairs Committee of the House of Representatives, to insure that such abuses cease forthwith in the Federal establishment, should, indeed, there be any. I feel confident, sir, that you earnestly share my desire that the Department responsible for the defense of our nation stand above and beyond reproach at all times."*

Sam did not smile when it was reported to him that the annoyed Secretary of War, ordering a subordinate to send the ledgers to the House, remarked, "Damn that Houston! I might have

73

known he'd be a gadfly, and should have squashed him when I could."

The first blow had been struck in an unrelenting campaign.

The affairs of Andrew Jackson were not prospering in Washington City. Sam and the other members of the Tennessee Congressional delegation made a quiet survey, and found that, in the impending election, Old Hickory, although the most popular candidate, lacked the support to obtain a majority vote in the Electoral College. The busy Sam immediately sent a letter to the Hermitage.

"The avowed candidates, Secretary of State Adams, Speaker Clay and Senator Crawford, are all here in Washington City, where they are in a position to advocate their causes by and through their proximity to the Congressional delegations of the States. Your cause suffers because of your absence, General. You should be here."

Jackson, true to his own beliefs, refused to take any active step to further his candidacy.

But Sam knew how he would react, and, along with Grundy and others, explained the situation in detail to Governor Carroll, Polk, and others in Tennessee who wanted to see Old Hickory in the White House. Carroll and Polk went to work at once, and the Tennessee Legislature responded to the emergency by electing Andrew Jackson to the United States Senate. Unable to refuse this demand that he serve his country, he reluctantly went off to Washington.

Neither Sam nor any of his other friends could persuade him to take any positive action in his own behalf, however, and in the presidential election on December 1, 1824, he received 99 electoral votes, less than a majority. John Quincy Adams stood second with 84, Senator Crawford, who fell ill, received 41, and many of his supporters joined the ranks of Henry Clay, who had 37.

Sam was even more disappointed than his Tennessee colleagues, since John C. Calhoun was elected Vice-President of the United States.

The election of the President, under the Constitution, now

went to the House of Representatives, and it was immediately obvious to everyone interested in politics that Henry Clay was a "king-maker." Although unable to win the presidency himself, his support would virtually guarantee victory for either Jackson or Adams, and Old Hickory's friends went to him, one by one, to urge that he make an arrangement with the Speaker.

"I'm sure," Sam said, "that if you offer him the post of Secretary of State, the Congressional delegations lined up behind him will move to you."

"You've caught political fever sooner than I thought you would, boy." Jackson pounded the floor of his sitting room in the suite at Brown's Hotel that he, too, had taken, and then gestured with his walking stick, wielding it like a sword. "I refuse to make a deal of any kind with anyone!"

"But Adams—"

"John Quincy Adams is an honorable man, Sam. I'll grant you he may be difficult to know, but he has too great a respect for the presidency to trade with Clay or his supporters. What's at stake here is the highest office in this land, not a country seat in some backwater state legislature. The President will be a statesman, admired by all the people, only if the men who are considered for the office think and act as statesmen. Under no circumstances will I permit you—or any other friend—to approach Clay! The House of Representatives will make its selection on the basis of merit alone, as it must!"

Sam was disappointed, but felt unbounded admiration for a man who had a great prize within his grasp, yet refused to compromise with his principles in order to win it. No matter how the House voted, Andrew Jackson was a great man and a great American.

On February 9, 1824, the House of Representatives convened for the purpose of electing the sixth President of the United States. The state delegations pledged to Henry Clay cast their ballots for John Quincy Adams, who was declared the victor. Then, twenty-four hours later, President-elect Adams announced he was awarding the highest appointive post, that of Secretary of State, to Speaker Henry Clay.

The friends and supporters of Andrew Jackson were outraged, but Adams, replying to their charges with dignified calm, declared that he had made no deal, and had given Clay the Secretaryship because he was better qualified for it than any other man in the nation. There were few, other than those who knew him intimately and were aware of his personal integrity, who believed him.

"The Presidency of the United States," said a grim Andrew Jackson, "has been auctioned from the block like a racing horse. I didn't want to be President, but I would have accepted had it been the people's will. The citizens of this nation were given no real choice. Now things are different. I'm going to start running, right now, and I won't stop until I win in '28!"

Sam Houston was even more thoroughly disillusioned. "There's only one thing that counts," he said. "The power to control votes. No matter how high a man's ideals, he can't help the people unless he carries a heavy club, and is willing to use it. I was an amateur at this game, a play-actor who assumed that everybody else was a gentleman. But no more. From now on, I'll know how to behave!"

Congressman Sam Houston of the 9th Tennessee District displayed seemingly inexhaustible energy, and rapidly moved into a position of leadership in the newly emerging Democratic party that was opposed to the administration of President Adams. Reelected, he worked ceaselessly for his own constituents, for roads and other improvements that would help the entire West, and with undiminished zeal he continued to support Andrew Jackson for the presidency in 1828. Although he had never before shown talents as a writer, he was co-author of a biography of Old Hickory, and Senator John Eaton raised so much money for the publication of the book that copies flooded the country.

James K. Polk joined Sam in the House, and not a day passed without a speech made by one or the other praising Old Hickory. "Those Congressmen from Tennessee," President Adams remarked to his Cabinet, "are the noisiest hornets in Washington. When they aren't demanding funds to help the West, they're crowning Jackson with fresh laurel wreaths. They clamor so loudly for his election as my successor that they give me no chance to show my capabilities. I suppose I should be grateful they aren't demanding my impeachment."

Sam's reputation as a hothead was not diminished by an incident that caused a furor in Nashville during the summer of 1826. The city's postmastership fell vacant, and the candidate proposed by Sam was not appointed, the place going instead to one of the few Adams-Clay supporters in the area, John P. Erwin. Sam lost his temper, and sent a barrage of letters to the Nashville newspapers, accusing Erwin of incompetence, chicanery and, as his fury mounted, corrupt idiocy.

On August 16 Representative Houston arrived home, following the adjournment of Congress, and the next morning, when he emerged from the Inn after breakfast, he found two men waiting for him. One was a lawyer with whom he was acquainted, William A. White, who was a friend of Erwin's, and the other was a burly fellow who called himself "Colonel John T. Smith" and who, according to a vague rumor, was a professional duelist.

Scenting trouble, Sam nodded to them, pulled down the brim of his white beaver hat and started off up Market Street.

The pair fell in beside him, and "Colonel Smith" removed a folded sheet of paper sealed with a blob of wax from his pocket and tried to thrust it into the Congressman's hand.

Sam smiled and refused to accept it. "I make it a rule to read no letters from constituents except those sent to my office," he said.

"Are you a coward, sir?" the "Colonel" demanded.

"My record—and the scars of combat I carry on my body to this day prove I'm not, sir." Sam was pleased that, in moments of personal crisis, he remained unruffled. "Why does Erwin send others to do his errands for him?" He tipped his hat to a pretty girl whom he knew slightly and with whom he made up his mind to become better acquainted.

"John Erwin suffers from poor health, General Houston," White

77

said, "and is content to settle the issue in the newspapers. But his friends demand more direct satisfaction."

"You're his friend?" Sam, thinking rapidly, knew that White had been a wilderness hunter in his younger days, but couldn't see how a confrontation could be avoided.

"Both of us are his friends," the lawyer replied.

Sam stared with cold distaste at "Colonel Smith," and shook his head. "This person has never been presented to me, sir, and I don't defend my honor in fights with total strangers."

The "Colonel" shrugged, which indicated he would receive his pay regardless of whether he actively participated in a duel.

"But you know me, General," White persisted.

"Indeed I do, sir!"

"Are we on speaking terms that will permit you to write me a letter?"

The trap was so obvious that Sam chuckled. "The saddle is on the other horse, White!"

"Must I write to you at your office?"

"Save yourself the ink and paper." Sam halted near the entrance to the *Banner* office, and bowed the other man toward the door. "The requirements in such matters will be satisfied if the arrangements are made in the presence of witnesses."

All three entered the offices of the newspaper, and it was immediately apparent from the stir they created that the staff members already knew that a challenge would be issued.

Sam marched to a place near the desk of the assistant editor who happened to be in charge at the moment, and announced in a loud voice, "Gentlemen, you're about to witness a somewhat unorthodox procedure. Since I'm busy protecting the interests of the citizens of Nashville and am devoting every moment I can spare to helping General Jackson win the presidency, we are dispensing with the usual ritual performed by seconds. I believe Mr. White has something he wants to say to me."

"I do, General." White spoke slowly and clearly. "You have sullied the honor of Postmaster Erwin, whose frail health makes it impossible for him to defend himself. Therefore, in his name, I challenge you to meet me on the field of honor."

"I accept, sir!" Sam cut in quickly, before the lawyer had completed his sentence.

There was a silence, and one of the *Banner* staff murmured, "You have the choice of weapons, General Houston."

"So I do." Sam smiled without humor. "We'll fight one week from today, with pistols. Each man will be permitted two shots, and we'll stand twelve paces apart."

The spectators gasped, White became pale and even "Colonel Smith" looked uneasy. With the chance to fire two shots at such close range, it was almost inevitable that at least one contestant would be seriously wounded, perhaps killed.

"Listen to an old mule who learned his lessons with gunpowder," Andrew Jackson said. "I still carry two bullets in me that I earned in duels, and I damned near died in that stupid brawl I had with Tom Benton, who has become one of my strongest supporters ever since he moved to Missouri."

"Under some circumstances a duel can't be avoided, sir," Sam said.

Old Hickory tugged at his jaw. "Your enemies and mine are going to turn this into a real jamboree, boy."

"Are you suggesting I retract?" Sam jumped to his feet and began to pace the length of the Hermitage library.

"No. You can't! I'd disown you if you tried. I merely wanted to point out the consequences to you, if they hadn't crossed your mind."

"I'm well aware of them, sir." Sam's smile was wry.

"First off, I'll make you the loan of a brace of fine French pistols I've owned for years. Their hair triggers have been shaved fine, and they'll respond to the slightest touch. Practice with them at least an hour every day, boy. If you like, use my back pasture. Nobody will disturb you there."

"Thank you, General."

Old Hickory pulled himself to his feet with an effort and went to the windows that looked out across the broad green lawns of his estate. "I reckon I'll have to go with you myself to the duel to make sure no mischief is done."

Sam was horrified. "I can't permit it, sir!"

Jackson ignored the protest. "Jamie wants to act as your other second. It would be best to oblige him."

"General, the Adams-Clay people are already calling you a blood-thirsty murderer. Can you imagine what they'd say if you acted as a second in a duel fought by one of your close supporters? Don't take my word for it. Senator Eaton and Felix will forbid you to go, and Billy Carroll—"

"Have you ever known me to take orders from any man?" Andrew Jackson drew himself to his full height in a vain attempt to meet Sam at eye level.

"Hang it, sir—"

"Boy, this duel is being fought on my account. Erwin was given his appointment because he was opposed to me. You hit out at him because he's an Adams-Clay man. Maybe you hit a mite too hard, everything considered, but a little show of honest temper never hurt anyone. And then you were inveigled into this duel because my enemies want to embarrass me. Well, I intend to show them I stand with my friends."

Sam was overwhelmed. "You're very generous, sir. But I wish you'd find out what Eaton and Jamie and some of the others think before you do something you might regret."

"When I've made up my mind, I've yet to meet the man who can persuade me to change it!" Jackson softened as he returned to his chair. "Jamie sounded as you did when I first told him my intentions, but by the time I was done he was swearing he'll let no one else act as your other second."

"I'm grateful to both of you."

"Gratitude has never won a gunfight at close range, Sam. Hie yourself out into that pasture and practice!"

An early morning mist settled over the hills west of Nashville, obscuring the forest treetops and soaking the path that followed the south bank of the Cumberland River. Branches were dripping, and the horses occasionally sidestepped to avoid a drooping limb or bush. The three men, all of them dressed in somber black relieved by the glitter of their sword hilts, rode in single file, and only Andrew Jackson, who naturally took the lead, was loquacious.

"This reminds me of my younger days, although the woods were much thicker then. You know, I rode on this same path to fight three of my duels. I still shiver when I remember them."

Congressman Polk wished, for Sam's sake, that he would stop dwelling on the subject of fear, and there was a subtle, scoffing note in his polite laugh.

Old Hickory heard it. "Jamie," he said, "you're not the type of man who'll ever fight a duel, and that's a blessing. You're too intelligent, and your mind keeps a tight rein on your feelings. We need more like you in this country, which is one reason you'll go far, mark my words. But Sam, here, is more like me. We're two buzzards from the same flock. That's why I know that right now he's shaking so hard his boots may drop off his feet."

"What makes you so certain, sir?" Sam spoke quietly.

"It's one thing when you flare up like a torch soaked in pitch when you're in the midst of battle. But right now you're riding to a murder—maybe Willie White's, maybe your own."

Polk tried desperately to think of some way to change the subject.

But Sam grinned. "Damned if you aren't a sly old fox, General."

Jackson twisted around in his saddle and glared. "I resent accusations, General Houston!"

"We're buzzards from the same flock, right enough." Sam chuckled again. "You're doing just what I'd do if our positions were reversed. For one thing, you're trying to shame me into calming myself."

Andrew Jackson pretended to peer off through the fog at the river. "Well, now—"

"And for another, you know I can't do anything to prevent White from killing me, but you're trying to warn me there might be nasty political repercussions if I do worse than wound him. You don't want to discourage me or take the fine edge off my spirit. But, at the same time, you don't want me to ruin my own career or hurt your chances in '28."

Polk fastened his cloak more tightly to protect his collar, and marveled at the ability of these two to understand each other.

"I'm not quite sure what scares me more," Sam continued, "the thought of dying or of being branded a murderer. But I've never avoided a fight in my life, and at thirty-three years of age I'm too old to start forming new habits."

Jackson's slow nod indicated his approval, and he became quiet.

None of the trio spoke again, and shortly after daybreak, after another half-hour's ride, they came to a natural, grassy clearing. There a number of men were already assembled, among them William White and his seconds, also dressed in black, two physicians and a small group of Democratic political leaders whose presence was unexpected. The rotund Senator Eaton looked concerned, Felix Grundy wore his habitual scowl, and Representative Cave Johnson, a tall, laconic young frontiersman who was rapidly moving higher in the ranks of Jackson's followers, was the only man who moved.

Raising his hat to Old Hickory, he quickly came forward and took Sam's bridle. "How do you feel?"

"Tolerable."

"Good. White has been boasting that he's going to put his first bullet through your heart."

"That'll take some extra-fancy shooting." Sam dismounted and took care to bow to everyone except his opponent. It was essential that a gentleman observe the amenities of a duel.

It was said there were no neutrals in Tennessee, that most men were in Andrew Jackson's camp, while his relatively few foes hated him passionately. The claim was only a slight exaggeration of the truth; certainly retired Judge George P. Wilson was on cordial terms with everyone. A resident of Knoxville from the days that Tennessee had been denied admission to the Union and had, briefly, organized herself as a separate nation called Franklin, he had moved to Nashville in order to be near his married daughters, and took no active part in the state's political life.

He had been an obvious choice as referee, and it was plain from his authoritative manner as he moved to the center of the clearing that duels were no novelty to him. "May I have your attention, gentlemen? Be good enough to tether your horses near the river, so they won't be menaced by stray shots."

Several men hastened to move the horses.

"Under the code of affairs of blood, I am required to ask the principals whether they are willing to be reconciled. Mr. White?"

"The honor of John Erwin makes it impossible for me to be reconciled." White spoke in a firm voice.

"General Houston?"

"My own honor prevents a reconciliation."

Judge Wilson summoned the seconds, and began to confer with them.

Sam stood apart, turned his back on everyone and looked off into the trees. A yellow poplar, taller and fuller than those in Virginia, reminded him of his father, but he hastily checked his thoughts. This was no time to be moved by sentiment. Near the water's edge was a cluster of dew-heavy wildflowers, and he recalled the impression he had made on a young lady in Washington City to whom he had recently presented a bouquet he had picked in a patch of woods in nearby Maryland. The girl had read too much significance into the gift, unfortunately, and he had been forced to stop seeing her. That sort of thing happened all too often; there had been so many women in his life, but none of them had meant anything to him.

Now, when it might be too late, was no time to wonder whether he should have made it his business to find a wife and settle down with her. His life had been far lonelier than he had allowed himself to realize, but he could blame no one except himself. Perhaps he was one of those men destined for bachelorhood. Yet, with the possible end so near, he couldn't help wishing he had sired a son to whom he could give his name—and his father's.

The scent of the pines was strong, and Sam inhaled deeply. Losing one's life in personal combat was not the same as dying in battle for a cause to which one's whole being was devoted. On the other hand, nothing was more sacred than a man's honor, and he twisted the gold ring on the little finger of his left hand.

Andrew Jackson touched his shoulder, and startled him.

"You'll use both sets of pistols, Sam. One of mine, that you've been using for practice all week, and one of Willie White's. I gave his seconds their choice of the pistols. I didn't think it mattered."

Sam saw that Jamie and one of White's seconds were inspecting and carefully loading the pistols. Everyone was watching them, and the low murmur of conversation had stopped. For an instant the glances of Sam and his adversary locked, then White turned away.

Finally Judge Wilson summoned the two principals, while the seconds moved aside with the weapons. "You'll stand back to back," the referee said, "and then you'll be handed your firearms. When I start counting, you'll each take six paces. Once I've called out number six, you're free to turn and fire whenever you please. Each of you has two shots. Fire them whenever you wish. If one of you is killed or hurt by the first shot, though, you're not allowed to fire the second. The drawing of blood means honor has been satisfied. Do you understand me, gentlemen?"

White merely nodded.

"I do, sir," Sam said.

"If either of you fires before I've counted to six, or if you fire a second shot after drawing blood with the first, I'll be obliged to shoot you myself. In my opinion, a quick death is too good for any man who knowingly breaks the code of gentlemen. Now, for the last time, if either of you is willing to reconcile, speak up!"

Both contestants remained silent.

"Stand back to back!"

White's second gave Sam two pistols, which he inspected. Both were loaded and appeared to be in good working order. A plan had formed in his mind, and he kept White's pistol in his left hand. General Jackson's, with which he was familiar, he held in his right.

"One!" Judge Wilson called.

Sam was mildly surprised to discover that his step was firm and that the tugging feeling in the pit of his stomach had disappeared.

"Two!"

The sun was beginning to rise, but would neither cut through the fog nor rise above the level of the treetops before the shooting began, and therefore would not be a factor in the duel.

"Three!"

Sam knew the presidency of the United States as well as his

own career might depend on his ability to draw blood without killing or inflicting serious injury, while, at the same time, incapacitating his opponent so that he himself would not die. The challenge might be greater than his skills.

"Four!"

No matter how great the task, however, he had to accomplish it. There was no alternative, no margin for error.

"Five!"

The responsibility he had assumed, both for Andrew Jackson and for himself, was enormous, yet he was discovering that the drama of the situation stimulated him. Perhaps that was why his fear had vanished and he had become so calm.

"Six!"

Both men turned, and Sam fired with the pistol in his left hand as he wheeled around. He was no more than a split second faster than White, but the very slight advantage was enough. His shot struck the other man's pistol, knocking it from his hand, just as White squeezed the trigger, and the lawyer's bullet went high into the air.

Now White had to transfer his other pistol to his right hand. This respite gave Sam all the time he needed. He already held Old Hickory's French dueling pistol in his right hand, and took rapid but deliberate aim with it, ignoring the flicker of terror he saw in his adversary's eyes. There was a surprisingly gentle crack, and White fell to the ground with a wound in the fleshy part of his thigh.

Judge Wilson immediately stepped into the center of the clearing, giving White no chance to fire his own second shot, and his seconds went to him in order to disarm him before he could fire again from a prone position. Blood had been drawn, so honor had been satisfied.

Sam quietly surrendered his own pistols to Jamie Polk, then walked slowly toward his opponent, waiting until the two physicians completed their preliminary examination.

"It will be the work of only a few minutes to remove the bullet and stop the flow of blood," one of them said. "There's no permanent injury, I'm sure."

Sam looked down at his opponent. "I'm sorry I had to do it," he said, "but you gave me no choice."

"I know. You could have killed me just now, General Houston, but you were generous. I'm grateful to you, and I bear you no grudge for wounding me." White extended his hand.

Sam grasped it. "I have no personal quarrel with you, or with any man." He thought of Vice-President Calhoun, and amended his statement. "In Tennessee."

He recrossed the clearing to the place where his friends had gathered, and were waiting to congratulate him.

"Why didn't you tell us you could shoot with both hands?" Andrew Jackson demanded. "You'd have saved us a heap of worry. How did you ever learn to shoot left-handed?"

Emotion choked Sam. "My father taught me, when I was a youngster," he said. "He aways told me the day might come when I'd find it convenient to use firearms with either hand." No matter how high in the world he had risen, no matter how much higher he might climb, he would never be able to repay his debt to the father who remained his idol.

Under Tennessee law a governor of the state was not allowed to succeed himself, so the Democratic leaders gathered in the private dining room of the Nashville Inn to select a new candidate. The last to arrive was Andrew Jackson, and the younger men stood as he walked to the dinner table.

"I'm blamed if I know why we had to meet here when I offered you the hospitality of the Hermitage," he said.

Several men started to speak simultaneously, but Governor Carroll silenced them. "We wouldn't want it said that we were using your house for politicking, sir."

Old Hickory grimaced. "Don't you read the Adams-Clay newspapers? They're claiming I urged Sam to run his sword through Willie White after wounding him. They'll make any claim against me, hoping that somewhere there are men foolish enough to believe it."

The others laughed. "I'm not a betting man," Sam told him, "but I've offered a wager of any sum up to one thousand dollars, at five to one odds, that you'll be the next President. So far I can't find anyone who'll accept, not even Newton Cannon, who'll probably become the Whig candidate for governor. When I ran into him yesterday, I challenged him, but he said he doesn't believe in making personal wagers."

"Cannon is a wise man," Polk observed, "but not quite wise enough. He'll be beaten if he tries to become governor, provided we put up the right candidate."

"What have you boys decided?" Andrew Jackson asked.

"Nothing, sir," Carroll told him. "We've been waiting for you, and haven't even discussed the situation."

Jackson sighed. "You lads have minds of your own, and I'm damned if I'm going to express my opinions until I hear what you have to say. In a democracy, every man thinks for himself. Billy?"

Carroll picked up a whisky jug, poured some liquor into his glass and passed the jug around the table. Everyone except Polk, who didn't drink, helped himself. "I've been giving the problem a great deal of thought," Carroll said. "Unlike the rest of you, I have no interest in holding any office that will take me away from Tennessee. I'd like to return to the governorship after my successor serves his term—"

"No man of integrity would agree to that!" Jackson said sharply. "I'll grant you that he couldn't succeed himself, either, but if he's honest he won't be a party to a private arrangement. We want the candidate who is best qualified, and will make the best impression on the voters."

Carroll managed to smile. "I guarantee all of you there will be no private arrangement. As to the man best qualified, I believe Sam Houston would make a first-rate governor. What's more, no one in the state except General Jackson is more popular."

The thought of becoming governor had not occurred to Sam, and he laughed self-deprecatingly.

Jackson pointed at John Eaton. "Senator, what are your views?"

"Sam is the obvious candidate. The way he handled Willie White in their duel won him even more support than all his speeches in favor of strengthening the Union and obeying the spirit of the Constitution."

Again the bony finger jabbed. "Felix?"

"Sam," said Congressman Grundy, who didn't believe in wasting words.

"Cave?"

Representative Johnson grinned. "You're going to believe we've held a private caucus, but we haven't. It's been plain to me for a long time that Sam ought to move into Billy's place."

"Jamie?"

Congressman Polk was thoughtful. "After a man has served in Washington City and has concentrated on the problems of a whole nation, he sometimes doesn't want to focus only on local issues. So I don't believe we have the right to force anyone to make what he might consider as a sacrifice. If Sam is willing, though, he's the natural choice."

Sam was overwhelmed by the unanimity of their views.

"What do you think, sir?" Carroll asked Jackson.

"I've had only one man in mind for a long time." Old Hickory turned in his seat and looked at Sam. "The governorship is a mighty important post. It can also be a steppingstone." He did not elaborate. "So, I'd say, everything depends on what you yourself want. If you're willing to be a candidate, I'll be available for as much campaign help as you'd like."

Sam saw all the others looking at him, and tried to clear his mind. Jackson's hint had been plain enough: some day, assuming that Old Hickory himself became President, he would use his influence to groom a favorite protégé for the nation's highest office. Too much could happen, however, for anyone to look years ahead. The governorship had to be considered on its own merits.

"I reckon we ought to give him a few days to think it over," Andrew Jackson said. "It isn't fair to ask him to make a commitment before he can weigh it."

"That won't be necessary, sir," Sam said. "I appreciate the confidence my friends show in me. If I was an amateur politician when I first went to Washington City, I've changed. I hope to spend the rest of my life serving the people. I'd be happier in Congress, I suppose, because I'd enjoy working for the administration's program when General Jackson becomes President. But

88

I'll do what's best for the electorate. If you think I can become an effective governor, I'll bow to your judgment."

The newspapers of Tennessee were in unanimous agreement that Sam Houston's campaign was spectacular. He visited every township of every county in the state, mounted on a magnificent gray stallion. He wore a white beaver hat, a coat with a standing collar that gave him a military appearance, a ruffled shirt and black satin waistcoat, and on his pumps were burnished silver buckles. Instead of a cloak, a beaded Indian hunting shirt was thrown over his shoulders, and was held in place by a sash of scarlet silk.

"*The candidate of the Democrats,*" said the Nashville *Whig,* "*resembles either a play-actor or a peddler of herb medicines. He does not comport himself with the dignity we expect of our state's first citizen.*"

Sam drew tremendous crowds everywhere, and blithely ignored the criticism. He confined himself to two campaign themes, and hammered at both relentlessly. "The Union of our sovereign states is sacred, and must be respected," he said again and again. "Under the Constitution it will grow and flourish. If the Union is strong, our beloved Tennessee will grow stronger and more prosperous. I intend, as governor, to devote all of my waking moments to her increased prosperity and strength."

The election was held on September 8, 1827, and three days later Congressman Polk brought the final returns to his friend, who had just returned to the Inn after visiting his mother. "Sam, we won't be making the journey to Washington together, and I'm sorry. But there are compensations. You'll be giving up this room for that grand new mansion Billy Carroll built."

Sam looked around the small room that had been his home for so long, and there was genuine regret in his voice when he said, "I've become attached to this place, and I have no use for a mansion."

"Like it or not, that's where you're moving."

"You picked up the final returns from the *Banner* office, Jamie?"

"All but a few scattered villages have reported, and you've won the biggest victory in history. More than forty-two thousand votes to thirty-one thousand for Cannon. Congratulations."

Sam shook his hand. "For a man who wanted to retire from public life four years ago," he said, "I seem to find myself in strange circumstances."

"Sometimes I think you're serious when you speak of retirement."

Sam's smile faded. "It's odd to say this when I've just been elected to the highest office in the state, but sometimes I believe I'm serious, too. Maybe the years I spent with the Cherokee marked me more than I know, but every now and again I get a craving for solitude."

"What you need is a wife."

"Now you sound like my mother, Jamie, and Old Hickory. Find me the right woman, and I'll marry her."

Governor Sam Houston took the oath of office on October 1, 1827, before a crowd so large that the ceremonies were transferred from the State House of Representatives to the First Baptist Church, Nashville's largest building. His mother was in attendance, escorted by General Jackson, and a number of Sam's other relatives were also present.

Demonstrating his grasp of Tennessee's problems, Governor Houston made a number of strong recommendations. He intended to appoint a board of engineers to recommend the building of new roads to tie the various parts of the state together, and would ask the legislature for appropriate funds after the engineers reported to him. Tennessee, he declared, was growing rapidly, and he proposed that lands in the public domain be sold only to men who intended to build homes and factories. He deplored the practice of allowing "our land, next to our freedom our most precious heritage," to fall into the hands of speculators. Care should be taken to exclude these "vultures who would feed upon the body politic," and all funds derived from land sales should be spent on schools, roads, and other internal improvements.

He was particularly emphatic in discussing the future of Tennessee's schools. "When I was young," he said, "I was foolish, and had it not been for my mother, I would today be uneducated. I propose that no child in this state be given the opportunity to exercise the prerogative of stubborn stupidity that so often afflicts the young. I propose that education be made compulsory for every boy until he reaches his fifteenth birthday, and that schools be supported by state funds."

While his audience was digesting his radical suggestion, he made another. "Ever since the first settlers moved into the Tennessee Valley," he said, "man has been handicapped by the rapids on the Tennessee River known as Muscle Shoals. These fearsome rapids, more than thirty-five miles in length, prevent the use of a natural waterway that would link this state with her neighbors to the south. I therefore intend to appoint a board of the most competent engineers I can find to deal with the problem, and will instruct its members to prepare plans for the building of a canal that will circumvent Muscle Shoals. The forces of nature must be made to bend to the will of man."

The idea was so sensible that the audience, as the *Banner* reported the following day, "wondered why no one had ever before made such a practical suggestion."

In closing, Governor Houston enunciated the principles that would guide him for the rest of his life. "One of my primary obligations, one of my first duties, now and always, is to support the Constitution of the United States. It is the cement that binds together our Union, and let no man misunderstand me, now or ever. I love this nation!

"I am sensible of the sacred and important character of the Constitution, and that it ought not to be violated—its provisions should be regarded, and extended in their operations, to the purposes of its adoption."

General Jackson led an outburst of applause, which interrupted the speaker.

"But at the same time," Governor Houston continued, when the audience became quiet again, "at the same time that we hold that production of our ancestors sacred, we should observe with vigilance, and guard with firmness, our own Tennessee Constitution—which is the guarantee of our sovereignty—whenever an infraction of it is attempted by the General Government.

"Thus, while we support the Federal Constitution according to its *essential* principles, with a view to the preservation of the national confederacy on the one hand—we are bound, on the other, to watch over and preserve the rights of our state.

"I am, above all, a citizen of the United States. I am, simultaneously, the elected shepherd of the Tennessee flock. I see no conflict between the two. Their responsibilities join and flow in one steady stream. To you who are gathered here, I swear that I shall be true to the trust placed in me, for I place honor above all."

The Democratic Party, in its first convention, unanimously nominated Andrew Jackson of Tennessee as its candidate for President of the United States. Old Hickory did not attend the convention himself, but was represented by Governor Sam Houston, who placed his name before the delegates.

The National Republican Party, some of whose branches called themselves Whigs, and which itself would soon revert to the name of the Whig Party, nominated the incumbent President, John Quincy Adams. Not even the President's most ardent supporters believed he had much chance of being re-elected.

The election was held on December 3, 1828, and one week later virtually all of the votes were tallied. As anticipated, Jackson won, with about 650,000 votes to Adams' 500,000. Vice-President Calhoun, with whom Andrew Jackson soon would break, was virtually unopposed, and easily won a new term.

Nashville, which had been celebrating for days, went wild when the official election results were received. Offices and business establishments closed for the day, courts were adjourned and taverns, including the staid Nashville Inn, were crowded with merrymakers. Huge bonfires were lighted, and citizens by the hundreds began a spontaneous march out to the Hermitage. Everyone, including the few who had voted for President Adams, agreed there had never been such a day in Tennessee's history.

At the Executive Mansion the atmosphere was more subdued, but there was an undercurrent of excitement in the air. Governor

Houston had been seeing visitors, but, soon after Congressman Polk arrived to tell him the news, an aide appeared in the anteroom and announced that all pending appointments were being postponed. When the visitors learned the reason, they cheered, even though some had been waiting for hours.

Inside the simply furnished office, from which most of Billy Carroll's ornate decorations had been stripped, Sam leaned back in his chair and grinned. "We've had no doubts, Jamie, but it's good to know the outcome. I wish you drank. I hate to toast the old man alone."

"On an occasion like this," Representative Polk said, "I'm pleased to break my rule."

Sam went to a cabinet, and removed a jug of whisky. "We'll have to ride out to the Hermitage this evening. Eaton and Felix and the others will want to go, too." He poured generous quantities of liquor into two silver cups. "I give you the President-elect of the United States!"

Polk took a token sip. "I have another toast I'd like to make, too. I want to drink to the man who has removed himself from Washington, where he can make no new enemies for himself. The man who holds a high office in his own right, and whose name everyone at the convention mentioned as the inevitable candidate when Old Hickory retires. The man who is closer to Andrew Jackson, both in person and in spirit, than anyone else. To the future President—Sam Houston!"

FOUR

1829–31

Eliza Allen of Gallatin, a small town northeast of Nashville, came to the capital with her parents to visit relatives during the rounds of banquets and grand balls, assemblies and barbecues celebrating the victory of President-elect Jackson. Sam first became aware of her at a reception he himself gave in the Executive Mansion ten days before Christmas. Among those present were his current mistress and two other women whose favors he had enjoyed, but he immediately forgot all other members of the opposite sex as he whispered to Senator Eaton, "Who is that girl with the yellow hair and blue eyes?"

She seemed self-conscious when Sam was presented to her, and he promptly did his gallant best to put her at her ease. "Has anyone told you that you're the prettiest girl here?"

Eliza blushed furiously.

"I've always said that a gown of simple white is far more effective than the colored silks with ostrich feathers and suchlike that some ladies wear." His comment on her dress of plain linen gave him the opportunity to admire her trim figure without the need to ogle surreptitiously.

The girl giggled. "This was my graduation dress. When I left Miss Overton's Academy. That was the only time I ever wore it, and Mama insisted I get some use out of it." She looked at him suspiciously, lashes sweeping down over her huge eyes. "Did my parents ask you to compliment me, Your Excellency? I was ashamed to wear a school dress to a grand party like this."

"I scarcely know your parents, and I give you my solemn word that I am a member of no conspiracy."

Eliza peered at him still more intently, and was satisfied that he was sincere. "Thank you for making me feel a little better. I cried all afternoon yesterday, and again this morning."

"I'll issue an executive decree making it a crime for anyone to bring tears to a face as lovely as yours."

She averted her eyes in a gesture totally lacking in coquetry.

Sam realized that the lavish praise relished by more mature women was upsetting her, and was afraid she might be even younger than he had imagined. "I know very little about academies for young ladies. I assume yours is the one operated by Judge Overton's sister."

Eliza nodded. "I was awarded my certificate last month."

His discomfort increased. "If you'll forgive my bluntness, I assume you're about nineteen."

"Eighteen, Your Excellency."

He would be thirty-six in less than three months, and was literally twice her age. "Your poise," he lied, "makes you seem much older."

She saw that scores of guests in the large main parlor of the Executive Mansion were staring at them, but she had no idea how to escape gracefully. Unsure of how to converse with this self-assured giant who was the most important man in Tennessee, she merely smiled at him.

Sam discovered, to his surprise, that he was riding the crest of a rising wave of excitement. "Will you have another glass of sack?" He signaled to a servant, who came to him at once.

"One glass is more than enough for me, Your Excellency," Eliza said, and belatedly remembered her manners. "But thank you."

"Nonsense!" he said. "Sack is the least intoxicating of spirits, and helps purify the blood. Not that you need it, I'm sure. Refill Miss Allen's glass, and bring me another whisky."

95

She knew it would be useless to protest again, and it was apparent that what her father and his friends said about the governor were true. She hadn't paid too much attention to the subject, but had gleaned that he was a very forceful man who had his own way in all things.

Sam took her glass from the servant and handed it to her with a bow. "To you," he said, and scarcely felt his own strong drink as it slid down.

Eliza began to enjoy her triumph. She would try to remember all of it to repeat to her friends when she returned home, and was pleased there were enough witnesses to testify that she wasn't exaggerating. Then she caught sight of her parents at the far side of the room and, seeing her mother whispering excitedly, felt her joy drain away. The moment a man paid the slightest attention to her, Mama jumped to conclusions, but it would be absurd to think that someone as old and as prominent as Governor Houston was doing more than being gallantly polite to her.

She decided to terminate the conversation before Mama began to tell people he was paying court to her. "Please don't neglect your other guests for me, Your Excellency."

Sam saw Jamie Polk and John Eaton grinning at him across the room. "They're looking after themselves very nicely, and I believe I'm entitled to the most pleasant interlude I've known in years."

Eliza saw he was standing directly in front of her, and realized it would be rude to sidle past him. She forced herself to accept the inevitable.

"I reckon you're happy that General Jackson was elected."

"I—I suppose I am. I know Papa was happy, but I'm rather ignorant on matters of politics."

"To be sure." He had been wrong to assume that a young female might know or care about such things. "What are your interests?"

She thought for a moment. "Well, I like to read."

"Splendid! What books in particular do you like?"

"I love the poetry of John Keats."

"I'm afraid I'm not familiar with the work of Mr. Keats." The name was vaguely familiar, and he believed that the man was an

English poet who had died a few years earlier. But it would be a tactical error to admit that all poetry bored him. "Do you know the works of Ovid?"

"Only what we had to read in school." All older people, Eliza thought, seemed to prefer literature written in Latin or Greek.

Sam thought it wise to shift ground. "Do you ride?"

"Oh, yes! I have two mares of my own at home—"

"Then you shall select one from my stable, and I'll consider it a rare privilege to ride with you for an hour before breakfast tomorrow morning. Perhaps you and your parents would like to join me here for breakfast."

She knew her father would be delighted. "You're very kind, Your Excellency," she said faintly.

"That's what strangers call me. I hate formality."

It dawned on her that his interest was more than perfunctory, and, in a strange way, she enjoyed the sense of power she was exerting. Certainly none of her classmates at Miss Overton's Academy had known a similar experience. "I'll do as you say, sir." She began, for the first time, to flirt with him.

It occurred to Sam that he would be prudent to back off before he became involved with a girl who was naïve and simple, little more than a child. For years he had confined his romances to sophisticated women capable of sustaining their disappointment when it became evident to them that he had no intention of marrying them. Under no circumstances could he permit himself to tamper with the affections of someone as ingenuous as Eliza Allen; he was attracted to her, perhaps, because she was so unlike all the others.

It was far too early to know what he wanted in a relationship with her, but he already realized that her fresh beauty wasn't the only reason he was drawn to her. He felt an almost overpowering desire to protect her, and his instinct warned him that, as never before, he might become serious. It would be ridiculous, of course, to hold back because of the difference in their ages. Many men married far younger women, and he was infinitely stronger and more vigorous than anyone of his own generation whom he knew.

Eliza waited patiently for his answer.

Sam wanted to show off. "Most of my acquaintances call me General, but you're neither in politics, nor in the Army. I'm known as the Raven to the Cherokee—I suppose you've heard I lived with them for several years when I was a boy. And occasionally I hear from people who still call me Congressman instead of Governor. But titles are too stiff." He pretended to ponder for a few moments. "I reckon there's only one solution. You'll have to call me by my Christian name, Eliza."

Their friendship, if that's what it was, seemed to be moving far more rapidly than she had anticipated. "I'll try." She took a deep breath. "Sam."

"That's settled!" Preening, he beamed at her. "Eliza, will you do me the honor of allowing me to escort you to supper?"

He offered her his arm, and she thought it simply had not crossed his mind that she might refuse. She had no choice, and slipped her hand inside the bend of his elbow.

There was a stir as the governor and his young guest led the procession into the dining room of the Executive Mansion.

Eliza found it unusual, and more exciting than she had imagined, to be the object of so much attention. Obviously Governor Houston was long accustomed to the limelight, and relished it, but she felt almost painfully self-conscious with so many people staring at her and whispering.

Sam, however, blithely ignored the commotion and gossip. Arming himself with two plates, he led the girl on a march from table to table, directing the servants stationed behind each to heap their plates high. He saw to it that they were given generous portions of poached, cold salmon and grilled trout, venison steak that had been marinated in a sauce of peppers and wine, sizzling bear chops brought on order from the kitchen outbuildings, pheasant and wild turkey, and wafer-thin slices of pungent wild boar ham. Sam particularly liked the roasted eggs of wildfowl, and would have given Eliza as many as he had heaped on his own plate had she not protested.

In side dishes, carried to a dining table for them by a servant, was raw cabbage that had been soaked in vinegar and maple syrup, topped with quantities of raw, shredded carrot. The very idea of eating raw vegetables did not appeal to the girl, but Sam was proud of the concoction, saying it was a favorite of the Cherokee, and that many citizens of both Nashville and Washington City had tried the recipe and found it delicious. She politely tried a little, and found it difficult not to gag. Sam seemed unaware of her problem, and in a display of casual informality reached over to her plate for the food she could not eat.

His appetite was prodigious, and he consumed every morsel of his own supper while simultaneously conversing with the girl and exchanging greetings with the endless procession of guests who came to their table to speak a few words to him. Frequently wiping his two-pronged silver fork on a special napkin of heavy linen that he kept beside him for the purpose, he proved himself a master of the art of talking and eating without pause. His memory was extraordinary, too, and he presented at least seventy-five guests to Eliza without once faltering or forgetting a name.

Even more astonishing was his ability to consume large quantities of whisky without showing the effects of the liquor. He drank constantly through the meal, which he called a "light supper," and was as sober at its end as he had been when he had first conducted the girl into the dining room.

After eating a large portion of a cake made with corn flour and raisins, he belched politely, tried in vain to persuade Eliza to share some brandywine with him and effortlessly emptied the contents of a silver cup. "I'm afraid," he said as he held her chair for her, "that my hospitality didn't appeal to you."

"I ate so much I'll have no appetite for breakfast."

"But you'll come?" he asked, suddenly anxious.

"I'm looking forward to it." That was the truth, she thought, fascinated by this man who lived on a scale vaster than she had ever known.

"Our ride will make you hungry. But," he hastened to add, "I'll make sure you take a gentle mare."

"There's no need for that," Eliza said proudly. "I've broken in several of Papa's horses."

He grinned at her. "In that case, maybe we could arrange a friendly little race. I'll gladly give you a handicap."

"You assume I'll need one."

Her spirit delighted him. "It could be you'll beat Sam Houston in a horse race. If you do, you'll be the first, and I'll give you one of the seals of Tennessee I use on official documents as a memento. But if I win, I'll want a prize of my own."

She was almost afraid to ask, "What's that?"

"A kiss, of course." The softness of his smile belied his bold words.

Eliza realized that, without quite knowing how it had happened, a door had opened, and she had no idea how to close it again.

Nashville's matrons looked wise when it was learned that Governor Houston had left the city to spend Christmas in Gallatin, and the rumors flew still more rapidly when he went there again to see in the New Year of 1829 with the Allen family. There were few in the capital who knew, however, that Sam was unable to leave the burdens of his office behind, and that, as a consequence, he conducted a curious courtship.

Two secretaries accompanied him, and were also given quarters in the large Allen farmhouse. The party arrived at noon on the last day of the old year and pack mules carried large files of correspondence and other papers that required the governor's attention. Sam immediately retired to a suite his host had made available for the purpose, and plunged into work, eating his midday meal from a tray that was sent in to him. He did not plan to see Eliza until evening, and the other members of the family, who had become accustomed to his habits, expected him to spend the entire afternoon in the suite.

So John Allen was surprised, late in the afternoon, when his guest suddenly appeared at the entrance to the parlor and asked to see him in private.

"Please come in, Governor." Allen, who had never been active in politics, was awed by the presence of such a distinguished man under his roof.

Sam carefully closed the door behind him. "I've been finding it a mite hard to concentrate this afternoon. I want a few words with you."

"Of course, sir."

"I wonder if you can keep a secret of some importance. Obviously, Mr. Allen, I believe you can, or I wouldn't confide in you."

The Gallatin farmer bowed.

"You may have been wondering about my future, sir."

Allen stared down at the hooked rug that covered the hardwood floor. "Well, I don't know more than anybody else. I've heard rumors that you might join the Cabinet after your term expires."

"Senator Eaton will become Secretary of War. It hasn't been announced as yet, so I must ask you to be discreet."

"Certainly."

"It may have escaped your attention," Sam said, "that the Legislature recently changed the law on the rights of succession. A governor is now permitted to serve two consecutive terms of office. The press reported the bill very briefly. Even the *Banner* has been assuming that Billy Carroll will seek another term."

"I guess that's what just about everybody in the state has been expecting, Governor."

"I don't know Billy's plans. It may be that he hopes to run. Regardless of his intentions, the *Banner* will announce on January 2nd that I'm going to run for re-election."

Even a complete amateur in the world of politics understood the significance of Sam's simple statement. It was clear that there had been a major split in the ranks of the state's Democratic party, and that the candidate who had the support of Andrew Jackson would win. "Forgive my curiosity, Governor, but what does General Jackson—"

"I'm not privileged to reveal anything regarding my private conversations with the President-elect," Sam said. Relaxing a little, he smiled. "Between you and me, though, he knows my plans."

"I see." Allen saw a great deal. Old Hickory had given Governor Houston his blessings, which meant that former Governor Carroll would have to seek some other office. No man could hope to win an election in Tennessee if Jackson supported his opponent.

"I've told you all this for a reason, sir." Sam curbed a desire to pace up and down the parlor. "You have a right to know something about my future, and as near as I can judge, I'll expect to spend several more years in the Executive Mansion at Nashville."

There was an uncomfortable silence. "I'm grateful for your confidence," Allen said at last, "but I don't quite see why you think I have a right to know your plans."

"Damnation! I'm botching this, but I've had no experience in speaking to a girl's father. Mr. Allen, I love your daughter. I've been no better than any man in my day, and maybe worse than most, but I'm in love for the first time in my life, and I feel like a young colt. I'd like your permission, sir, to propose marriage to Eliza."

Allen's smile was broad. "I'd be a hypocrite if I pretended to be surprised, Governor. Mrs. Allen and I have been expecting something like this, even though your romance has developed rather suddenly. It was only two weeks ago that you and Eliza met."

"I'm a man who knows his own mind."

"The voters of this state have known it for a long time, sir, and now I'm privileged to see it at close range." Allen held out his hand. "It'll be a great honor to be Sam Houston's father-in-law. Why, just last night Mrs. Allen was saying how strange it would feel to visit Washington City and live in a guest suite at the White House." Suddenly Allen looked embarrassed, aware he had said too much.

Sam was relieved, even though he had calculated correctly when he had thought Eliza's parents ambitious. "As I told you, sir, I'm looking forward to spending the next few years in Nashville. And it's my hope that President Jackson will be in the White House himself for a long time to come."

"I share that hope, naturally," Allen said hurriedly.

Sam hooked his thumbs in the pockets of his green satin waistcoat. "Would it be breaking a confidence, Mr. Allen, to tell me how you think Eliza might react to my proposal?"

"I can give you positive assurances, Governor," the girl's father said firmly, "that she'll be receptive. Most receptive!"

Sam breathed freely for the first time in days. Ever since Eliza had appeared so unexpectedly in his life he had known the torments of love, and now he would reap the joys. The prospect staggered him, and he was glad he had waited so many years for the right woman. "I'll speak to her right now, rather than tonight. I don't want to waste a single minute."

Eliza Allen and Governor Sam Houston planned to be married on January 22, 1829, at Gallatin, in a quiet ceremony attended only by members of their families. The untimely death of Rachel Jackson less than a month earlier had caused the cancellation of numerous public events and celebrations, and Sam had vetoed the suggestion of his bride's parents that a post-wedding reception be held in the Executive Mansion in Nashville.

"It wouldn't be seemly," he said. "I have too high a regard for General Jackson, and grieve too deeply for the loss of Mrs. Jackson."

In spite of his desire to be married as soon as possible, he preferred to postpone the ceremony until the President-elect left for Washington City. The grieving Jackson departed on January 18, accompanied by most members of the Tennessee Congressional delegation, several relatives and a number of friends who were joining his personal staff. Sam awaited him in Nashville, and they rode together to the steamship that would carry Old Hickory on the first leg of his long journey eastward.

Other members of the party fell behind to give the two men a chance to confer privately, but they rode toward the wharf in a silence which Jackson was the first to break.

"Billy Carroll would have wanted the governorship, if there had been a choice, but he'll be satisfied, I think, with the first vacancy that comes up in the Senate."

Even in a time of personal tragedy Old Hickory did not forget those who were loyal to him, and Sam swallowed hard. "Thanks very much, sir. A fight with Billy would have split the party."

Andrew Jackson nodded vaguely and stared off into the distance.

"I hope, Mr. President, that you'll let me know when there's something I can do for you."

A smile appeared on Jackson's leathery face for the first time in many days. "Everybody else has been asking favors. You're the only one who has offered help. Sam, I won't forget it!"

"There's nothing I want from you, sir."

"When there is, you shall have it."

Sam couldn't imagine anything he might desire. His political future was assured, Eliza soon would be his, and his life would become complete.

"When are you being married, boy?"

"In four days, Mr. President."

"Do you love her?"

"More than I thought it possible for me to love any woman."

Jackson continued to stare off into space. "I know the feeling. It happens to a man, if he's lucky, once in his lifetime. Kiss her for me, Sam, and bring her to Washington so I can meet her. I'm going to be lonely."

"We'll come in October, sir, right after the election."

They reached the wharf, and several militia officers came forward to take their horses.

"Don't dismount, boy," the President-elect said. "You'll want to clean off your desk, so go back to your office. I hate farewells."

They leaned toward each other to shake hands. "God bless you, Mr. President," Sam said huskily, "and the country with you."

Andrew Jackson turned away abruptly.

Riding back through the streets of Nashville to the Executive Mansion, Sam felt guilty because his own happiness was so great.

The bride's mother wept, as did most of the younger women who attended the wedding, but Elizabeth Houston remained dry-eyed. "Remember," she told her son after the party arrived at the Allen house for dinner, "that Eliza is very young. Be gentle with her, and above all, be patient."

Sam tugged at his white silk waistcoat and grinned. "You sound as though you're afraid I'm an ogre."

"No, but you're impulsive. And demanding. And you've always been impatient."

"I'll tell you a secret." Sam bent down to whisper, with mock solemnity, in his mother's ear. "I love my wife!"

Elizabeth did not smile. "All the more reason to keep in mind that life isn't going to be easy for her. She's little more than a schoolgirl, and all at once she finds herself married to one of the most prominent men in the United States. It may take her time to adjust to a new gait."

"I reckon it's a mother's right to exaggerate. I'll grant you I've made something of a name for myself west of the mountains, but in the seaboard states people have never heard of me."

"They will," Elizabeth said, "which is all the more reason to keep in mind what I've told you."

Several of Sam's brothers came to take him into the parlor for pre-dinner toasts, and the old lady released him.

Eventually everyone sat down to a feast of turkey gumbo soup, broiled lake bass, larded beef and the traditional wedding dish, roast goose stuffed with chestnut dressing. There were salad greens of watercress and dandelions, three kinds of fruit pie and one of John Allen's own cheeses, which the groom pronounced delicious. Five different wines were served with the meal, and at its end toasts were consumed in port, then brandywine and, finally, whisky.

Sam ate his usual hearty meal, accepting second helpings of everything and drinking each glass set before him. He dominated the conversation, as always, delivering a monologue on the wedding customs of the ancient Greeks, Romans, Phoenicians, and Carthaginians, and then repeated some of the stories that invariably drew applause when he spoke at banquets. He was witty, his ear for the dialects of Scotsmen, Irishmen, and Englishmen was accurate, and he had most of the guests laughing throughout the meal. In brief, he enjoyed himself.

Eliza, seated beside him, remained silent and had no appetite. She picked at her food, scarcely touching most dishes, and took only token sips of the wines. At Sam's insistence she tried taking somewhat larger swallows in response to the toasts, but the effort was too great for her, and she looked relieved when the feast came to an end.

When evening came the lamps were lighted, and in honor of the occasion a scented oil made in Hartford and carried across the mountains at great expense was used in liberal quantities. A fire of hickory logs and fragrant fir branches burned in the parlor hearth, and Sam, keeping a tight hold on Eliza's hand as they sat together on a divan opposite the fireplace, continued to draw stories from his endless supply. His dialect became that of frontier woodsmen, and some of the guests laughed so hard they wept when he imitated the French-speaking citizens of New Orleans.

Eliza, looking very pale, did not say a single word.

Sam did not desist until his mother caught his eye and glared at him. Then, at last, he took the hint.

The bride's relatives departed for their own homes, and those of Sam's family who were staying with neighbors also left. Elizabeth Houston kissed her new daughter-in-law and son, and was followed up the stairs by the bride's parents.

Eliza and Sam found themselves alone in the parlor, where fresh logs were crackling in the hearth. He kissed her, and she accepted his embrace passively, but did not respond.

He assumed she was nervous and frightened. "It's a shame to leave all this good brandywine," he said, standing and reaching for a decanter of heavy cut-glass.

"Papa bought it just for today."

"I admire his taste. You'll join me in a nightcap?"

"No, Sam. I—I couldn't."

He thought it wise not to insist. "You won't mind if I have a last glass?"

"Of course not." Eliza smiled very faintly.

"What I mean," Sam explained, "is that the odor of brandywine is rather strong. I wouldn't want you to find it offensive on my breath."

"I won't." It had not occurred to him, she thought, that his breath was already heavy.

He raised his glass. "To my wife, whom I love more than I've ever cared for anyone in this world."

She bowed her blond head, but was unable to reply.

Sam drained his glass.

Suddenly Eliza jumped to her feet. "Excuse me," she murmured, and gathering her full skirt of white satin, hurried to the stairs.

He had the sense not to follow her, but watched her as she climbed to the second floor landing. Absently refilling his glass, he stared into the fire. His mother had been right, of course, and he was grateful for her warning. The situation would be terrifying for any young woman in Eliza's position, and he realized he sometimes had a tendency to overpower people. But she would change when she learned the depth and sincerity of his devotion to her. Then, he felt certain, she would feel more at ease with him, and they would enjoy the perfect union he had envisaged.

Forcing himself to remain in the parlor, he sipped his brandywine very slowly, and every few minutes he reached for the gold watch in his waistcoat pocket. After a half-hour had passed he could stand the suspense no longer; he had given his bride ample time to compose herself and change her attire. Straightening the stock of black silk that encircled his high, starched collar, he went to the staircase, and mounted it slowly.

The door of the outer chamber of the two-room suite that had been Eliza's since childhood was ajar, and Sam went in, shutting it silently behind him. Smokeless French tapers were burning in wrought-iron sconces, and he grinned when he caught sight of a battered wooden doll with a painted face propped in the seat of a rocking chair. It pleased him that Eliza had kept her childhood toys, which, some day, would be passed on to their own youngsters.

Sam tapped lightly on the door to the inner chamber, but there was no response. He raised the latch, and when he stepped inside he was surprised to see Eliza, still attired in her wedding gown, sitting in a straight-backed chair near a window. The reflection of the light cast by the lamp on the night table, combined with the fullness of the chintz curtains on either side of the window made it impossible for her to see into the orchard of fruit trees below.

He went to her and, very gently, put a hand on her shoulder.

Eliza gasped and shrank from him.

Sam immediately withdrew his hand.

"I'm sorry." She spoke in such a low voice he had to strain in order to hear her. "You have no idea how badly I feel."

He wanted to take her into his arms to caress and soothe her, but forced himself to remain several feet from her. "You needn't be afraid of me, my dear," he said, overwhelmed by a feeling of possessive tenderness.

"You don't understand," she murmured, pushing back a long blond curl that had fallen across her face.

"Tell me."

"It's—being here—that upsets me. This is where I've lived all my life. I—I was born down the hall. I had the five-year-old Indian cough here, and the ague when I was eight. Just a few weeks before I broke my leg when I was thrown by my first horse, I was given this very bed. Do you see what I mean?"

Sam was afraid he did understand, but wanted to be sure, and although he knew he was subjecting her to additional strain, he shook his head.

Eliza glanced at him for an instant, then quickly looked away again. "We shouldn't—have stayed here. Not tonight." Her murmur was still lower, barely audible.

Sam found it almost impossible to follow the workings of a woman's mind. He could see no rational reason why his bride should be reluctant to begin her marriage in the same room in which she had lived since earliest childhood, but he had only two alternatives. Either he could accept her feeling as valid, and wait to make her his wife in more than name, or he could make an attempt to change her attitude. In any other situation he would take the offensive and fight for an immediate victory, but his marriage was too precious to be spoiled by a single false move. In spite of his eagerness it would be best to show that, when necessary, he was capable of exercising patience.

"I'll do whatever you think best," he said, clenching his fists.

"Thank you, Sam. You're kinder—than I thought you'd be." The pain in her eyes seemed to have diminished as she glanced up at him for an instant.

Acutely aware of her distaste for physical contact of any sort in these surroundings, he did not kiss her again. Instead, feeling ludicrous, he bowed and retreated to the sitting room, where he spent a long, sleepless night on a divan that was too short for him.

On the day following their marriage, Sam and his bride set out for Nashville, Eliza's belongings having been sent ahead in wagons. They started late in the morning, planning to stop somewhere for a light meal. Even by traveling at a leisurely pace, Sam reasoned, they would reach the Executive Mansion long before sundown.

But the winter weather intervened, and two hours after the couple started out, they were pelted by a cold, driving rain that soon turned to sleet. Sam was indifferent to bad weather, and would have continued the journey had he been alone, but he could not permit a fragile girl to be exposed to the elements. Ignoring his own comfort, he threw his cape over her shoulders, and pointed down the road.

"Bob Martin lives no more than a mile or two from here," he said. "I'll soon have you there."

They continued on the main road, then turned down a side lane, and a short time later, thoroughly soaked, appeared at the front door of Speaker Robert Martin of the Tennessee Legislature. Martin and his wife were delighted, and while Sam stood before a roaring fire in the main parlor, the eldest of the Martin daughters, a girl of about Eliza's age, took the bride off to dry out and make herself more presentable.

"You sure as hell can't leave again today, Governor," the host said, handing Sam a glass of whisky. "This storm is one of those northwesters that will last for at least twenty-four hours."

Sam peered out of the nearest window as thunder rumbled in the distance. "I'm afraid you're right, Bob. But I hate like the very devil to inconvenience you."

"This is an event that my family will talk about for months." Speaker Martin laughed. "There are nine of us, you know, so two more won't matter."

"Mrs. Houston and I are obliged to you." Sam sipped the whisky and edged closer to the fire.

"There's just one thing that bothers me." Martin seemed embarrassed. "You've only been married a short time—"

"Since yesterday."

"Well, Governor, Mrs. Martin and I would be happy to turn our bedchamber over to you, but we have the two youngest sleeping with us until I can rebuild the wing that was burned down in last autumn's fire."

Sam began to smile, feebly.

"I'm afraid we'll be obliged to put Mrs. Houston in with the girls, and I'll have to ask you to sleep with my boys."

"You're putting yourselves out to be hospitable, Bob, so we won't mind in the least."

Speaker Martin couldn't understand why Houston laughed so loudly.

The storm gave Eliza a severe chill, and by the time she and Sam reached Nashville the next day, she was running a high fever. The alarmed bridegroom took her to the home of his cousins, the Robert McEwens, rather than risk setting up housekeeping in the Executive Mansion. A physician was summoned, and he announced, after examining the patient, that she was suffering a severe case of the ague.

Mrs. McEwen immediately isolated her in a third floor bedchamber. There she would remain for at least a week, Sam knew, and went off to Market Street for a supply of mustard to be used in poultices. That night he slept alone in the Executive Mansion.

Eliza recovered slowly, and two weeks passed before the physician said she could be moved from the McEwen home. Sam, who visited her several times each day, was present when the physician said she was strong enough to leave, and as soon as he was alone with her, he moved to her bedside, beaming.

"You'll soon be fit again," he told her in the hearty voice that the perennially healthy so often used when addressing invalids. "I'm putting in a stock of beef tea for you, and—"

"Sam." Eliza's voice was as wan as her appearance.

"Whatever you want, you shall have!"

"There's just one thing I want right now." She plucked at the quilted cover with listless fingers. "I don't have the strength to start keeping house in a strange place. Not yet."

"Maybe we can get your mother to come down from Gallatin for a week or two. Of course, the staff at the Mansion know my ways, but I reckon it'll be different for them with a new mistress in the house."

"Very different, and I can't cope with serving maids and cooks and the like just yet. Do you mind?"

"Certainly not! That's why I suggested—"

"I don't want Mama here with me, but thank you for the thought."

Perhaps she wanted to return to Gallatin for her convalescence, but he was afraid to ask.

"You won't be angry?"

"I give you my word," he said, and felt a flicker of annoyance. He was being unfair to her, perhaps, but there were times when he felt he was dealing with a child.

"It would be wonderful if we could move to the Inn until I'm completely well."

He was so relieved he slapped his thigh, startling her. "Why in all unholy Hades didn't I think of that?"

A rare smile appeared on Eliza's face. "It occurred to me that we could order our meals at any hour, and wouldn't have to worry about buying meats or sending to the greengrocer's. But— can we afford the expense of a suite at the Inn for several weeks, Sam?"

Money was the least of his concerns, even though he was insisting on paying the McEwens for their hospitality and had not yet received the physician's bill. "Don't give it another thought. But I wonder if we need a big suite. A parlor and a bedroom will be enough."

"Two bedchambers would be much better," Eliza said.

Sam frowned.

"The doctor said I need my sleep, and—well—until we grow accustomed to each other—" Her voice dwindled away.

The request was reasonable, Sam knew, but he couldn't help wondering if Eliza was deliberately trying to avoid him. In all justice to her, she had not been to blame for the crowded conditions at the Martin house any more than she had been at fault for her subsequent illness. But, whether she knew it or not, she was straining his patience to the limit.

"If that's the arrangement you want," he said, "it's what we'll have. Now, if you don't mind, I'll go downstairs to join Cousin Bob in a drink of whisky before I go back to my office and write a message to the Legislature."

Ten days after Governor and Mrs. Houston moved into the Nashville Inn they began to accept a few invitations to dinners, and within a short time were caught up in the social life of the capital. Sam was the first citizen of Tennessee, his bride was lovely and became increasingly vivacious, and together they charmed everyone they saw. Both appeared happy, and everyone who saw them concluded that their marriage was successful.

Only Sam and Eliza knew they were living a lie, and she refused to admit it. She was pronounced in good health again, completely recovered from the ague, but she continued to find reasons for staying on at the Inn. She wanted to hire her own domestics, she said, and preferred to wait until she assembled them before moving into the Executive Mansion. Three or four days a week she interviewed cooks and serving maids, but her standards were very high, and she found almost no staff members who suited her.

Sam's patience was exhausted, and on three different occasions he went to her bedchamber when he returned to the Inn after spending part of the evening at his office, but each time he found the door bolted. Had they not been living at a hostelry, he would have been tempted to batter down the door.

A trip to Knoxville, which he made with several members of the Legislature, postponed the confrontation that had become inevitable. But, by the time Sam returned to Nashville in early April, he was unwilling to procrastinate any longer. His love for his wife had grown deeper, and he was in a state of never-ending misery, yearning for her, living on the far side of a barred door from her.

He went straight to their suite at the Inn on his return, and found Eliza in the parlor of their suite, writing a letter. He threw his beaver hat and scarlet silk-lined cloak onto a chair, and went straight to her.

She raised her cheek for his kiss.

Sam grasped her shoulders and drew her to her feet. The thought crossed his mind that she was trying to block his view of her letter, but he dismissed the idea. There were far more important issues to be settled.

"I've waited long enough," he said.

Eliza started to reply, saw his expression and suddenly could not speak.

He tried to pull her closer.

But she resisted, and in a sudden surge of panic broke away from him.

"I'll be damned," he said, "if I'm going to have to hog-tie my own wife so I can make love to her."

She opened her mouth, but was unable to make a sound.

"We've been married for two and a half months, and we're still not man and wife. I love you, and I can't stand this torture any more."

Eliza raised her hands to her face and began to weep, silently.

"Have I done something to offend you?" He raised his voice. "Answer me!"

She sobbed, rocking back and forth.

"I beg you, don't torment us any longer."

Her sobs became wild and unrestrained.

Sam had little experience in dealing with a woman's hysteria, but he knew she needed a shock to jar her back to sensibility. He caught hold of her shoulders again, and, as he began to shake her, his own frustrations caused him to lose all self-control. He wanted to hurt her, to punish her for the pain and humiliation she had caused him to suffer, and his fingers bit hard into her flesh.

Fear sobered Eliza. "Please stop!" she gasped.

He released her so suddenly she almost fell to the floor. He passed a hand across his eyes, and then stood erect. "We can't lose our dignity again, but I deserve an explanation."

"You do." She forced herself to meet his steady gaze, and winced when she saw how badly he had been injured.

"If I'm to blame for anything that—"

"You aren't, Sam. I've been a coward, and I've done dreadful things to you."

He thought she was thawing, and took a step toward her.

Eliza backed off, putting the desk between them. "Hear me out, I beg you."

Sam halted, his hands at his sides.

"I shouldn't have married you," she said.

He felt as he had when Creek bullets had smashed his shoulder.

"I didn't love you. I was giddy because a—a great man was paying court to me, and I let myself be influenced by Mama and Papa."

He had known from the start, of course, that her parents had been his strongest allies. But that was in the past. "We're married now, so it no longer matters how you once felt. I'm sure you can learn to return my feelings—"

"No!" Eliza shouted the word, hurling it at him as a challenge.

"Am I so repugnant to you?" he demanded hoarsely.

"You're a fine and good man." She lowered her face, and he could see only the crown of her blond head. "I've been wickedly unfair to you."

A sudden, inexplicable instinct caused him to reach for the partly written letter on the desk.

Eliza snatched it, crushing the sheet of paper as she held it close.

"I see," Sam said.

"I—I've loved someone else all along." There was an air of bravado behind her words.

He stared at her, and his voice became metallic. "Who is he? I'll put a bullet between the bastard's eyes."

"Then you'd be committing a crime against yourself—as well as against him. I've never been untrue to you."

"Do you expect me to believe that?"

Slowly, with trembling hands, she smoothed the crumpled letter and handed it to him.

He was reluctant to take it, and could not read it. In the long run it was far better to accept her word.

"I've written many letters," she said, "but I've never sent him a single one."

He was silent for a time. "I dreamed all this in my nightmares," he said at last. "What do you want to do now?"

"If you wish, we can stay together as we've been doing. I don't want to cause you any more harm, or damage your career—"

"Impossible," he said curtly. "If you stayed with me, I'd— No, Eliza. If you love someone else, I'll set you free. That's the greatest gift in my power."

"My God, my God," she whispered, weeping again, "I wish I could love you, but I can't."

Sam picked up his hat and cloak, then left the room without looking in her direction again. He called for his horse and, as he rode to the Executive Mansion, responded automatically to the greetings of citizens.

Staff members saw him as he entered the building, and tried to claim his attention, coming to him armed with sheaves of documents. But, almost in a daze, he brushed past them without speaking. When he reached his own office he bolted the door behind him, and suddenly collapsed into the nearest chair. For some moments he was too numb to feel or think, but suddenly, for the first time since the death of his father, he wept without restraint.

Nashville,
April 16, 1829

The Senate and
House of Representatives,
State of Tennessee.
Gentlemen:

It has become my duty to resign the office of Chief Magistrate of the State, & to place in your hands the authority & responsi-

bility, which on such an event, devolves on you by the provisions of our Constitution.

In dissolving the political connection which has so long & in
such a variety of forms existed between the people of Tennessee
and myself, no private afflictions, however deep or incurable,
can forbid an expression of the grateful recollections so emi-
nently due to the kind partialities of an indulgent public. From
my earliest youth, whatever of talent was committed to my care
has been honestly cultivated & expended for the common good;
and at no period of a life, which has certainly been marked by
a full portion of interesting events, have any views of private interests or private ambition been permitted to mingle in the
higher duties of public trust.

In viewing the past, I can only regret that my capacity for being
useful was so unequal to the devotion of my heart, and it is one
of the few remaining consolations of my life that even had I been
blessed with ability equal to my zeal, my country's generous support in every vicissitude of my life has been more than equal
to them both.

That veneration for public opinion, by which I have measured
every act of my official life, has taught me to hold no delegated
power which would not daily be renewed by my constituents,
could the choice be daily submitted to a sensible expression of
their will.

And although shielded by a perfect consciousness of undiminished claim to the confidence & support of my fellow citizens,
yet delicately circumstanced as I am, & by my own misfortunes,
more than by the fault or contrivance of anyone, overwhelmed
by sudden calamities, it is certainly due to myself & more respect-
ful to the world, that I should retire from a position which, in
the public judgment, I might seem to occupy by questionable
authority.

Submitted with my deep respect,
& in deeper sorrow,
Sam Houston

Dr. William Hume, the Presbyterian clergyman who had married Sam and Eliza, summed up the reaction of a shocked citizenry. "*Sic transit gloria mundi,*" he said. "Oh, what a fall for a major general, a member of the Congress of the United States and the present governor of so respectable and great a state as Tennessee."

Speaker Robert Martin of the State Legislature stood at the windows in the study of former Governor William Carroll. "I went to his quarters at the Inn, Billy, and found him packing his belongings. Mrs. Houston wasn't there, and he refused to talk about her—"

"I understand she's returned to her family in Gallatin. I was told she left yesterday." Carroll's voice was expressionless.

"I heard the same thing."

"What confuses me, Billy, is that they seemed so happy together when they stopped at my house the day after their marriage. I can't imagine what could have happened to them."

Carroll shrugged. "There will be rumors by the score in the next few days. You can rely on it."

"How can you take all this so calmly?"

Carroll allowed himself a small, tight smile. "Sam has chosen his course."

"Maybe you didn't hear what I told you when I first came in here. He's leaving—today—for the Arkansas Territory. He insists he's going to live with the Cherokee."

Carroll's smile broadened. "It isn't a life I'd choose for myself. But Sam is old enough to know what he's doing and what he wants."

"You're wrong, Billy. Something has happened that's made him temporarily deranged. He doesn't sound or look or act like himself. He either mutters things you can't understand, or he shouts. And when he laughs, which he does constantly, you think he's going to burst into tears. It's terrible!"

"I know nothing about his personal tragedy, and I feel very sorry for him." Carroll was quietly firm. "But I'd rather not pry into his private affairs."

"Someone has got to stop him from throwing away the most

117

promising political career of any man in the United States!" Martin was no longer able to control his own feelings, and pounded on a table with such force that several books toppled.

"He's already resigned, Bob. The damage is done."

"No, he—"

"I beg to disagree with you. Even if he were to rescind his resignation, the voters wouldn't trust him again. He'd have no chance of being re-elected governor, and I don't think the people of Tennessee would want to take another chance with him, ever, in any public office."

"I begged him to get the advice of President Jackson before he does anything more drastic. He'll always listen to the President. But he refused. He said he's written a letter to Jackson, but he isn't waiting for a reply. He intends to present the President with an accomplished fact."

"It would take several weeks for a courier traveling at a fast clip to reach Washington and bring back an answer, Bob."

"Most of the men who have been close to him—Jamie Polk, John Eaton, Cave Johnson—are in Washington. You're probably the only friend in the state at the moment who might influence him."

"He wouldn't heed me, Bob."

"You've got to try, Billy."

Carroll rose from his chair, clipped the end from a *segaro* and lighted it with a spill which he plunged into the coal fire burning in the grate. "That would be presumptuous of me. Sam and I were allies—of a sort. But we were never intimate friends, and I'm positive he'd resent my intrusion."

"He'd at least listen to you, Billy!"

"I won't embarrass Sam—or myself," Carroll said with finality, and was silent for a moment. "You say he's leaving today, Bob."

"Yes! That's why—"

"I'll play it safe. I'll wait until tomorrow before I announce my own candidacy for governor."

Cherokee who had known Sam since childhood continued to call him the Raven, but the younger warriors, who had never seen him until he stumbled into the nation's principal town, near the village of Little Rock, gave him the name of the Big Drunk. Even the squaws and children mocked him behind his back, but Oo-loo-te-ka silenced the tribe by appointing his adopted son to the Cherokee ruling council. Then no one, not even the most irreverent, dared to laugh at him.

But Sam refused to accept responsibilities, even when he learned that the Cherokee were in need of his help. Agents appointed by the United States had repeatedly violated the rights of the Indians, who had no friends in high places to intercede with the Federal government on their behalf. Sam listened with sympathetic indignation in the council lodge to the woes of the Cherokee, but seemed incapable of rousing himself from his liquor-induced stupor long enough to take any positive steps.

His whiskers grew long, and his plaited hair was unkempt. His white doeskin shirt became filthy, as did his leggings of heavier leather and the blanket thrown over his shoulders; even the eagle feathers that adorned his hair were bedraggled. Often he vanished for many days at a time into the forests of pine and black walnut and cypress, and occasionally he disappeared into the rugged mountain ranges to the west for even longer periods.

These trips, he claimed, were hunting expeditions, but he rarely returned to the Cherokee town with game, and the senior warriors found that, after most of these journeys, his rifle had never been discharged. As the months passed, he became gaunt and hollow-cheeked, and as his physical strength ebbed he took on the appearance of an old man who walked with a shuffling gait and stared down at the ground.

Only when he received letters from President Andrew Jackson did he force himself to become sober enough to send long, rambling replies. Then, exhausted by his efforts, he turned again to whisky for solace. Oo-loo-te-ka repeatedly begged him to change his ways before he killed himself, but he seemed either unwilling or unable to follow the good advice.

At last the sachem could tolerate no more, and called the other members of the Cherokee council to a meeting in his lodge. "The son of Oo-loo-te-ka," he said, "shames the warriors of the

Cherokee. Even the squaws and children laugh at him. He who was the chief of many is not now the chief of himself."

The members of the council, by unanimous vote, agreed to expel him from his seat in the ruling body, and Sam was summoned to hear their verdict.

Filthy and unkempt, his hair and beard matted, he stood with his feet apart to brace himself, weaving slightly, and tried to concentrate on what the sachem said to him.

Oo-loo-te-ka had to repeat his solemn words before Sam understood them.

Flushing slightly, then growing pale beneath his tan, he staggered back to his own hut. His overwhelming feeling was one of self-pity, but guilt nagged at him, too, making him uncomfortable, so he tried to drown all sensation by gulping large quantities of raw corn whisky that seemed to set his insides on fire. He realized, dimly, that he had descended to the bottom of a deep, dark pit, but he had no pride, no desire to help himself, no reason to recover his reason. No one else cared what became of him, he thought dully, and it would not matter to anyone if he killed himself in this remote wilderness.

"Your mother is dying and wants to see you," Robert McEwen wrote from Nashville. *"I have heard stories about you that I find difficult to believe, but if they be true, I beg you not to torment your mother in her last days on this earth. Rather than cause her needless pain, it would be far better if you stayed away."*

Sam had to read the brief letter several times before it made sense to him. Then, with a demonstration of coordinated energy that astonished the Cherokee, he filled a saddlebag with parched corn and jerked venison, saddled a horse and started out on the long journey to Tennessee.

The first days of his trip were a torment. His craving for liquor was insatiable, but he refused to drink, even though he was tempted, more than once, to trade his rifle for whisky. He was shaken and sick, and sometimes thought he would expire in the saddle, yet he pressed on, rarely resting, sleeping only in brief snatches. Only a man whose will was stronger than his emaciated body could have survived, much less reached Tennessee, but he had stopped thinking of himself, and was consumed by a dread that he would arrive too late.

When less than twenty-four hours from his destination he scrubbed himself and his ragged clothes in the cold waters of a stream, hacked off his beard with his skinning knife and cleaned his long hair. Then, far more presentable than he had been in months, he went on to Baker's Creek Valley.

Many of his relatives were gathered at the Houston homestead, and he knew from their anxiety that his mother was still alive. So he wasted no time in greeting any of them, but went straight to his mother's bedchamber.

Elizabeth was propped up on several pillows, her leathery, lined face ashen, her breathing shallow. She appeared to be asleep, but opened her eyes when her son stood beside her. "I knew you'd come," she said in a voice that was weak but clear.

Unable to trust himself and afraid he might break down, he could only nod.

"You look older, Sam. You've been suffering."

"Whatever has happened to me has been my own doing, Ma," he said. "I have no one else to blame."

"There are some who claim you were wrong to resign as Governor. But I say with Matthew, 'Judge not, that ye be not judged.' You have only one enemy, boy. Conquer yourself, and you can still live up to the greatness that's in you."

Someone at the entrance to the darkened room coughed in warning. "Ma is tired out and needs rest. Leave her be now, Sam."

Elizabeth roused herself. "Let *him* be," she said, showing a touch of her old asperity. "I can rest for all eternity, and I want a few words with him." The effort was too much for her, and her hand fluttered on the coverlet.

Sam reached down to grasp it.

His mother smiled faintly, and touched the gold ring that was loose on his thin finger. "You still wear it."

"Yes, Ma." He found it difficult to meet her steady gaze.

"If you've been true to the motto inside, you have no need to be ashamed. If you haven't, mend your ways, boy."

"I will, Ma."

Suddenly her voice fell to a whisper. "I've been separated from your father for a long time. A very long time. It will be good to see him again, and not to be lonely any more."

Sam realized he had to retain his composure, and again he nodded.

"Don't you grieve. Save your strength for the living. You're not like any of the others, boy, and you have work to do." Elizabeth closed her eyes for an instant, and when she reopened them, a film seemed to cover them. "Pray for me," she murmured. "But softly, so the others won't know."

He dropped to his knees beside the bed and whispered the words of the Lord's Prayer close to her ear. She appeared to fall asleep, and not until he had finished did he realize her breathing had stopped. He repeated the prayer, silently, then pulled himself to his feet.

Gazing down at the frail body of his mother, Sam knew he could not allow himself the luxury of tears. The time for self-indulgence had ended, and now he had to prove he was worthy of being the son of Elizabeth and Samuel Houston.

He walked to the door, and in a low but steady voice called his brothers and sisters into the room.

FIVE

1832–36

The trading post flourished, and word spread from the Cherokee to the other Indian nations of the wilderness that Sam Houston was the one man from whom they could buy merchandise with complete confidence. He refused to sell shoddy goods, he was scrupulously fair, and his prices were absurdly low.

As a matter of fact, Sam refused to take a profit on any of his dealings. The Cherokee had seen him through a period of black insanity, and he wanted to repay his debt to them in a practical way. Most of their purchasing had been done through greedy Indian agents, men who inflated prices and pocketed huge gains for themselves, and he hoped that his example would drive costs down. His success in the enterprise was immediate, and only in one endeavor did he fail. He tried to obtain government-owned merchandise from Secretary of War John Eaton, but for political reasons that were not clear to him, Eaton was unable to deliver the supplies he wanted.

In spite of Sam's efforts, however, the Cherokee continued to suffer at the hands of the agents, whose operations were unhampered because of the indifference of government officials in Washington City. Oo-loo-te-ka finally decided to send a delegation to the capital to appeal for justice and help, and Sam immediately volunteered to accompany his friends as an unofficial member of the group. The sachem tried to dissuade him, afraid he might be embarrassed because of his past close associations with so many men who now held high office, but Sam would not listen to talk of escape.

"My brothers," he said, "gave me a home here when I was too drunk to make sense. I won't desert them now."

The party traveled east by way of Tennessee, and most of Sam's old friends in Nashville were delighted to see him. Governor Carroll, apparently afraid that the visit might be a prelude to a return to state politics, absented himself from the city. Sam left a polite note for him before going out to the Hermitage to cut himself a hickory walking stick, a gesture that, the Nashville *Banner* noted, might be a symbol of things to come.

When the group reached Washington City after spending long weeks on the road, Sam remembered the furor he had caused so many years earlier when he had lived with the Cherokee in their tents, and not wanting to create any problems for President Jackson, quietly engaged himself a room at Brown's Hotel.

Then, after shaving carefully, he went straight to the White House, where Andy Donelson, the President's nephew and secretary, greeted him exuberantly. "I've heard for the past week that you were coming, Sam, but I couldn't believe it."

"I'm here, but I'm not sure I'm welcome."

"You'll see for yourself. The President is in a meeting, but he wouldn't forgive me if I didn't tell him at once that you're here."

While Donelson hurried off down the corridor, Sam waited in his small office, feeling strangely uncomfortable. Three years had passed since Andrew Jackson had first come to this place as President of the United States. Three years had vanished from Sam's own life, and he was overcome by a sensation of unaccustomed diffidence. Perhaps, for the sake of what they had meant to each other, Old Hickory would receive him, but he wouldn't be surprised if he was greeted with chilly reserve. A man who had been the logical heir to the presidency, and who had systematically destroyed his own future, had no right to any welcome worthy of the name.

After what seemed like an interminable wait, Donelson reappeared. "He's unusually busy today, what with the Whigs in Congress kicking up their heels, but come along."

Sam felt reluctant. "I can come back another time, Andy."

"He wants to see you now." Donelson led the way down a corridor lined with portraits of the first six Presidents, then stood aside to let a number of gentlemen leave the large room at the end of the hall.

Several looked at Sam, who felt increasingly ill at ease in his shabby, worn buckskins, and although he felt certain he knew a number of them, none spoke to him. Then Donelson pushed him through the entrance, and the door closed behind him.

Andrew Jackson, seated at a large desk beneath a portrait of his wife, had aged since Sam had last seen him. His sparse hair was white, his complexion was that of a man who rarely spent any time outdoors, and his hands looked frail and thin. He was signing papers with a stubby quill pen, and the spectacles that had slid part-way down the bridge of his nose gave him the unexpected appearance of a stern schoolmaster.

Sam swallowed hard and found his voice. "Good morning, Mr. President."

Old Hickory glanced up, leaped to his feet and threw aside his spectacles. "By the Eternal, I never thought I'd see you again in this world!"

The lump in Sam's throat grew larger as the President embraced him. "Let me look at you, boy. You've changed, Sam. My God, it's a wonder you're alive."

"I guess I don't kill easy, Mr. President." He refused to sit in the chair Old Hickory offered him until Jackson returned to his own place behind the desk. "I can't even take any credit for staying alive."

The President saw his smile was genuine, and was encouraged. "I think I know how you felt. When I found myself alone, I didn't have much heart left, either, but at least I had a lifetime of a good marriage to cushion me." He changed the subject abruptly. "It won't give Vice-President Calhoun much pleasure to know you're alive—and in Washington City."

"I wasn't planning to call on him, sir."

"My friends aren't welcome at his house," Jackson said. "I broke with him personally when I learned he tried to have me court-martialed back in the days when I was conducting the campaign in the Floridas and he was Secretary of War. And I reckon you've heard how I put him in his place two years ago, when he was threatening to lead South Carolina out of the Union—and I said, publicly, that the nation must be preserved."

"I'm glad you did, sir, but I must admit I haven't known much of what's been happening in the civilized world."

"I guarantee you that your Cherokee friends will get a fair hearing in every government department. You're going back to the Arkansas Territory with them?"

Sam had been making plans he had revealed to no one, and, not wanting to commit himself, confined his response to a cautious nod.

"A man of your talents is wasted operating a trading post—at no personal profit."

"I've been developing some ideas, Mr. President. My store is in the wilderness, but you'd be surprised how many travelers come there, and I've been keeping my ears open." Sam found himself saying more than he had intended. "Men from all over the country are going down to Stephen Austin's settlements in Texas. I thought I'd see for myself if prospects are as bright there as Austin and his friends claim."

The President's pale blue eyes suddenly glowed. "I've been told so many different things I don't know what to believe. What do you hear, Sam?"

"All I know, sir, is that Mexico has a province, bordering on the United States, that's almost unoccupied. Men who have been down there say some of the land is richer than any they've ever seen. Americans are bound to be attracted to Texas, Mr. President, no matter how much it upsets the Mexican government to see us settling there. We're a frontier people, and we have the wilderness in our blood. We pushed across the Appalachians, we're expanding as far west as the Rocky Mountains—"

"When I first went out to Nashville, it was a village in the forest. That was before your day."

"I'm sorry, Mr. President. I don't need to tell you how the whole country feels about staking homesteads in virgin lands. It's like waving a jug of whisky under the nose of a drunk." Sam grinned wryly. "A drunk who hasn't learned his lesson. Americans by the thousands are staking claims to farmlands down in Texas, sir, no matter how many laws the Mexican government passes to bind and gag them."

"Are you thinking of settling there yourself, Sam?"

There was no reason to hold back anything. "It could be, Mr. President. I've recovered from the sickness in my soul, but I have no future in Tennessee. If the climate is right for me in Texas, I might stay there."

"Down in Mexico City they're trying to make Texas too hot for any Americans."

Sam laughed. "Nobody knows exactly how big the province is. According to the maps I've seen, it fills at least a quarter of a million square miles. That's one hell of a big territory."

"I've seen a few maps myself."

"The way I look at it, sir, maybe I'd have a new chance to build a life for myself down there. I failed the voters of Tennessee, and I couldn't blame them if they had no use for me, ever. But everybody is getting a fresh start down in Texas."

The President chuckled. "The Sam Houston I knew," he said, "wouldn't be satisfied to own a property and farm it. He'd get into politicking, no matter where he lived."

"You told me a long time ago that office-holding is a hankering a man never loses, once he's had a taste of it." The years slipped away, and Sam found it surprisingly easy to confess his ambitions to his mentor.

Old Hickory looked out of the window at the azalea bushes he had planted in his wife's memory. "According to reports I've been getting from New Orleans, a great many men going down to Texas are empire builders who want to establish a new country of their own. Do you agree with them, Sam?"

"I'm an American, Mr. President! I won't insult you by saying

I love this country more than you do, but I sure love it just as much."

Jackson turned in his chair and faced his visitor again. "That's what I thought, but I had to hear you say it yourself. Sam, the way I see it, Texas is going to be the cause of trouble. If Mexico wanted to settle the territory herself, she'd have every right. Or if she tried to keep Americans out, that would be her privilege, too. But she's doing neither. She's allowing Americans to enter, and is then hobbling them with second-class citizenship. Our people won't stand for that. The adventurers and rogues are already agitating for a separate country. I couldn't tolerate a nation of unstable expatriates on our border. No President could."

"Most of the men who have stopped off at my trading post," Sam said, "seem to take it for granted that one of these years Texas will become part of the United States."

"The idea has crossed my mind," Jackson admitted, "but if I showed any interest in it, the Mexicans would declare war on the United States. It's a delicate situation."

"It'd be easier all around, sir, if Texans applied for admission to the Union."

"Much easier, provided they were free of Mexico."

"I'm taking nothing for granted," Sam said, "but whenever another thousand Americans settle there, it brings the day closer." He and Old Hickory exchanged a long look.

"You understand that in my official capacity I can do nothing to help or encourage such a movement."

"Of course, Mr. President. And you know I'd be the last to cause embarrassment for the United States government."

"I do. But it would be a big help if I heard regularly from a reliable friend there. Someone I know I can trust."

"I've neglected my correspondence as badly as I ruined my future in Tennessee. I won't make the same mistakes again." Again they looked at each other, and the silent bargain was sealed.

"Enough of business matters," the President said abruptly. "How long has it been since you've eaten a good dinner, Sam? You need filling out, so I reckon you'd better come back tonight. I'd starve if I waited as late every night as the Easterners and Europeans do, so we usually sit down around six o'clock."

Sam rose, flattered by the unexpected invitation. "If you're sure you want me, I'll be here, sir."

"I'll tell Emily Donelson to make certain the cook roasts a turkey with chestnut stuffing for you." The President stood, too, trying in vain to sound casual. "I hear you're staying at Brown's. I suppose you've heard their rooms cost a dollar per day now. They've raised their prices, like everybody else."

Sam knew what he was trying to say, and reddened. "I'm going to collect some old debts while I'm here."

"Then you'd best start with me. I never did pay you that last wager I lost to you when we were racing horses at the Hermitage."

There had been no such wager, and Sam tried to protest.

But the President, digging into his inner coat pocket, gave him no chance. "You've been with the Cherokee so long that maybe you've forgotten a man in public life must be careful of his appearance. I assume you brought some suitable cothes with you."

Sam could not admit that he was wearing his entire wardrobe. "We—left the Arkansas Territory so suddenly—"

"I lost two hundred dollars to you in that wager," Jackson said loudly, took the money from his purse and thrust it at Sam. "Stop standing there, boy, blinking at me. I have work to do!"

Sam remained in Washington far longer than he had anticipated. He paid two brief visits to New York, where private banking firms interested in investing funds in the Texas settlements gave him enough money in advance payments to restore him to financial solvency. He insisted on repaying President Jackson, and was planning to leave the city when, on March 31, 1832, Representative William Stanbery of Ohio, a Jacksonian Democrat no less, tried to embarrass Old Hickory by claiming, in an address on the floor of the House, that Sam and John Eaton had been engaged in a fraudulent conspiracy to supply the Cherokee with rations. They would have made a fortune, Stanbery declared, "but even President Jackson could not stomach so bold a scheme, and canceled the contract, sending Eaton away to become Governor of the Florida Territory."

The charge would have been forgotten overnight had Sam

ignored it, but he had been absent from the political arena so long that he had become thin-skinned and lost his temper. Armed with his hickory walking stick, he went to the lobby of the House of Representatives to wait for Stanbery.

Jamie Polk, the administration leader in the House, managed to coax him out of the building and took him home for dinner.

Sam's temper did not abate, however, and the following day he insisted that Representative Cave Johnson deliver a viciously insulting note to Stanbery on the floor of the House.

Had the customs of the West prevailed, a duel would have been fought within twenty-four hours. But Stanbery observed the more civilized code of the East, and ignored the communication. Having been warned, however, he armed himself with a brace of pistols, and wore them wherever he went.

Sam postponed his departure from Washington until, as he told Polk, "I attend to a private matter."

Polk, Johnson, and Sam's other friends from Tennessee could not persuade him to drop the matter, and Andrew Donelson reported that the President, with grim humor, said he could not use his influence in an affair of honor.

On April 13, while Sam was walking with Senator Alexander Buckner of Missouri and Representative John Blair of Tennessee, en route to dinner, he suddenly came face to face with Stanbery. Pennsylvania Avenue, Washington's principal thoroughfare, was crowded, and Sam shouldered aside several pedestrians, pulling away from his companions who tried to restrain him.

"Are you Mr. Stanbery?" he demanded, his roar causing others to stop and stare.

Stanbery, almost as tall as Sam, eyed him coldly. "I am, sir."

"You're a damned rascal!" The walking stick lashed out, striking the Ohioan across the shoulder.

Determined to avoid a scandalous incident, Stanbery ignored the blow and turned away.

Sam was equally determined to avenge himself, and leaped onto the back of the man who had made a false charge against him. They rolled over and over on the ground, as scores of passers-by halted in astonishment to gape.

Suddenly Stanbery managed to draw one of his pistols, cocked it and pulled the trigger. There was a clicking sound, but the weapon did not fire.

Sam knocked the pistol from Stanbery's hand and, in the same motion, jumped to his feet.

Stanbery tried to rise, too, but a blow from the walking stick across his backside sent him sprawling again.

Men in the crowd laughed, and some began to cheer.

Sam caught hold of the Congressman, and, grasping his feet with one hand and rendering him helpless, struck him repeatedly across the seat of his trousers, completing his humiliation.

The entire throng was enjoying the spectacle now, but Sam was unaware of the crowd's presence and interest.

"I've given you the punishment," he said, "that a liar and coward deserves." Tucking the walking stick under his arm, he rejoined Buckner and Blair, and, not bothering to glance in the direction of the crumpled Stanbery again, strolled away.

The incident made headlines in every newspaper in the United States. Administration supporters crowed, the Whigs took up Stanbery's cause, and a minor brawl became a national issue. Congressman Stanbery's friends were determined not to let the matter rest, and a resolution was offered in the House for the arrest of "one Sam Houston, former Governor of Tennessee."

A number of Democrats were afraid that the dignity of the House had been irreparably damaged, and voted with the Whigs in favor of the resolution, in spite of the efforts of Polk, Johnson, Felix Grundy, and Speaker Andrew Stevenson to defeat it.

Sam was arrested, called before the House and given forty-eight hours to prepare his defense.

President Jackson could no longer remain a bystander, and at his instigation one of the most distinguished attorneys in the country, Francis Scott Key, was engaged to act as counsel for the defense. The trial occupied the attention of the House for three weeks, and the newspapers reported every word. Sam, elegantly attired in a suit of black broadcloth, a stylish high collar and a white satin cravat, with a matching waistcoat, sat each day at the defense table in the well of the House, but did not take the witness stand. The President became increasingly concerned, as did a number of staunch administration supporters. Senator Thomas Hart Benton of Missouri, who had been Sam's commanding officer in the Creek War, summed up their views when he told Key, "Sam Houston may be the finest orator in the country. In God's name, let him speak for himself!"

Key, however, insisted that the defendant remain silent until the last possible moment, and Sam agreed with his strategy. "I'm working on a speech," he said, "and when the right moment comes, I'll deliver it."

That moment arrived on May 8. The defense had been ordered to close its case that day, and when it was rumored that the erratic Governor Houston intended to take the stand, the galleries of the House were crowded with ministers from the foreign legations, Cabinet members and the highest-ranking officers in the Army and Navy. A number of ladies were present, and there was a stir when Andrew Donelson, the President's secretary, arrived with his pretty wife, Emily, who was the official White House hostess.

Promptly at noon Speaker Stevenson called the House to order, and Sam Houston was sworn in as a witness. He bowed to the Speaker, and, ignoring the galleries, addressed himself exclusively to the members of the House, even pretending not to see the Senators who crowded the rear of the chamber. He began in a quiet, humble tone.

"Arraigned for the first time in my life on a charge of violating the laws of my country," he said, "I feel all that embarrassment which my peculiar situation is calculated to inspire. The charge which has been preferred against me is one of no ordinary character. If I shall be convicted of having acted from the motive alleged by my accuser, lasting infamy must be the necessary consequence.

"I am accused of lying in wait, for the purpose of depriving a fellow man of the efficient use of his person, if not of existence itself. Mr. Speaker, can there be a greater crime? Who, but a wretch unworthy of the name of man, could ever be guilty of it?

"I disclaim, utterly, every motive unworthy of an honorable

man. If, when deeply wronged, I have followed the generous impulse of my heart, and have violated the laws of my country, or trespassed on the prerogatives of this honorable body, I am willing to be held to my responsibility for so doing."

The members of the House were attentive, the Senators neither whispered nor moved, and the galleries were still, absorbing every word. Sam knew he had won the first skirmish in his battle, that of gaining the interest and, perhaps, the sympathy of his audience. Departing from his prepared text, he dwelt at some length on his love for the House, reminded the Congressmen that he had once been a member of the body, and then stressed that the decline in his personal fortunes in no way touched his honor, which he considered inviolate.

He reminded his listeners that he had carried only a walking stick on the day of the attack, and that, had he intended to kill or wound Stanbery, he would have been armed. Then, his voice rising, he emphasized that Stanbery had been armed with two loaded pistols.

Gradually, changing his approach subtly, he built to the heart of his argument, accusing his foes—and President Jackson's—of what he called "legislative tyranny," while repeating that the spokesmen of liberty were supporting him. Lawyers and other students of the Constitution began to shift in their seats, knowing the House was vulnerable to the charges for which Sam was carefully preparing his ground.

"I have violated no law," he said, his voice rising, "I have transgressed no precept known to the people of this land. If I have violated any privilege, that privilege must be somewhere declared. If it exists at all, it lies as a little spark deeply covered; not even the smoke of it has appeared. It is a privilege which American people do not know; and I demand, on their behalf, to know what it is."

He pounded on the wooden railing of the witness box, and jabbed an accusing forefinger at the members of the House. "I shall bow to that privilege when it shall have been defined, and when it shall have become Constitutional, by the people's acquiescence. But where there is no law, there is no transgression.

"I freely admit that the members of this House have privileges, and that their persons ought to be protected, because they represent the citizens of this Republic. But, when a member of this House places himself out of the protection of this privilege by trespassing on my rights, I shall view him in his individual capacity, and deal with him as with any other private man."

There were cheers and applause in the galleries, and Speaker Stevenson gaveled for silence.

Sam seemed unaware of the outburst. "When a member of this House, entrenched in his privilege, brands a private citizen, in the face of the whole nation, as a fraudulent villain, he forgets the dignity of his station and renders himself answerable to the party aggrieved.

"Are honorable gentlemen to send abroad their calumnies unquestioned?

"Are they to use the privilege which they have received from the citizens of this country as a means to injure the citizens? If gentlemen disregard the ordinary rules of decorum, and use, in their place, language injurious to individuals, can they expect to be protected by privileges which they have forfeited?

"Apprehensions seem to be entertained by members of this House, lest violence should some day be employed to abridge this honorable body in the enjoyment of its rights; and precedents have been referred to to show that the deliberations of a legislature may be controlled by armed mobs.

"All history will show that no tyrant ever grasped the reins of power until they were put into his hands by corrupt and obsequious legislative bodies. If I apprehend the subversion of our liberties, I shall look not to the Executive, but to the Legislative department.

"Men never can be conquered so long as the spirit of liberty breathes in their bosoms. But let their legislature once become corrupt and servile, then the freedom of the people becomes an easy prey."

Again applause erupted, and this time the smiling Stevenson waited until it began to die out before going through the motions of rapping his gavel for silence.

Sam had completed his argument, and ended his address on a patriotic note. Looking up at an American flag on a staff a few feet away, he pointed toward it in a dramatic gesture. "Mr. Speaker, so long as that flag shall bear aloft its glittering stars —bearing them amidst the din of battle, and waving them triumphantly above the storms of the ocean, so long, I trust, shall the rights of American citizens be preserved safe and unimpaired, and transmitted as a sacred legacy from one generation to another, until discord shall wreck the spheres—the grand march of time shall cease—and not one fragment of all Creation be left to chafe on the bosom of eternity's waves."

He bowed to the House, and, seemingly conscious of the galleries for the first time, inclined his head toward them in a gracious gesture. His audience went wild, and even Whig Representatives stood and cheered him as he returned to his seat at the defense table. It was apparent to everyone present that he had scored a major personal triumph.

The Whigs made an attempt to clear the House of all visitors so the deliberations could be concluded in private, but the attempt was defeated. Then the Democrats tried to have the charges against Sam dismissed, but their motion was beaten. The original motion was thrown out, too, and a new one was introduced, the members then voting that "Governor Sam Houston is guilty of a contempt in violation of the privileges of this House, and that he be reprimanded accordingly, but that due clemency be shown him."

The House had salvaged its dignity, but, for all practical purposes, Sam was being punished with a gentle slap on the hand. The new resolution was voted accordingly, and Speaker Stevenson, after saying, "I reprimand you in accordance with the will of this House," spent ten minutes praising Sam as a great patriot.

The entire country knew who had won the verbal war, but Sam was not satisfied. He brought a civil suit against Stanbery, and proved himself innocent of the original charges made against him and John Eaton by the Congressman from Ohio. Finally, in late June 1832, Sam was able to leave Washington City for Texas.

On the night before his departure a small White House dinner was given in his honor, with a few of his friends in attendance, and he made the only reference to the whole Stanbery affair. "I was dying politically," he said to Andrew Jackson, "and had they taken me before a justice of the peace and fined me ten dollars, it would have killed me. But they gave me a national tribunal for a theater, and that set me up again."

Having done everything in his power to aid the Cherokee, Sam returned with them to the Arkansas Territory, and then proceeded to Texas. There, on December 24, 1832, he applied for membership in the colony of Stephen F. Austin, and was accepted. Seven weeks later he wrote a long, confidential letter to President Jackson.

In it he pointed out, succinctly, that Mexico was in a state of civil war, that Americans in the province of Texas were being given no protection by either faction, and that "nineteen-twentieths of the population" favored the acquisition of the territory by the United States. Correctly judging the temperament of the frontier settlers, he also emphasized that, regardless of any action the United States might or might not take, Texans were determined to separate from Mexico, and, if necessary, establish their own government.

Then, after coldly analyzing the political situation, he suddenly became emotional. "I have traveled hundreds of miles across Texas," he wrote, "and am now enabled to judge pretty correctly of the soil, and the resources of the country, and I have no hesitancy in pronouncing it *the finest country to its extent upon the globe*. The greater part of it is even richer and more healthy, in my opinion, than western Tennessee!

"There can be no doubt but the country east of the River Grand of the north would sustain a population of ten millions of souls.

"My opinion is that Texas will by her members in convention by the 1st April declare all that country as Texas proper and form a state constitution. I expect to be present at the convention and will apprise you of the course adopted, as soon as its members have taken a final action.

"It is probable that I shall make Texas my abiding place! In adopting this course, I will never forget the country of my birth."

Sam's love affair with Texas had begun, and would continue unabated until the day he died.

The newcomer settled in the little town of Nacogdoches, in east Texas, built himself a small, primitive cabin there, and told a pretty young neighbor, Anna Raguet, who soon became his confidante and friend, that he hoped to practice law. But the demands of politics were more pressing, and the former Governor of Tennessee soon found himself elected a delegate to the convention of Texans at San Felipe.

There his fellow settlers quickly discovered that a new leader had arrived in their midst. The conservative, quiet Austin, whom Sam liked personally but opposed politically, was reluctant to break with Mexico, but Sam favored a severing of relations as soon as possible, and most of the delegates supported him.

The new arrival was made chairman of a committee ordered to draw up a new constitution, and himself wrote the better part of it. Less than five months after his arrival he had become the principal spokesman of the majority of settlers, and thought of himself exclusively as a Texan. It did not matter to him that the tiny wages he drew barely paid for his food, most of which he cooked himself, that he was too poor to rent lodgings when traveling, and usually slept in the open.

"There are things in this world far more important than money," he told Anna Raguet and her parents. "Of these, the freedom of Texas is paramount. I have been searching all my life for a cause to which I can devote myself without reservation, and I rejoice that, at last, I have found it!"

Events in Mexico, as in Texas, moved rapidly. Antonio López de Santa Anna, a Mexican-born soldier who had fought in the Spanish Army, who had been one of the leaders of the revolution that had won Mexico her independence and then had begun to agitate in favor of his own cause, became President of the young republic. Sometimes calling himself a liberal, frequently admitting he was an opportunistic revolutionist, he confided to intimates that he intended to make a permanent name for himself as the Napoleon of the Western Hemisphere.

Sam, who had started the practice of law in Nacogdoches in what he called his spare time, heard of the boast, which became a topic of conversation at a sociable given by the Raguet family. "I reckon," he said, "that Santa Anna doesn't know his history. Napoleon lost his throne at Waterloo, and was lucky to be sent into exile. It's strange, you know, but any time a man, no matter how important he is, gets too big for his breeches, somebody cuts him down to ordinary size. Maybe I ought to be Santa Anna's Duke of Wellington."

Although he laughed heartily at his own witticism, only the teen-aged Anna Raguet noticed that there was no humor in his eyes.

The rest of the company, like everyone else he met, was taking Sam very seriously. He had, overnight, become a major figure in the political affairs of Texas, he had more law business than he could handle and he was becoming a property owner of consequence, too. With two other men, who furnished the cash for the purpose, he bought a tract of almost one hundred and fifty thousand acres. Not satisfied with a part-ownership, he bought for himself another property of ten thousand acres, paying for it with his income from the law.

"I'm proving," he said, "that I have complete faith in the future of Texas. What's more, I'm here to stay."

One item of an intensely personal nature remained to be settled. On November 30, 1833, he applied in the Texas courts for a divorce from Eliza Allen Houston, bluntly stating that they had been separated for four years and that, in spite of his own feelings in the matter, there was no chance of a reconciliation.

Two fellow attorneys were foolish enough to ask him about the petition, but Sam's reply caused them to lose interest in the subject. "I have two pistols," he said, "and my trigger fingers are itching to close the mouths of people who don't tend to their own affairs."

No one else asked him about the divorce.

Besides, the decrees issued by President Santa Anna furnished a far more fascinating—and infuriating—topic for discussion. The new head of the Mexican government busied himself promulgating decrees that curtailed the personal liberties of the people; most of these edicts were directed at the Americans who had settled in Texas, but they blithely ignored the laws, gathering in groups of ten and more when they pleased, publishing newspapers attacking the regime in Mexico City, and, the majority of them being Protestants, worshiping in churches they built. What really confused Santa Anna and his subordinates was that the Americans who were Roman Catholics happily joined in the "conspiracy" of their Protestant friends and helped in the construction of these churches. In the United States, they said, men worshiped as they wished, and no American intended to abandon the principle of religious freedom.

Stephen F. Austin went to Mexico City, hoping to work out reasonable agreements with Santa Anna that would satisfy both Mexicans and the Americans in Texas. He was cast into prison, and the garrison of Mexican troops in the city of San Antonio was strengthened. Even the Texas moderates became angry, and Sam Houston cast aside the last shreds of caution.

"An armed clash between Texas and Mexico has become inevitable," he said in November 1834. "When the rights of peaceful men are curtailed by the musket and bayonet, they must defend their liberties."

Tension continued to rise in 1835. Committees of Vigilance and Safety were formed by the settlers, who patterned them on similar groups that had been active immediately prior to the American Revolution, and Sam was active in all of them. Then, on September 1, 1835, a gaunt Stephen Austin returned from prison, and spoke in a new voice. It was impossible, he declared, to consult with tyrants or deal reasonably with them.

The last doubts were swept away, and Sam addressed a mass meeting in Nacogdoches, the largest assemblage ever held in east

Texas. "The work of liberty has begun," he declared, and his words were repeated throughout the province. He, even more than Austin, James W. Fannin, Thomas J. Rusk, and James Bowie, was emerging as the leader behind whom all Texans were uniting.

He took his pre-eminence more or less for granted. He was working toward a goal in which he believed, and he assumed that others would accept and follow him. His self-confidence was completely restored, his energy seemed inexhaustible and he was convinced that Texas would emerge triumphant from her difficulties. He took care, however, not to take sides in the dispute between the moderates, who hoped to establish a semi-independent state under Mexican suzerainty, and the radicals, who were demanding complete independence.

"In my opinion," he wrote President Jackson, "the ambitions of Texans cannot be realized within the boundaries of the Mexican Republic. But I am standing aside until events make this clear to the entire population. I can best serve Texas and her citizens if I am recognized as the servant of all the people." Old Hickory's pupil was becoming a master politician in his own right.

Sam was a delegate to the convention that met at Columbia in October 1835, and in San Felipe the following month, to establish a provisional government. One of the first acts of his colleagues was to elect him, by an almost unanimous vote, to the post of commander-in-chief of the Texas Army, with the rank of major general.

Leaving politics to others, he plunged into the task of recruiting, financing, training, and equipping a military force. His problems appeared almost insuperable. The provisional government was virtually bankrupt, so he had to solicit—sometimes beg—the wealthier citizens for funds. His recruiting parties met with less success than he had hoped, principally because so many independent companies of volunteers were being formed, and refused to submit to any authority other than their own. He had to send volunteers to New Orleans for many badly needed supplies, among them lead and flour, shoe leather and even soap. Privately, consulting no one, he wrote to President Jackson, asking for a substantial loan from the United States.

Santa Anna had no intention of waiting until the Texas insurrectionists organized their military forces before taking action, and in the late autumn of 1835 seized the initiative. Everywhere the outnumbered Texans were forced to give ground, and their future appeared bleak. By March 2, 1836, the day that Texas declared her independence, a strong Mexican corps was besieging a tiny garrison of less than two hundred men at the Alamo, and an even larger force threatened the single strongest unit of Texans, which was stationed at Goliad.

The desperate situation required a swift, desperate response. Sam's authority was broadened, and all who bore arms, including the volunteer companies, were placed under his direct command. Volunteers by the hundreds began to appear at recruiting centers, most of them carrying their own arms and ammunition. There was no time to train them, much less subject them to the discipline that Sam considered essential to the success of operations. Pessimists were afraid that all Texas would be overrun by Mexican troops, and that the war would end almost before it began.

On March 6, after a siege of thirteen days, the Alamo, in San Antonio, was captured by the Mexicans. Only five members of the defending force, commanded by Colonels William B. Travis, David Crockett, and James Bowie, were still alive when the attackers burst into the fort. These five were murdered, and Texans everywhere were convinced Santa Anna himself had given orders that no prisoners were to be taken.

Sam heard the tragic news of the Alamo's fall when he reached the little town of Gonzales, where a tiny force of only three hundred and seventy-four armed men awaited him. Surrounded by his ragged volunteers in buckskins, he remained silent for some moments after the courier reported to him. Then, very softly, but in a voice that carried, he said, "If we fail, the cause of liberty itself will perish. Every free Texan must remember the Alamo."

"Remember the Alamo!" became a rallying cry, but Santa Anna still held the initiative. Sam ordered Fannin, who was commanding the Goliad garrison, to evacuate the town and join him, but

Fannin hesitated, and his entire force was slaughtered by an overwhelming Mexican force.

Sam was forced to retreat eastward, as was the provisional government of President David G. Burnet. Only Rusk, who held the position of Secretary of War, urged his colleagues to stand firm and set an example for the people. But the panicky Burnet and his colleagues ran, and frightened settlers evacuated their households, afraid they would be massacred by the oncoming Mexicans.

Only Sam refused to become discouraged, and was heartened by the steady growth of his little corps. Reinforcements swelled his ranks to six hundred, then to nine hundred as he continued to conduct his slow, careful retreat eastward across the rolling Texas countryside. The burly Rusk, whose intellect belied his appearance, joined him, and approved of his decision to burn down San Felipe in order to discourage the enemy from taking and ransacking the town.

Texans everywhere were in despair, and refugees believed they had lost their homes and their future in what had been a land of rare promise. But Sam, after crossing the Brazos River, called his troops together on the bank of the stream, at the edge of a field of wild clover. The men, grimy and bearded, many of them hungry, either sat or squatted on the ground, and their general mounted his horse so they could see and hear him.

"Boys," he said, "it's customary for officers to sit in a council of war, but I prefer to tell all of you what's on my mind—and to hear what you're thinking."

A heavy-set sergeant wiped his face with the back of a ragged sleeve. "Sam," he shouted, "there's only one thing I can think about. A beefsteak with trimmings!"

The men laughed, shouted, and applauded.

"Now that you mention it," Sam replied, "I wouldn't mind a good meal myself. But I reckon we'll have to be satisfied with cracked corn and cold potatoes a little longer."

The troops groaned.

The commander-in-chief grinned at them, then sobered and held up a hand for silence. "It isn't in the nature of Texans to run away from a fight. This past month hasn't been easy on any of us. Me, now, I'm mighty damned tired of running, so I aim to do something about it."

A sudden tension gripped the troops, and no one moved.

"I've just had a report," Sam continued, "that General Santa Anna and his army tried to capture President Burnet and the rest of the government at Harrisburg, off to the south. Well, our people got away, and Santa Anna burned Harrisburg to the ground."

"The bastard!" someone in the rear ranks called.

"He's a smart bastard, and he has an army of nearly two thousand men, so he outnumbers us by about two to one. But he isn't as smart as he thinks. Right now he's resting his corps near Buffalo Bayou on the San Jacinto River. With the river on his flank and the bayou in front of him, he's limited his ability to maneuver. I've been waiting patiently for him to put himself into a trap."

The men exchanged glances, and many of them began to fondle their rifles.

"You and I," Sam told them, "offer Santa Anna the last organized resistance in Texas. If he can beat us, or drive us out, our Declaration of Independence becomes a paper that isn't worth the ink used to write it. We'll have to clear out."

"The hell we will!" The heavy-set sergeant jumped to his feet and shook a clenched fist.

"That's precisely the way I feel. The hell we will! Texas is our home, and here we stay!" Sam made no attempt to curb the fresh outburst that greeted his words.

Rusk, who was also mounted, moved closer to him. "Are you sure this is the way to handle it?" he asked cautiously.

"Positive!" Sam replied, and turned back to his troops. "Boys, I have a question for you. Can one Texan whip one Mexican?"

The roar sent a flock of birds soaring high into the air.

"All right, then. Another question. Can one Texan whip two Mexicans?"

Again the men roared.

"Think carefully, boys. Those are the odds against us, and if they beat us, it means the end of Texas. So I want to put this to a vote. I don't aim to attack Santa Anna unless all of us are in agreement. How many of you are in favor of a battle?"

Almost to a man the troops stood, shouting until they became hoarse.

"That settles it," Sam told them when the hubbub subsided. "Any man who doesn't want to come with us is free to leave. Now. With no hard feelings. Our food supplies are nearly exhausted, our ammunition and powder is limited, and we have no artillery except some old pieces that may explode when they're fired. So I sure couldn't blame anyone for wanting no part in an attack." He scanned the ranks, waiting.

Not one man left his place.

Sam's manner changed. "Captain Archer!"

"Sir?" A man in a broad-brimmed hat who stood beside his horse stiffened to attention.

"We've got to let Santa Anna know we're coming, so he won't go some place where the terrain is more favorable to him. Take your company of Rangers down to the San Jacinto River, and give the Mexicans our regards. Make nuisances of yourselves. Raid their outposts at night. Let them see you, and then show them that Texas cavalry can ride faster and farther than their own. But don't go too far from Santa Anna's base camp. I want to make absolutely certain he stays there until I can join you with the main body."

"Yes, sir." The young Ranger officer hesitated for an instant. "Is it all right with you, General, if we leave right off?"

Sam joined in the laugh, then shook hands with each of the Rangers before Archer led his forty men off to the south.

"Keep your powder dry, boys, and don't waste bullets on game," the commander-in-chief said. "In another week, at the most, Texas will either be free or all of us will be dead men." He paused, deliberately, and then declared in ringing tones, "Remember the Alamo!"

The corps moved slowly toward the south, conserving its strength. Food supplies were no longer rationed, and the men were permitted to eat whatever they pleased. "If we lose," Sam said repeatedly, "we'll have no need for food. But we're not going to lose."

His senior officers were sparked by his determination, and Rusk, although technically his superior, placed himself under Sam's command and offered to serve in any capacity the General wished. Sam immediately made the Secretary of War his deputy.

On April 19, when the Army was drawing close to the San Jacinto River, and had made camp for the night in a wooded patch of scrub pines, a Ranger from Archer's company arrived at the bivouac. "The enemy know you're coming, General," he said, "and they're waiting for you."

"Are they still in position between the San Jacinto and Buffalo Bayou?" Sam wanted to know.

"Yes, sir. They haven't budged. A couple of times they got a mite restless, but Captain Archer took their minds off moving by finding some new ways to harass their sentry outposts."

"My compliments to Captain Archer," Sam said. "Tell him to rejoin us on the march tomorrow morning. We'll see some real action before the day ends."

The corps broke camp at dawn on April 20, and moved cautiously south of Buffalo Bayou into a position facing Santa Anna. The two forces were no more than a mile and a half apart now, and on the afternoon of the same day the cavalry of both sides skirmished intermittently, each trying to scout the main body of the other. Shots were exchanged throughout the afternoon, but casualties were negligible.

The Texas Army waited until sundown to make ready for battle. Baggage wagons and mules were sent to the rear, and Sam's two six-pounder cannon were brought forward to support the infantry. Rain had fallen heavily for days, making the rich prairie earth soggy, and the wheels of the gun caissons sank hub-deep in the mud. Sam, who had developed a sixth sense when trouble developed, appeared at once, stripped off the coat of his uniform and began to haul one of the cannon free. Scores of volunteers came to his aid, and, without an order being issued, the guns were moved to firmer ground.

A strong detachment had remained on the far side of the

bayou as a rear guard, but Sam, after a brief consultation with Rusk, decided to gamble that the enemy would not try to sneak away. The two men agreed that Santa Anna, with a far larger and better-equipped corps, had no reason to leave, but would welcome an engagement that could destroy the Texans' last hope of obtaining their freedom.

The bayou was treacherous by day and doubly so by night. About fifty yards wide and more than twenty feet deep in the center, it provided no firm footing anywhere. Not only could men drown if they took a false step, but several members of the army who came from Harrisburg swore that poisonous snakes, virtually invisible at night, lived in the marshes at the sides.

The commander-in-chief and his deputy decided that the best way to raise the spirits of the entire force would be to act as their own guides. While Rusk stood in ankle-deep water holding an oil lamp, Sam skirted the bayou to the far side, then led the rear guard back to safety. Neither thought their feat remarkable, and were surprised, subsequently, when newspapers in Texas and the United States applauded their extraordinary courage.

Later that evening, by the light of the same lamp, Sam wrote a message to the people of Texas: *"We stand on the eve of battle. We are nerved for the contest, and must conquer or perish. It is vain to look for present aid; none is at hand. We must now act or abandon all hope. Rally to the standard! Be men, freemen, that your children may bless their fathers' names.*

"We shall use our best efforts to fight the enemy to such advantages as will insure victory, though the odds are greatly against us. I leave the result in the hands of a wise God, and rely upon His providence.

"Our country will do justice to those who serve her. The rights for which we fight will be secured and Texas free."

To the surprise of his aides, Sam slept soundly. He had requested the previous night that he be awakened two hours before dawn, and ate a breakfast of smoked beef and cracked corn, which he washed down with several cups of water from the San Jacinto, no other beverages being available. Then, calling in his unit commanders, he gave them the order of battle.

146

The Rangers were directed to act as mobile vanguard, supported by a battalion of frontier marksmen. Companies of inexperienced recruits were split into platoons and scattered through the corps so that, in the event that a few men panicked, the disease would not spread. And two hundred infantrymen were assigned to guard the campsite and act as a reserve. This left a striking force of only seven hundred men to oppose a foe whose total strength Captain Archer estimated at fifteen hundred to eighteen hundred.

The war drums rolled and the trumpets blared, but the Texans did not move. Sam had decided to entice the enemy into attacking, if he could, believing he could inflict heavier losses on the Mexicans if his own troops held fixed positions. But Santa Anna immediately understood his motives, and adopted the same tactics. His own buglers and drummers responded to the Texans, but the Mexican corps remained in formation near the banks of the San Jacinto.

The sky was overcast, and a light rain fell in midmorning, but the sun came out shortly before noon. The Texans were hungry and restless, and unit commanders had been begging Sam to act, but he heeded no counsel except his own, coldly analyzing the situation. It was evident that Santa Anna had no intention of taking the initiative at present, and Sam grew increasingly afraid that his own men, especially those totally lacking in combat experience, would lose their ardor for battle.

He realized he would be taking a great risk if he ordered an attack, but his chance of being defeated, eventually, would be far greater if he failed to change his tactics. So, a few minutes after noon, he spoke calmly to his deputy.

"Colonel Rusk," he said, "be good enough to pass the word to all unit commanders. We'll attack in five minutes. But I want the trumpeters and drummers to keep quiet. It may upset the enemy if we launch the assault in silence."

The seven hundred men of the Texas striking force moved forward in a single wave, and Sam, ignoring the pleas of his aides to protect himself, insisted on riding with the Rangers. The cavalrymen trotted in formation, and as soon as they came within rifle range of the enemy they opened fire.

147

The Mexican horsemen moved forward to meet them, meeting fire with spirited fire, but the ranks of the Rangers held steady, and the Mexican cavalry retreated. Sam wasted no time in utilizing the slight advantage. He ordered his horsemen to charge at full tilt, and, half-standing in his saddle, urged his foot soldiers forward by waving his sword.

The frontiersmen could fire and reload their rifles in forty seconds, even when running, and the steady roar of their weapons was disconcerting to an enemy accustomed to a more leisurely tempo of battle. The Rangers, driving hard, created an opening in the Mexican lines, and the infantry, close behind the horsemen, quickly widened the breach.

The defenders fought courageously, but were bewildered by the ruthlessness of their foes. Falling back, yet unable to maneuver freely because the river and bayou hampered them, the Mexicans tried repeatedly to reorganize their lines and make a stand. The Texans gave them no chance. Sam's troops cut through to the rear, then pushed back in the opposite direction, their own ranks firm, and systematically cut their enemy to shreds, isolating companies, platoons, and small squads, annihilating them and then renewing their attack.

Sam himself realized that victory was assured, and, forgetting momentarily that he was a forty-three-year-old commander-in-chief, he found himself caught up in the spirit of the exhilarating fury that had taken possession of his troops. He directed each thrust, then participated in it himself, wielding his sword like a scythe and, when he could, reloading his smoking pistols.

Suddenly, when the fighting was at its height, he felt an agonizing stab of pain in his right leg. Glancing down, he saw that his shin had been shattered by a bullet, and that he was bleeding heavily. The pain quickly spread up his leg, and in a moment or two his entire body was suffused, but he could not allow himself to withdraw. No one else knew he had been wounded, so he continued to direct the fight and participate in it.

In a short time, little more than two hours after the battle had begun, it came to an abrupt end. Mexican losses had been heavy, and the survivors, losing heart for combat, fled from the field, their corps suddenly disintegrating and becoming a mob in which every man was concerned only for his own safety.

"Follow them, boys!" Sam shouted. "Take as many prisoners as you can capture!" Secure in the knowledge that his victory was complete, he slumped unconscious in the saddle.

Tears came to Sam's eyes and his aides were afraid he might faint when the surgeon poured whisky onto his wound to clean it. But he managed to joke about his plight. "That's a damnable waste of good drinking liquor," he gasped.

Two men held him while the surgeon set the broken bone in his leg, but after the splints and a dressing had been applied, he insisted on resuming the direction of the Army. He slept for a few hours on the night following the battle, and the next morning sent a brief report to President Burnet:

"*Texas is free. We met the enemy at San Jacinto, and beat him soundly. As of the present, we have counted six hundred and thirty-four Mexican dead, and have taken more than seven hundred prisoners, many of them wounded. Santa Anna's corps no longer exists.*

"*The Almighty was merciful to us, and our own losses were light. Nine of our brave boys were killed, and thirty-four were wounded.*"

It did not occur to him to mention that he himself was one of the injured. So his statistics were inaccurate.

At the insistence of the surgeon, Sam spent the better part of the day resting on a pallet. Foraging parties had gone out through the countryside to search for food, and patrols continued to bring in frightened, hungry Mexican prisoners, who were astonished to find themselves being held under guard rather than cold-bloodedly murdered. One of the captives rounded up during the afternoon was a short, slight man who wore a faded blue peasant's smock and dirty red carpet slippers, which he had substituted for his uniform.

When the other prisoners saw him, they began to murmur, "*El Presidente*," and the alert Lieutenant in charge of the guard detail immediately escorted the man to the commander-in-chief, who was stretched out on his pallet under a tree.

Sam glanced up in mild curiosity.

The prisoner stepped forward and bowed. "I am General Antonio López de Santa Anna," he said, speaking in almost unaccented English, "President of Mexico and commander of the Army of Operations. I place myself at the disposal of the brave General Houston."

Stunned by the revelation, Sam could only mutter, "Ah. Indeed." Then, feeling a little foolish, he added, "Take a seat, General. I'm glad to see you."

Texans were appearing from every part of the camp to look at the celebrated prisoner.

But Sam waved them back. In control of himself now, he said, "I'm afraid I can't offer you anything to drink but water. We've been too busy lately to carry any wines in our baggage train."

Santa Anna appreciated his humor, and managed to smile. "I will be grateful for a cup of water, General."

An aide went to fetch it, and the two commanders eyed each other a trifle warily.

Santa Anna cleared his throat. "That man may consider himself born to no common destiny," he said pompously, "who has conquered the Napoleon of the West."

Sam inclined his head, but had to turn away his face to hide his grin.

"It now remains for the conqueror to be generous to the vanquished," Santa Anna said, accepting the cup of water and sipping.

Sam's smile faded, and his eyes became hard. "You should have thought of that at the Alamo," he said.

There was a long, tense silence, and Santa Anna stared at the ground, believing he would be executed.

"Unlike the enemy we've beaten," Sam continued in a harsh voice, "Texans are civilized. We don't kill helpless prisoners. You're safe enough, and so are your men."

Santa Anna stammered his thanks.

"Colonel Rusk," Sam said to his deputy, who had joined them,

"I want every last soldier in the Army notified that anyone who molests, wounds, or kills a prisoner will be directly responsible to me."

Rusk went off to transmit the order to unit commanders.

The uncomfortable Santa Anna relaxed a little, and his professional curiosity overcame his personal embarrassment. "I wonder if you will tell me something, General Houston. It confuses me that you did not attack two days ago. My men were so anxious for battle that I could scarcely keep them in their ranks."

Sam nodded soberly. "That's exactly why I didn't fight. I knew you were expecting me to begin the battle that day, and were prepared for it. So I was right. Besides, I thought there was no use in having two bites at one cherry."

"But you were taking a chance, General," Santa Anna said. "Suppose reinforcements had reached me?"

"Your reinforcements wouldn't matter, General," Sam replied. "You never can conquer freemen."

The war was won, and Sam's victory in the Battle of San Jacinto on April 21, 1836, combined with his subsequent capture of Santa Anna, made him the most popular man in Texas. Celebrations in his honor were planned in every town, but had to be postponed. Sam's physicians would not allow him to be moved until his wound began to heal satisfactorily, and he remained at the site of the battlefield until May 5.

In the meantime all Mexican troops withdrew from the soil of Texas, the government in Mexico City recognized the Rio Grande as the border and promised to reimburse Texas for her losses. Santa Anna remained a hostage until the final peace treaty was signed.

Only President Burnet was unhappy. He and the colleagues in his administration who had fled from the Mexicans were being ridiculed by the rejoicing citizens of Texas, and he hated Sam for making him appear a coward. A simple statement from the hero of San Jacinto might have helped restore Burnet to public favor, but Sam had no intention of telling the people that the civilians had been wise to run away from the Mexican troops. Burnet's reputation meant nothing to him, and only two matters were on his mind, the final peace treaty guaranteeing the independence of Texas, and the state of his own health.

The physicians felt that no facilities were available in Texas to help speed Sam's recuperation, so he was taken to Galveston, and there sailed to the United States. Late in May an operation was performed on his leg in New Orleans, and a week later he was allowed to leave his bed for limited periods, provided he used crutches. He would be wise, the physicians told him, if he remained in New Orleans for about eight weeks.

But disturbing news reached him from Texas. Although the Mexican government had scrupulously observed all of the conditions in the preliminary peace treaty, Santa Anna was still being held as a prisoner, and his life was in jeopardy. President Burnet, hoping to regain public favor, and supported by new waves of immigrants just arriving in Texas from the United States, was allowing it to be known that he intended to submit the President of Mexico to a court-martial trial, following which he would be executed.

Sam was outraged. *"Texas badly needs to be regarded favorably by the civilized nations of the world,"* he wrote Thomas Rusk. *"If Santa Anna is executed, we will rightly be regarded as barbarians."*

In a letter to his friend, Henry Raguet, Anna's father, he revealed still another reason for his distress. *"I gave Santa Anna my personal pledge that he would not be molested or harmed. My own honor is at stake!"*

Too restless to remain inactive, he ignored the warnings of the medical men and sailed for Texas on June 15. Dr. Robert Irion, a young friend and admirer, met him on his arrival to dress his wound, and traveled with him to Nacogdoches, trying in vain on the journey to force his patient to rest. The task was compounded by the enthusiasm of the people.

Settlers traveled as far as two hundred miles to catch a glimpse of the hero of San Jacinto. Barbecues were held in his honor every night, he was pelted with flowers, shook the hands of hundreds and accepted countless jugs of whisky, smoked hams and roasted turkeys as gifts. By the time he reached Nacogdoches he was so

exhausted that Dr. Irion put him to bed in the Raguet home
and told Anna to bar his room to all visitors.

But not even the devoted girl and her parents could accomplish
the impossible and Sam refused to be isolated. He sought news
of the outside world from Henry Raguet and the many visitors
who came to pay their respects to him. By late July he lost his
temper again and sent another angry letter to Rusk. He had heard
a rumor, he said, that Santa Anna would be taken to Goliad for
execution following a secret court-martial. But he found it "too
incredible to be believed."

Such action, he declared, would be contrary to the true policy
of Texas. Not only would it be a gross violation of the rules of
civilized warfare, but the execution would be a disregard of the
national character of Texans. It would place the lives of Texans
still being held prisoner in Mexico in grave jeopardy, he added.

Rusk, himself now a major general and in temporary command of the Army, replied that he would use all his influence
to prevent such a trial, and, if necessary, would protect Santa
Anna's person with the troops.

Sam had been insisting to visitors that he had no interest in
politics. Now that the independence of Texas had been secured,
he wanted to look after his personal interests, develop his law
practice and farm some of the property he had purchased. His
reasons were valid, he told himself, but he was finding the lure
of politics irresistible now that an election of a permanent government to replace the provisional regime was pending.

Two men had already announced their candidacies for President, Stephen Austin and Henry Smith, but a spontaneous campaign for Sam was making it increasingly difficult for him to
resist. Newspapers urged him to run, Rusk issued a statement to
the effect that he was the man best suited for the post, and a
large majority of the convention delegates who had voted for independence signed a petition in his favor. Private citizens joined
in the clamor, and so many wrote him letters that the Nacogdoches
post office fell hopelessly behind in its task of sorting the mail.

Sam was genuinely torn. On one hand he truly wanted the
opportunity to put his own affairs on a sound financial basis,

and his injured leg was causing him more trouble than he wanted
to admit. He had to remind himself, too, that Texas was still at
war with Mexico, at least technically, and that, when his health
permitted his return to the field, his place was with the Army.
There were rumors, too, of an impending Creek Indian uprising
on the eastern frontier, and, to be on the safe side, he ordered
the militia of that area mustered.

But he discovered that he had politics in his blood, and that
the lure of high office was beyond his ability to resist. He had
rehabilitated himself, and knew that the reputation he had won
at San Jacinto had earned him a permanent place in the history
of Texas, so it would be sensible to spend the rest of his days
making himself comfortable. But, no matter how hard he tried,
he could not forget Andrew Jackson's prediction that a man who
had held high elective office would not be satisfied in life with
less.

Finally, at the end of the summer, he compromised with himself, and issued a brief statement to the press. "I have yielded to
the wishes of my friends in allowing my name to be run for President. The crisis requires it, or I would not have yielded." He refrained from adding that, as President, he would make certain
Santa Anna was returned unharmed to Mexico. And he saw no
reason to mention his private decision to conduct no campaign
on his own behalf. If he should be elected, it would be because
the people themselves wanted him.

From the day he made his announcement, his opponents took
it for granted that he would win. Austin had been embroiled in
too many quarrels during the long, lean years of his leadership as
Texas' principal colonizer, and knew it. In fact, he privately made
plans for a permanent retirement from public life. And Smith,
although he did not withdraw from the ballot, made speeches
urging the citizens to vote for General Houston.

The election was held on September 5, 1836, and Sam received
more than five thousand votes. The combined total of the other
candidates, including a number whose names were written in, was
approximately fifteen hundred.

In October 1836 the First Congress of the Republic of Texas

convened in the little town of Columbia, and on October 22, at four o'clock in the afternoon, General Sam Houston took the oath of office as President. Since the streets were not paved and it had rained that morning, his boots, like those of everyone else, were caked with soft mud.

Legislators and private citizens who had heard that their new chief executive was a great orator were disappointed. Sam's Inaugural Address was as short as it was sharp. There was work to be done by the entire nation, he said, and he intended to waste no time doing his share. This, he declared, was not a time for talk.

His principal Cabinet appointments, which he revealed that same day, demonstrated his statesmanship. Stephen F. Austin became Secretary of State, and Henry Smith was made Secretary of the Treasury. No one was surprised when the President's friend, Thomas Rusk, returned to his position of Secretary of War.

That evening the members of the administration, their families and their friends gathered for a celebration, but no building was large enough to house such a throng. So barbecue pits were dug in the open, near Washington Street, the main thoroughfare, and sides of beef and oxen were roasted. The President, in his shirtsleeves and munching ears of sweet corn, greeted all of the guests, even though he still needed a cane when he walked or stood. Late in the evening, after the crowd thinned, the President, the Secretary of War and four others retired to the log cabin that had been erected, hastily, as a "temporary White House," and ended the evening by consuming an impressive quantity of corn whisky.

Sam, wrapped in a blanket on the floor in one corner of the cabin, awakened at dawn. His mouth felt dry, a reminder of the days when his overindulgence had been habitual, but he was clear-headed and felt alert. Limping out to the well behind the cabin, he hauled up a bucket of water, washed and began to shave. Most of his friends and colleagues were still asleep, and in the early morning quiet he had an opportunity to reflect on the enormity of the problems he would be required to solve.

Texas was an incredibly vast domain, and although new immigrants were arriving every day, the total population of the Republic was approximately thirty thousand. There were no law courts, no jails, and the few constables were self-appointed. The land surveys that had been made were primitive, virtually no records of real estate transactions had been kept anywhere, and there would be utter chaos if order was not established in the immediate future.

A state of war still existed with Mexico, Santa Anna was being held prisoner and the members of the new Senate had made it plain the preceding night that they had no intention of agreeing to his release.

Diplomatic relations had to be established with the United States, Great Britain, France and Spain, legations had to be opened in their capitals and, somehow, competent men had to be found to serve in them.

Worst of all, the Treasury was empty, and there were no sources of revenue to pay wages, even those of the troops on guard at the Mexican border or on patrol in the eastern frontier district. The House of Representatives was opposed to Sam's idea of establishing tariffs on imports, and the Senate already was threatening to reject property taxation. No matter how his Congress felt, Sam knew that both forms of fund-raising were imperative.

Despite the immediate difficulties, however, he had no doubts in his mind about the future of Texas. The soil was rich, the forests of yellow pine and oak were thick, and farmers had already demonstrated that cotton, wheat, and vegetables grew far more rapidly and easily than in most parts of the United States. Cattle thrived, fish were plentiful off the Gulf of Mexico and anyone with imagination knew that Galveston, which was growing rapidly, would be a great seaport.

Yet, in spite of his optimism, Sam felt strangely depressed. He had conquered himself and had risen above the black despair that had threatened to destroy him after he and Eliza had parted, and he knew he had cause to be proud of his accomplishments. Certainly he had earned the right to wear the gold ring his mother had given him so long ago. Why, then, was he so gloomy?

He could rationalize, he supposed, and say that his leg had not yet entirely healed, and that his health was still impaired. He could claim, with justice, that the responsibilities he had assumed the previous day were staggering.

The basic cause of his unhappiness, he reluctantly admitted to himself, was irrelevant to the burdens of his office or to the state of his health, which was sure to improve. As soon as he established the courts, his petition for a divorce from Eliza would be granted, and then he would be alone, legally as well as in fact. He was acquainted with many men of forty-three who were grandfathers, but he was a bachelor, and likely to remain one for the rest of his days.

He, who needed a wife's love and wanted children, appeared doomed to spend his life by himself. It would be easy enough for a man in his position to find a bride, of course, but he had made that mistake once, and had no intention of repeating it. There was literally no woman he knew in whom he could become interested. He was fond of Anna Raguet, but she was only a child, and he felt like her uncle, not her prospective husband.

Texas, like all frontier lands, was still a man's country, and the few single women who came here were either harlots or adventuresses—or both. The ladies of his acquaintance were already married, and another generation would grow to womanhood before an honorable man could find himself a wife.

The first President of the Republic of Texas started a fire in the outdoor pit, sliced some bacon and made some dough for biscuits. Then, filling a kettle with ground coffee beans and water, he cooked breakfast for his advisers and himself.

Two pungent candles provided the illumination in the President's cabin, and occasionally Secretary of State Austin, whose health was frail, went out into the open to breathe some fresh air. Secretary of the Treasury Smith and Secretary of War Rusk sipped their whisky and water from battered mugs, as did the President, who occasionally gave them additional whisky from the jug on the dirt floor beside him. The fire of pine logs in the hearth crackled, but there were so many openings between the logs of the cabin that the room was cold, and the men huddled in cloaks as they talked.

After spending a month in office, all were bone-weary, but accepted their late evening meeting as inevitable. Eighteen-hour days had become routine. Each went through the papers stacked before him, pending business was discussed, and questions were resolved when possible, with solutions postponed only when there was no choice.

At last Sam slumped in a chair, took a swallow of his whisky and ran a hand through his rapidly graying hair. "That disposes of the day's ordinary matters, gentlemen."

Austin yawned and glanced at his watch.

"I won't keep you much longer, Stephen," Sam said. "I know you're testifying before a Senate committee tomorrow morning on the appropriations for legations."

"Before that," Austin said with a hollow laugh, "I'm having breakfast with my staff."

"I have only one more matter to talk about tonight," Sam said. "Let me review it briefly. Twenty-four hours after I took office, I sent a message to the Senate requesting a bill authorizing the release of Santa Anna—"

"We know," Smith interrupted testily. "The Senate refused to pass such a bill. Then you issued a decree setting Santa Anna free, and the Senate refused to ratify it. There's been a stalemate for the past two weeks."

"Forgive my bluntness, Sam," Austin said, "but it's a waste of time to discuss the Santa Anna problem until we find some new approach. We've exhausted every Constitutional alternative to set him free."

The President and his Secretary of War exchanged surreptitious grins. "To my mind," Sam said briskly, "the matter is paramount. The Mexican government has failed to live up to one provision of the peace treaty, that of recognizing our independence. I can't blame them, of course, since we still hold Santa

Anna. But the issue is vital. Until Mexico admits our independence, the legality of our status is dubious."

"I'll grant you," Austin said, "that there isn't much chance the United States will admit Texas to the Union as a state until Mexico legally sets us free."

"Let me finish my summary." Again Sam drank some whisky. "When I spoke to Santa Anna last Tuesday, he told me he'd gladly go to Washington City in order to use his influence, from there, to change the position of his government. His successors aren't any too anxious to see him return to Mexico, but he's still the most popular of all Mexicans, and he can do our cause a great deal of good working from Washington."

"Until we can find a way to set him free," Smith said, "I see no point in speculating on the good he might do us."

Sam was silent for a moment. "If there are two men in all of Texas I'd trust with any assignment, they're Colonel George Hockley and Major Bill Patton. They served under you after I was wounded at San Jacinto, Tom. Do you think they're reliable?"

"There's no doubt of it. They follow instructions to the letter."

"This noon," Sam said, "Congress adjourned for a week. Most members left Columbia immediately, and they showed good sense. There isn't much to keep a man here when he can go home for a few days. Help yourself to more whisky, Henry. At this very minute Colonel Hockley and Major Patton are riding toward the border of the United States. They're leading a company of Rangers, and they have orders to let no one stop them. They're going straight on to Washington City." He paused, then added casually, "They're escorting a former prisoner of the Republic of Texas, General Santa Anna."

Austin and Smith were speechless, and could only stare at him.

"Colonel Hockley and Major Patton acted on my written instructions. A short time after sundown tonight they went to the house where we were holding Santa Anna, released him and rode off with him."

Smith was the first to find his voice. "You've defied the Senate!"

"I reckon I have," Sam said.

"When Congress reconvenes and Sam tells the Houses what

he's done," Rusk added, "he's going to remind them that it was he who made Santa Anna prisoner—and worked out the basic peace treaty with him."

"The Senate," Sam said, "can either accept what I've done, or try to impeach me. They don't have enough votes to do it, and the people wouldn't stand for it."

Austin was frowning. "I'm not sure whether what you've done is Constitutional."

"I've exercised my Executive prerogative," Sam said firmly. "It's my duty to secure the safety and honor of Texas. I was elected by the people, not the Senate, and I intend to serve in the best interests of the people. The Senate ratifies treaties, but the Executive implements them. And this Executive is going to use a little common sense as long as he holds office. If the voters disagree with me, they can retire me in two years. I hold with Andrew Jackson that the Presidency is only as strong as the man, and I'll be damned if I'm going to let a pack of narrow-minded Senators stop me from doing what I know is right!"

SIX

1837–40

Rarely in the history of any nation had one man done so much in so short a time. The first months of Sam's administration were frantically active, and Vice-President Mirabeau Lamar, Burnet's friend, who disliked the President, was forced to admit, "Houston is a whirlwind. I don't know when he sleeps, or if he sleeps. He appears determined to accomplish in a year what other nations do over generations."

Less than a week before the end of 1836, Secretary of State Stephen Austin died, and Sam lost his most dedicated and widely respected associate. "The father of Texas is no more," he told the people, and proposed that a city be named for the great pioneer.

Law courts were established under an unusual but effective system devised by the President. The judges whom he appointed and their bailiffs traveled through the districts under their jurisdiction, heavily armed, and whenever their authority was questioned, quietly offered to settle the issue with dissenters in "wilderness style," with the principals aided by a few friends. The "friends" of the judges were revealed to be one or more companies of mounted Rangers, who had remained out of sight until the challenge had been made. Nowhere did local citizens, even the most belligerent, accept the offer, and by the early months of 1837 the courts were dispensing justice everywhere.

The command of the Army was given to General Albert Sidney Johnston, an exceptionally able professional soldier. A Kentuckian by birth, he graduated from the United States Military Academy at West Point in 1826 and had a long and honorable record of service prior to his immigration to Texas. A modest, almost shy farm owner in his early thirties who had thought his military career ended when he left the United States, he had enlisted as a private in 1836, served throughout the campaign with Mexico and had risen rapidly through the ranks. Sam, quick to recognize his extraordinary talents, did not hesitate to promote him to the top command, and even the disgruntled Senate, which was conducting a feud with the President, had to admit the choice was a good one.

Always sensitive to Indians, Sam made peace with the Comanche, one of the most ferocious of the savage nations, who were living within the borders of Texas. Simultaneously he offered friendship and abiding peace to the Cherokee, who were so elated by his election that they were moving in large numbers from the Arkansas Territory into Texas.

Relations between the President and the Senate became strained as soon as it became public knowledge that Sam had freed Santa Anna and sent him to Washington. Difficulties with the House soon followed, too. No sooner had the first tax bills become law than the legislators wanted to share in the financial windfalls, and both Houses were flooded with measures appropriating funds for post offices, forts, and roads. Sam impartially vetoed all of them, finally announcing, "The income of this Republic is modest, and must be used for the benefit of all our people. As long as I am President, no man will grow rich at government expense, and no legislative district will get more than its fair share of internal improvements."

The rate of immigration increased, and since most newcomers were former residents of Southern states, many brought their slaves with them. "*I am afraid,*" Sam wrote to Henry Raguet, "*that the very considerable rise in our slave population will,*" *some day, impede our efforts to persuade the United States to annex Texas. Whether I, either as President or private citizen, approve of the institution of slavery is irrelevant to the problem.*

"There are slaves in Texas, and more arrive each day. In New England, the Prairie States and other portions of the North the Abolitionist movement becomes stronger, so I need not be a seer to predict that in these parts of the United States there will be resistance to the admission of Texas into the Union when she applies.

"But it is already too late to find a compromise that will satisfy both slave-holders and Abolitionists. Just as we are larger, by far, than any state in the American Union, so our farms are larger, and our property owners, having discovered they cannot till their acreage themselves, have resorted to slave labor.

"Consequently we can only pray that the larger issue at stake will be resolved within the United States. For myself, I know only that I stand with President Jackson, that Calhoun and his Nullifiers who would tear apart a great nation must be put forever in their place, and that the Federal Union, of which Texas inevitably must become a part, will be preserved."

Two brothers, John and A. C. Allen, founded a new town at the navigational head of Buffalo Bayou, where ships from New York and Philadelphia, Charleston and New Orleans could reach it. This port city, they declared, would serve the heartland of Texas' richest agricultural district; crops could be grown in abundance in the rich soil of the area, "fresh fish, fowl, oysters and sea bathing" would be available only a few miles away. The climate was healthy, water supplies were ample for the support of a large population, and the very location of the community guaranteed that it would become the capital of Texas. Weeds were burned, trees were cut, although the brothers were so anxious to start building the new town that many tree stumps were left in the ground, and lots were offered to prospective buyers at low prices.

The Allens, not seeking the permission of the President, named the community after him and made him a gift of a lot that, they informed him, "was in the best of all possible locations."

Sam was simultaneously flattered and embarrassed. His permanent home was in Nacogdoches, but he told the brothers, "I am honored, and it is my hope, after I retire from office next year, that I can spend at least some portion of each year in the new city of Houston."

Sam's curiosity was greater than his patience, and in April 1837, he paid his first visit to the new community that bore his name. It was growing so rapidly that it promised to become the largest town in the nation within a very short time, and was already thriving as a shipping center and market for fish and vegetables. Manufacturers of consumer goods were building small factories, citizens of means were erecting handsome homes and Sam was delighted by all that he saw.

With the aid of several acquaintances he went to work on a house for himself, enjoying the first holiday he had taken since coming to Texas. But he refused to permit the construction of a large dwelling. "I live alone and have no need for a big house," he said. "What's more, I can't afford anything more pretentious than a modest place."

Not until then did anyone learn that, contrary to the custom of his peers in both Texas and the United States, he believed it wrong for a man who held high public office to accept an income from private sources. Not only had he given up his law practice, but had refused to take any profits from the Nacogdoches farm which Henry Raguet and other friends were operating on his behalf. Going even farther, he was receiving only a token portion of his wages as President.

"Until Texas becomes solvent," he declared, "I'll live on my savings. I must support no one but myself, and my needs are simple and few."

Vice-President Lamar, who hoped to succeed him in office, persuaded several newspapers friendly to his cause to print the charge that President Houston was bankrupt. These articles hinted that his trouble was caused by his spendthrift ways, and that Texas would be in similar difficulty if the Senate did not curb his extravagances.

Sam ignored the allegations, and refused to allow his friends to answer them. "I deserve no praise for insisting that the Treasury Department keep the better part of what is due me. The decision was a private one, and I don't care to make public capital of my private principles."

The matter was minor, he insisted, and something of far greater importance was on his mind. Andrew Jackson, in his final act before relinquishing the presidency of the United States to Martin Van Buren, officially recognized the independence of Texas. It would be far more difficult now for Mexico to renew the war in an attempt to reclaim her lost province, and Sam felt certain that Great Britain and France, not wanting to be outdone by the Americans, would grant recognition within the immediate future, too.

Texas' growing pains pleased the President and his supporters, but caused his opponents increasing anguish. Sam was a tyrant, Lamar and his other foes said, when he made no secret of Columbia's inadequate facilities and moved the seat of government to Houston. It was becoming obvious that, within a year, the nation's population would be doubled, and Sam, while ordering every department and bureau of his expanding government to plan accordingly, vetoed a score of bills, passed by his reckless Congress, that would have spent money foolishly.

He lived alone in his tiny house of whitewashed clapboard, and his habits confused the men who wanted to portray him to his fellow Texans as a power-hungry, would-be king. A man who fried his own beefsteaks and roasted his own eggs, who made his own bed and washed his own dishes was not threatening the freedom of ordinary men and women who performed the same chores.

Sam's greatest weakness was sartorial. He had waistcoats made in crimson silk and cloth-of-gold, ordered a new hat of white beaver, and startled his Cabinet by appearing at a meeting wearing a cravat adorned with gold tassels. His vanities directed attention away from his injured leg, and he had learned to handle a walking stick so adroitly that few men realized he still walked with a limp, could stand for no more than limited periods and sometimes, particularly when the weather was damp, suffered excruciating pains.

"*The President's courage*," Dr. Irion wrote to Anna Raguet, "*is remarkable. I have treated men who, with a condition far less severe than his, have taken to their beds for weeks. But he refuses to remain on his pallet more than four or five hours each night. Colonel Hockley and the other members of his staff cannot keep pace with him, nor can I. Work is his recreation and joy as well as his duty.*

"*If he suffers any serious fault, I suspect he sometimes drinks too much whisky or claret wine when alone, but I can offer no conclusive proof of this charge. Occasionally I have detected the strong odor of spirits on his breath, but at no time have I seen him in a state other than one of complete sobriety.*"

Sam realized, far better than did his young physician friend, that he was drinking too much, and once again was jeopardizing his future. Although he refused to touch either whisky or wine when working, he had convinced himself that a glass of spirits made it easier to fall asleep at night, and far too often, when no one was at hand to see him, he staggered to his pallet.

The responsibilities and cares of his office were enormous, and he tried to convince himself that a strong drink late at night was a reasonable, fitting substitute for a loving wife and family. All too often, however, he had to drink several cups of strong coffee at breakfast to clear his head, and knew he was flirting with a disgrace even greater than that which had ruined him after he had fled from Tennessee.

It was a feeble excuse to tell himself he was the kind of man who needed a wife and should not live alone. Others might not believe that the hero of San Jacinto, the aggressive, uncompromising President who was creating a stable, safe and prosperous Texas, had an Achilles heel. But it was the truth that necessity, not choice, made a bachelor of Sam Houston, whom thousands of Texans and millions of Americans respected and envied.

Under the terms of the Texas Constitution Sam could not succeed himself, and left office on December 12, 1838. Although he had declared in public on a number of occasions that he was retiring from politics, Lamar had been elected as the new President, and Sam, uncertain that he trusted him, wanted to leave the door open in case he decided he was needed again.

A large crowd gathered to hear the Inaugural of the new President, but Sam gave him no chance to make more than a token speech. The outgoing Chief Executive chose the occasion to make some remarks of his own, and after reviewing the history of Texas and of his own administration, he sketched the potential of the future. His address lasted for more than three and a half hours, and the crowd, after cheering him lustily, went home.

His achievements were solidly impressive. Texas' independence was recognized by all of the nations with whom she had wanted relations, and trade with all of them was growing. The courts of law were operating, the Treasury was solvent, the Army had become an organization of professionals and a small, efficient Navy had been created. Public schools were being built to educate the children of every citizen, and extensive plans were being perfected to create more universities, per capita, than could be found anywhere in the United States. New public roads made travel easy, and more were being built. Systematic land surveys had been made, and every homestead owner knew the precise boundaries of his property.

"President Houston," said Thomas Rusk, "has performed miracles. He deserves his retirement."

Sam's return to private life lasted only a few weeks. A vacancy occurred in the House of Representatives, and his East Texas neighbors prevailed on him to run for the seat. Lamar had already announced his intention of removing the capital to a new city he was building and naming after Austin, and Sam decided it might be wise to keep watch on the activities of his successor. He was elected to the House without opposition.

But he did have time now to look after his private interests, and plunged into farming and the practice of law with the same energy and enthusiasm he had shown in public life. The annexation of Texas by the United States was still of paramount importance to him, and he corresponded regularly on the subject with Andrew Jackson, who had retired to the Hermitage. Sam also confided in Old Hickory on other matters.

"*I am inclined to suspect that Lamar is a fool, a spendthrift and a saber-rattler who may get us embroiled in a new war with Mexico,*" he wrote. "*But I must be fair to him and give him a chance. I have formed a partnership in the law, at Houston, with John Birdsall. Together with George Hockley and several other friends I am active in a new company dedicated to the development of the city of Houston and the making of it the most important city in North America. I intend to enlarge my farming operations at Nacogdoches, and am particularly anxious to breed blooded cattle, which flourish in the salubrious climate there. In brief, sir, I am busy.*

"*I hope to visit the United States in the coming months, and plan to pay you a visit at the Hermitage.*"

Before his departure Sam encouraged Dr. Irion in a romance with Anna Raguet, and urged the girl to give Irion's suit serious consideration. He also made an attempt to mediate differences between the Cherokee and the authorities of the East Texas counties. But, in spite of his many activities, he found time dragging, and frequently spent his evenings drinking large quantities of whisky.

"I've learned how to handle liquor," he told the friends who showed concern.

The two people who were closest to him, Dr. Irion and Anna, disagreed, but were unable to persuade him that he was jeopardizing his future, taking risks that might destroy all he had achieved since coming to Texas.

Early in the summer Sam went off to the United States to buy horses and cattle from an Alabama dealer, Hickman Lewis. He sailed from the city of Houston, and, after arriving in Mobile, was invited to give two addresses there. On both occasions he drank too much, and although there were some in his audiences who were shocked, he managed to retain a sufficient grip on himself to make sense as he urged his auditors to emigrate to Texas.

He sobered in time for his negotiations with Lewis, at whose plantation he stayed, and there were so many in the neighborhood who wanted to entertain the distinguished visitor that Sam relaxed and began to enjoy his first holiday in years. Among the houses at which he dined was that of William Bledsoe and his handsome wife, Emily. It was there that he met Emily's sister, Margaret Lea.

Although it had become Sam's custom to drink several glasses of whisky before dinner, he found this young woman with grave, violet eyes watching him, her manner serene, so he refused any liquor, much to the surprise of his host. Margaret sat on his left at dinner, and although she said little, continued to observe him. At first he was uncomfortable, then slightly irritated. At the end of the meal, when the men were alone, he took only a few token sips of his port, and after rejoining the ladies made the feeble excuse of asking Margaret to show him the flower gardens.

As they strolled in silence toward the summerhouse at the far side of the lawn, it occurred to Sam that she was taller than he had realized. She wore her blond hair piled high on her head in the French mode, which gave her an added illusion of height, but, all the same, there weren't many women who could look at him without craning their necks.

"You really don't want to see the wisteria, Mr. President," Margaret said calmly.

Caught off guard, Sam replied bluntly. "That's right. And I wish you wouldn't call me Mr. President. I'm just an ordinary member of the Texas Congress these days."

"I very much doubt that you're ever ordinary, sir. Would you rather I call you General, as Mr. Lewis does?"

"Call me anything you please," he said ungraciously. "Miss Lea, you've been studying me ever since I was presented to you."

"I didn't know you were aware of it. I had no intention of embarrassing you. There's the wisteria, General. And a dozen flowers whose names I always confuse. You should have asked my sister to show you the garden."

"I wanted to talk to you. Why have you been watching me, Miss

Lea?" Sam knew he had no right to be rude, but persisted. "Am I a freak?"

"You're the first famous person other than Senator Calhoun I've ever met."

His muttered comment about John C. Calhoun was far from complimentary.

Margaret wisely ignored it. "What I find so interesting is that you're just like anyone else, General Houston. Oh, dear, that isn't what I meant." Refusing to become flustered, she halted and sought the right words. "What I should have said is that you don't put on airs."

"Why should I?"

When Margaret smiled, a dimple appeared in her right cheek. "I hadn't heard that modesty was one of your attributes, sir."

"It isn't. I know my attributes—and my failings. I could have sworn you were waiting to see me get drunk."

It was her turn to become disturbed. "Hardly, sir!"

"Then I apologize. I reckon I'm sensitive on the subject because I sometimes do drink too much." Sam was surprised by his own candor.

Margaret's violet eyes widened a trifle, but if she found the topic unorthodox she gave no other sign. "Why do you do it, General?"

"I'm damned if I know. Because I lack the character to give up liquor completely, even though I know it isn't good for me."

She pushed open the door of the cool, latticed summerhouse. "From what I've heard, you could do anything you want." Sitting, she arranged her voluminous skirt of light brown silk that matched her hair.

"I wonder what else you've heard." He stood before her, feet planted apart, thumbs hooked in the pocket of his pale green waistcoat. "Did anyone ever tell you I was married, and that I've been divorced?"

"There have been rumors about your marriage for years." She was meeting frankness with frankness.

"The truth of the matter," Sam said, "is that I was stupid and my wife was foolish. I married what I imagined her to be, and she married the Governor of Tennessee, not a man."

"Then she must have been very young—and very childish. Even famous men are—well, just people. That's what I was thinking all through dinner about you. It isn't very flattering, I'm afraid, but—"

"It's very reassuring." Sam chuckled, and found his antagonism fading.

"Why, General? And why are you telling me so much about yourself?"

Sam sat beside her on the summerhouse bench. "I want you to know the worst about me. If I have any good qualities, you'll find them out yourself."

"I will?" She knew what he was saying, but met his gaze without coyness or a hint of flirtatiousness.

"Don't tell this to my political enemies, Miss Lea, because they'll use any ammunition against me they can find. But my mind sometimes works slower than I like to think it does. I didn't realize until just now that I hope you and I are going to know each other a great deal better."

Margaret's soprano laugh was clear. "I must confess that now you do surprise me, General. I knew the first moment you looked at me that we'd see each other again."

Sam could have completed his business with Lewis in a few days, but deliberately complicated the negotiations so he could pay a visit to the Lea plantation every afternoon. Then, when he could delay no longer and had purchased his horses and cattle, his amused host invited him to remain as long as he pleased. He accepted, and increased the pace of his courtship.

His romance appeared to be common knowledge in the area. Men grinned at him when their paths crossed his on the dusty roads between the Lewis and Lea houses, ladies in carriages favored him with the special smile they reserved for someone in his situation, and hostesses engaged in an unspoken conspiracy. Dinner parties were given in Sam's honor nightly, and every evening he found that Margaret was his partner.

Finally, after he had spent almost a month in Alabama, he decided the time had come for a serious talk with her. He found her waiting for him in the main parlor of her parents' house, and it bothered him that she looked particularly lovely in a gown of peach-colored silk.

She invited him to sit, but he refused, and she became concerned. "Has something upset you, Sam?"

He nodded, and ran a hand through his thick gray hair. "I had a chat with your father after supper last night, and got his permission to speak to you."

"Papa told me." Her violet eyes became quizzical. "I should have known your proposal would be unorthodox."

"I'm not proposing. Margaret, I wonder if you realize I'm old enough to be your father."

"Not quite," she replied calmly. "A very young uncle, perhaps, although you haven't treated me as your niece, and I don't feel like one."

"The difference in our ages doesn't bother you?"

"It isn't that great. Besides, if it had upset me, I wouldn't have encouraged you."

"You don't know that my house in the city of Houston is just a shack, unfit for a lady to live in. And my place at Nacogdoches isn't much better."

"But I do know. You've described them to me many times."

"It might take me years to afford the kind of house I want for you. I'd like to build you a mansion."

"A woman who lives with the man she loves doesn't need a mansion."

"Damn it, Margaret, don't say things like that, or I'll lose my self-control. I want you to understand our situation!"

She obediently folded her hands in her lap and looked up at him, waiting.

"It may be years before I'm in a position to support a wife in style. I've had some mail from Texas this morning. President Lamar is spending money like a madman, and may bankrupt the country. He's been goading Mexico, trying to start a fight, and may have a new war on his hands. He's even gone out of his way to be insulting to the United States, which lessens our chances of annexation. So Anson Jones and some of my other friends are urging me to run for President again."

Margaret was not surprised, but obeyed his request and remained silent.

"I don't really want to run. I'm not interested in holding high office again these days, when I have important personal matters on my mind. But I don't believe I have any real choice. If I'm needed, I'll have to accept."

"Of course," Margaret murmured.

"It will be at least two years from the time I take office before I can start earning a good income."

"I'm sure many men support wives on less." She could not prevent herself from speaking.

He paid no attention to her comment, and continued doggedly. "The new capital, Austin, is no place for a lady. It's a frontier village of log cabins and muddy roads. I'm not sure I could move the capital back to Houston, and it might not be worth the effort, because I'd offend so many people. That means you and I would be separated for long periods."

"When a man gives of himself selflessly," Margaret said, "his wife must be prepared to make sacrifices, too."

Sam was shaken. "Don't start thinking I'm noble. In spite of all I say, I'm really itching to be President again."

She looked at him, her eyes indicating that she knew.

"Then there's something else," he added somberly. "My drinking."

"I haven't seen you take more than an occasional glass of wine, Sam. Aren't you exaggerating the problem?"

He made a wry face. "I've been trying to impress you, Margaret. And I haven't felt the craving for liquor. When it comes over me, I can't resist it. No matter how hard I try to stay away from the damned stuff, I drink myself into a stupor. Have you ever seen a man drink himself unconscious? It's an ugly sight."

"I've thought about your drinking, Sam, and I know how it torments you."

"I can't allow it to torment you."

"All I can say is that I want to help you fight the problem. I don't know how, really, and that's as honest as I can be. But I want to try. If I fail, we'll fail together."

"I don't deserve you."

"I wonder if all men who are known in every civilized land, as you are, deprecate themselves. I'm inclined to doubt it."

He wanted to tell her the feeling was new to him, that he had always been self-confident in his relations with women, but that her poise and reserve made him strangely diffident.

"None of the things you've mentioned will stop me from marrying you," Margaret said.

Sam was alarmed. "My divorce?"

"Oh, I'm certain people will talk. They always do when a man has been married and his former wife is still alive. But I can harden myself to gossip, so I'm sure I can survive it. No, Sam, this concerns only you and me."

He felt fear that was far more intense than he had ever known in battle.

"I know our love is genuine—"

"If you doubted me, Margaret, I'd—"

"You've had far more experience than I, yet I'm positive this is different for you. I can't explain why or how I can tell, but I know. It's real for me, too."

He took a step toward her, hands outstretched.

She held him off. "Wait. You have your fears, Sam, so respect mine. We've known each other a very short time, and I don't want to make your wife's mistake. I don't believe I will, but I won't be satisfied until I've proved it to myself—and to you. My parents have promised to take me to Texas next year, and if you still want me, I'll marry you. But we'll have to wait."

"I accept your conditions."

Suddenly Margaret's self-assurance vanished. "Until then, I suppose, we're betrothed."

Sam drew her to her feet and gently embraced her. "For the sake of propriety," he said huskily, "wait until I propose before you accept me."

The quiet at the Hermitage was startling after the busy years in Washington City. Andy Donelson and the former President's adopted son, Andrew Jackson, Jr., handled major correspondence, supervised the operations of the farm and arranged visits with invited guests so that only one or two came out from Nashville each day. An efficient staff of secretaries worked in what had been the auxiliary parlor, answering letters from every state and territory, and Emily Donelson handled the household staff with the ease of a woman who had long practice in the art.

Old Hickory made his headquarters in the sun parlor looking out on the broad, grassy lawn, and spent most of his waking hours in a rocking chair beneath his late wife's portrait, a shawl draped over his shoulders. Piles of correspondence and newspapers lay on a table beside him, but he seemed more interested in a roan mare and her colt grazing in the pasture beyond the lawn, and was easily distracted by a puppy frolicking near some shrubs.

"This whisky," he said, "comes from Kentucky. We make better, but the taste isn't bad. Try a glass, boy."

"Thanks," Sam said, "but I'm trying to rid myself of the habit."

"Pour a drop more into my cup, will you? My doctors are trying to limit me to one a day, but I can trust you not to tell them I'm having two this afternoon. This is an occasion."

Sam poured some liquor from a jug, averting his face slightly to avoid its smell.

"Van Buren," Jackson said abruptly, "stands a poor chance of being re-elected President, no matter how much he wants to stay in the White House. People are blaming him for the unemployment and high prices everywhere, and if you want the truth, boy, he's been less firm than you or I would have been. I hear the Whigs are thinking of running General Harrison, and if they do, he's almost sure to be elected. Van Buren is too elegant for the voters, and an Indian fighter like Harrison will appeal to them."

Old Hickory had aged, but his mind was still sharp, Sam thought.

"It's a damned shame you left Tennessee when you did. You could have served in the Cabinet during my second administration, then moved into the Senate, and you'd be a natural candidate in the next election."

"I'm looking forward to an election of my own in Texas, sir," Sam said diplomatically.

"You'll win it."

Sam grinned. "Not so fast, sir. I haven't told anybody I've agreed to run."

"As if that mattered. Some men have a genius for winning office, and you're one of them. Do you still have American citizenship?"

"I'm a citizen of Texas."

"But you haven't renounced your American citizenship? No matter. At my age, I find I daydream. If Van Buren is succeeded by a Whig, you're going to have trouble bringing Texas into the Union."

Sam agreed, but wanted to hear his reasons. "Why is that?"

"They'll prey on the country's fear that annexation will bring on a war with Mexico. What's more, the Whigs are growing stronger in the North. I spent eight years in the White House fighting sectionalism, but it's the first battle I've ever lost. Antislavery feelings aren't really very strong, except in New England, but the Whig politicians see their chance to win—and keep—both the White House and Congress. So they'll follow the Abolitionist line as long as they find it useful."

"That means," Sam said wryly, "that Texas must depend on the Nullifiers, anti-Constitution men like John Calhoun."

"To an extent. But only for the moment, I hope. The Democrats are still strong in the South and the West, even though Van Buren continues to offend them, and they're in favor of the admission of Texas because their bloc will be strengthened. What frightens me is that the Whigs, if they're in the majority, will put up a solid front to keep you out."

"Texas belongs in the Union," Sam said grimly.

"You and I know it," the old man replied, "but the Whigs take a different view, and it looks as though they're going to be in the saddle. I needn't tell you there's nobody as shortsighted as a politician protecting his own hide."

"There are ways to tan hides."

"By the Eternal, boy, you're a real fighter. Always were and always will be!"

"What advice can you give me, General Jackson? How can I win the admission of Texas to the Union?"

"I've been thinking about the problem, General Houston," the old man said formally. "And so far I've found no solution. I've never been very clever, you know." A plaintive note crept into his voice. "I've always had one strategy. Find the enemy and attack him. I did it as a soldier, and I did it as President. I couldn't have held back for a day, as you did at San Jacinto." He leaned forward in his chair and slapped Sam on the shoulder. "If they try to bar you from the Union, boy, you'll find a way to bring Texas in."

Almost immediately after Sam's return to Texas he became involved in partisan politics of his own. A brief and tragic war had been fought with the Cherokee during his absence, and he rose in his seat in the House of Representatives to condemn the shortsighted policy of President Mirabeau Lamar, who had made enemies of allies.

One of Lamar's supporters replied succinctly, and with what he believed to be sardonic humor presented Sam with the feathered headdress of the sachem who had led the Cherokee into battle.

The adopted son of Oo-loo-te-ka erupted in anger and made one of the most violent addresses of his long public career. Throwing aside both diplomacy and caution, he attacked everything that President Lamar and Vice-President Burnet had done since taking office, and his fury was so intense he scarcely bothered to pause when his fellow Congressmen interrupted to cheer him.

Then, after tracing the history of Texas-Cherokee relations and stressing the loyalty of the Indians to the young Republic during her fight for independence, his voice rose to a rasping, scornful pitch. "The Cherokee were a peaceful, industrious and profitable community. The arts had made considerable progress among them, and they lived nearly as comfortably as we live.

"They made great advances in civilization during my presidency. They looked upon Texans as their friends. They knew I was more than their friend, that I was their brother. I am their brother still. Their enemies are my enemies!

"For no reason other than the cheap and flimsy attempt to increase his own popularity with voters who were ignorant of the long, honorable and peaceful relations with the Cherokee, Lamar—the butcher—attacked these people who had done no harm to Texas. With a force of seven hundred men, some of them veterans of San Jacinto, Lamar—the butcher—commenced a war of extermination.

"Texas' finest troops, and there are no finer on this earth, carried ruin to the homes of the poor Cherokee. I do not and cannot blame the courageous men who fought so valiantly at my side. I blame only the man who ordered them into battle. Lamar, the butcher.

"His treatment of the Cherokee spread scenes of rapine and murder from the Red River to the Rio Grande. Honorable Texans forever will be ashamed of this bloody, disgraceful infamy, this foul page in our bright history.

"Were it not for the high regard I have for the office of the Presidency, I would warn Lamar, the butcher, to beware. I would not hesitate to scalp him with my Cherokee skinning knife, one of my proudest possessions. But the coward is safe. I will harm no hair on his evil head.

"Instead, gentlemen, I hail Lamar before the bar of justice. Let all Texans be his judges. Here, now, and for all time, I charge him with murder."

Austin,
January 10, 1840.

My Dear Margaret:

I had intended to write to you yesterday, but found myself exhausted after delivering a speech of more than two and one-half hours' duration in the House on the previous day.

Rather than allow myself to become upset anew by repeating even a portion of what I said, I enclose clippings from two of our newspapers, which should give you the gist of the address. The Telegraph & Texas Register has been friendly to Lamar, and, until now, has favored a candidate of his choice to succeed him as President. I gave the editors a strong bone to chew on, and although they misquote me in some places, their account is, mostly, a fair one.

The Texas Sentinel is edited by young men who lard their pages with irony, but in this instance the sobriety of my subject matter caused them to prepare a relatively somber and straight-forward report of what I said. Their subsequent comments hinting that I had the Presidency in mind when I spoke to the House may be totally ignored.

The plain truth of the matter, my dear, is that I was so angry I completely forgot politics, and must keep my feelings in tight rein to avoid exploding with wrath again.

Yet a strange thing has happened. Members of both Houses of Congress and my many friends in private life have come to me insisting that I become a candidate. The friends of Lamar, and it grieves me that he has friends, are equally insistent that I be kept from the presidency.

So, quite inadvertently, the coming campaign has already begun. I will not declare my candidacy; it appears that I am already a candidate. The Lamar faction does not yet know what candidate it will choose—I assume that Burnet has ambitions— but they unite on an anti-Houston platform. Mind you, there will be no formal campaign until next year! That is to say, no names will be placed in nomination until that time.

But my attack on Lamar has thrust me into the vanguard of those who hate him, and who despise the dishonor he brings to Texas. So be it. If it is necessary for me to stand against the Lamars and Burnets who slaughtered an innocent people, I will do it.

I am heartily sick of politics, however, and cannot make capital over the dead bodies of my slain Cherokee brothers. I am refusing the many offers of speaking engagements being made to me, and will not appear in public, other than on the floor of the House. I am dressed in mourning for the Cherokee.

My beloved Margaret, I beg you to consider a change in our plans. If you come to Texas with your family for a visit in the

179

spring, it will be summer before we can return to Alabama for the wedding. Summer is far off, and I am consumed by loneliness. There is within me a void that you alone can fill.

I have not wavered in my love, nor have you. Every letter I receive assures me of your continuing affection. So, I urge you, give earnest thought to the advancement of our wedding date.

When Congress adjourns I must go to Galveston on private law business, and could sail from there in April for Mobile, if you will but give your approval.

The murder of the Cherokee sickens me, and my need for you is great.

You will not be displeased to learn that, last night, I was successful in my efforts to avoid strong drink.

The house at Nacogdoches is being enlarged for you. A new kitchen building with a broad hearth and a wood stove are being installed for you, and I have given instructions for the construction of a sun parlor similar to General Jackson's at the Hermitage, which I know will be to your liking.

I send you my abiding love, dear Margaret, and remain

> *Yr obdt*
> *Samuel Houston*

Margaret and Sam were married at the home of the bride's brother, Henry Lea, at Marion, Perry County, Alabama, on May 9, 1840. Margaret wore a dress of white silk, and Sam was soberly attired; even his waistcoat was a dark gray, and his cravat matched his black suit. Colonel Hockley, who had accompanied his friend from Texas, stood up with him at the ceremony. Since Sam had been married previously, Margaret invited only relatives and a few close friends to attend the reception on the lawn at the Lea plantation. The guests were offered a simple meal of smoked ham and roasted chickens, duck that Sam and the man who had become his brother-in-law had shot on a brief hunting outing two days earlier, and, for those with delicate digestions, river trout.

Sam appeared subdued at the ceremony and reception, and responded quietly to the hearty jokes of the gentlemen. He avoided the limelight, and when called upon to offer a toast, raised a glass of wine silently to his bride. He ate heartily, but a number of those present noted that he took only a few sips of wine and avoided both whisky and rum.

After dark the party repaired into the house, and Margaret disappeared to change into a simple dress of blue muslin. Sam was waiting for her at the foot of the back stairs, and they slipped away, riding two borrowed horses to a small house of red brick, about three miles away, that also belonged to Henry Lea. Sam was making certain that no pranks were played on his bride, and halted frequently on the brief ride to make certain they were not being followed.

There were no servants in the little house, where they had stored some of their belongings the previous day, so Sam stabled the horses himself, then joined his bride in the tiny parlor. Margaret had lighted two smokeless French tapers and, although the night was warm, a fire of pine logs was burning in the hearth.

Sam halted to look at his bride, started to speak and changed his mind as he went to her.

"What did you want to say?" she asked.

He shook his head. "I thought my luck had run out a long time ago," he whispered, "but I was wrong."

Margaret held him at arm's length, and looked at him with concern. "Why do you decry yourself, Sam?"

"Just look at the calendar. I'm frightened, and that's the truth. I'm forty-seven years old, and you're not twenty-three yet!"

"If that had mattered to me, I wouldn't have married you."

"Some women are born wise, and I suppose I ought to be grateful for my blessings instead of questioning them." He took her in his arms, and other people, the very room faded from their consciousness.

A huge crowd gathered at the Houston homestead in Nacogdoches to greet Sam and his radiant bride. The women of the neighborhood had baked pies, bread, and cakes, men who had gone hunting for game were roasting sides of venison in the stone-lined pit behind the house, and long tables had been set up in the yard to accommodate the guests.

Margaret, overwhelmed by the warmth and size of her reception, saw her husband in a new light. He was more than a considerate lover and a kind, gentle man now. When he had first seen the throng gathered on the property he had assumed the mantle of a public figure, and the girl marveled at his ability to remember the names of the hundreds who shook his hand. He presented each to her, and with a brief anecdote or a few witty, descriptive words flattered the guest.

He laughed loudly at the jokes of the men, inquired after the welfare of children who were not present, and, sampling virtually every dish on the tables of scrubbed pine, praised the women who had baked and roasted, boiled and pickled the bewildering variety of foods. "Texas," he had told Margaret on their journey, "isn't like any place you've ever seen. I lived in Tennessee when it was frontier country, but Texas is different. You've never seen such generous people in all your days."

Margaret began to understand what he meant. Not only had the guests provided the food for the feast, but had filled her own larder with smoked meats, jars of vegetables preserved in vinegar, and huge sacks of corn and wheat. She and Sam would be able to live for weeks on the supplies that generous neighbors had brought them.

Only once did Sam lose his genial air. A guest came up to Margaret and inquired with seeming innocence, "Mrs. Houston, have you visited Shelby County?"

"Not yet," she replied. "Until we landed at Galveston I'd never been in Texas."

"You ought to go there, ma'am," the man said, chuckling. "General Houston has forty children there."

Margaret took a deep breath.

"Named after him, that is."

Sam's smile had faded. "Friend," he said, "you'd oblige me very much by connecting your sentences more closely."

Late in the afternoon some of the guests departed for the long ride to their own homes, but those who lived in the immediate neighborhood lingered. Several of the women took Margaret on a tour of the house that had become her new home, and she realized they were watching her carefully for any signs of disappointment. Aware that she was the wife of Texas' most prominent citizen and that any adverse reaction would be reported throughout the nation, she smiled steadily.

In spite of Sam's warnings she had been unable to picture the plainly furnished dwelling. In only two rooms were there small, hooked rugs; elsewhere the floors of rough pine were bare. In time she would become accustomed to a new way of life, but some day, perhaps, they would have enough money for her to buy furniture from Charleston and Europe that would remind her of the world from which she had come.

When the women returned with her to the yard, Margaret started toward Sam, then stopped in confusion. He was standing in the midst of a large, boisterous group of men, one of whom had just splashed whisky into a mug he was holding, and he downed it in a single swallow.

Someone touched Margaret's arm, and she found herself looking at a girl a year or two her junior.

"I met you earlier, but I'm sure you can't remember all these names. I'm Anna Raguet."

"Of course! Sam has spoken constantly of you and Dr. Irion. He says you're being married soon."

"We are." Anna linked her arm through Margaret's and drew her aside, whispering, "Don't look so concerned, or the friends of Lamar and Burnet will have something new to gossip about."

Margaret made an effort to compose herself.

"You're worried about Sam's drinking."

"How did—"

"All of us were worried, before he married you. But he'll be all right. A few drinks might make an ordinary man intoxicated, but Sam can drink more than anyone in Texas."

Margaret took a deep breath. "It's just that I've—never seen him drinking."

"Robert—my husband-to-be—is watching him. When he thinks Sam has had enough, he'll break up the conversation over there.

Robert has been Sam's physician for a long time, so he knows better than anyone how much he can take." Anna's dark eyes were sparkling and she was smiling broadly; anyone watching would assume she was engaging in harmless brides' chatter.

"I'm—grateful to you." Margaret made a supreme effort to look animated, too.

"Don't thank me. All of Sam's real friends are standing with you."

Until now Margaret had thought herself capable of handling the problem, but now she felt lost. Sam's booming, almost raucous laugh was not that of the man she had married, nor was his seemingly carefree attitude, and it occurred to her for the first time that she had taken too much for granted. "Help me," she begged.

"I'll do everything I can," Anna said.

"Tell me something. Why is he drinking? He looks as though he doesn't even realize what's in that mug!"

"I don't believe he does. I've known Sam since I was a child, and I have my own theories about his drinking. I may be wrong, of course—"

"Wrong or right, I want to know."

"They're talking politics over yonder. It's always that way here. When a half-dozen or so men get together, that's what they discuss."

"Sam loves politics." Margaret was becoming increasingly bewildered.

"Hear me out," Anna said. "He does—and yet he doesn't. Robert and I happen to know a great deal about his personal situation, so I hope you won't mind if I'm blunt."

Margaret steeled herself.

The other girl saw her growing tense, and patted her arm. "You'll be of more help to him than anyone. You see, Sam is in the same position as everyone else. He's property poor. He has this place, with his livestock, but it hasn't started bringing in much of an income yet."

"So he told me. And he doesn't have much time to practice law, either."

"Even when he does, his clients usually can't pay him in cash. It's the same with Robert's medical practice. We'll either have to wait for years to be paid by his patients, or else accept food as payment. Texas is growing faster than you can imagine, but we're still a frontier people, and cash is scarce."

"I think I understand."

"That's why Sam's problem with politics plagues him. I'm certain he wants to earn a good living for you. I know he's ashamed of this house—"

"He needn't be!"

The vigorous warmth of Margaret's loyalty made Anna smile more broadly. "He'd build you a palace, if he could. But he feels it's his obligation to accept the presidency again next year—if the voters want him, which they do. But even while he's cursing politics—and you'll hear him curse, I can tell you—he's fascinated. He has a genius for understanding what the people want. Robert says he's torn by a desire to live the life of a private citizen—and to spend the rest of his days as President of Texas. I'm inclined to agree."

Margaret nodded. "You mean that when he's being pulled in two directions at the same time, he drinks to forget his discomfort."

"I wouldn't have put it that way, but I believe that's the root of the trouble."

"Then he'll always be tormented. I can't imagine him retiring from public life."

"Neither can I," Anna said.

"Then it will be up to me—to make him contented with the life his own ambitions and conscience force him to lead. I don't know how I'll do it—but I must."

Sam was glassy-eyed and a little unsteady on his feet as he stood at the entrance to the parlor. The last of the guests had gone, taking with them the long tables and what had remained of the food. The fire in the roasting pit had been reduced to a few glowing embers, but the scent of wood smoke still drifted into the house through the open windows.

Margaret's legs and back ached, but she smiled at her husband and pretended to be unaware of his condition. "It's late, Sam," she said, "and this has been a very long day. Tell me which bedroom is ours."

He jerked a thumb in the direction of the largest chamber, which adjoined the tiny dining room. "You sleep in there," he muttered. "I'll go upstairs."

"This is our first night together in our own house." She found that, by concentrating, she could speak calmly, without sounding hurt.

"I have no right to sleep in the same room with you." He advanced two steps into the parlor, weaving slightly.

Margaret recalled a cousin who had been bitterly self-deprecatory when intoxicated, but had no other experience to guide her. Common sense, however, told her this was no time for a serious discussion. "You didn't expect all those people to be here, and you've done a hard day's work." She held out a hand, and continued to extend it when he failed to respond.

"If I'd thought about it, I'd have known they'd be here, just as you should have known I'd get drunk." His self-scorn seemed to consume him.

She was afraid he would walk out into the night if she went to him.

"They're the most wonderful people on earth," Sam said, "and I hate them."

Margaret discovered she could still laugh.

"Do you know why they gave this party for us?" he demanded. "I counted four Senators, eight Representatives, and three judges. Yes, and all of them brought greetings from others. They wanted to make sure marriage hadn't changed my mind about running for President next year."

"I'm sure they came here because they're your friends, Sam. They like you."

"Maybe so, but—even more—they like the way I can take a whole slate into office with me. The Congressmen are up for reelection next year, and the judges' terms of office will expire. They spent hours, all of them, telling me how Lamar and Burnet are leading Texas into ruin. And they're right, that's the worst of it!"

"We've known that you'll serve another term as President. You told me about it long ago, and I accept whatever you think is right."

Sam shoved back an unruly lock of hair. "My mother spent all her life in rough wilderness houses."

"Was she any the worse for it?"

"Certainly not! But I'll be damned if you're going to suffer inconveniences and hardships when I can earn you a comfortable living!"

An idea occurred to Margaret, but she gave herself no chance to think about it, knowing she would lose her courage if she hesitated. "Is that why you drink, Sam?"

He was startled. "I suppose it is."

"What was your reason before we met?" she asked softly.

Sam stared at her for a moment, then covered his face with his hands.

Margaret crossed the room to him and put an arm around his broad shoulders. It was comforting to know that this man of genius and valor had a deep need for the sympathy and warmth, understanding and love she offered him. "No matter what you do," she said, "I admire you."

With a great effort Sam drew himself erect. "May the Almighty help me, I won't disgrace you again. I've had my last drink."

"No one will be surprised," the New York *Post* commented on November 7, 1840, "if the Republic of Texas collapses. If the Government falls and public order vanishes, the United States, in her own interest, must be prepared to send troops into this nation, founded by our sons, before Mexico can intervene."

There were many in Texas who agreed with the New York newspaper's estimate. The extravagant President Lamar had issued so much paper money that the Texas dollar was worth only eighteen cents, and was still declining in value. Adventurers, both in Texas and in the United States, were preparing to stake out private empires if the young Republic floundered.

In a desperate attempt to bolster his administration, Lamar

proposed a treaty with France, under which the better part of the public debt would be assumed by the French, who, in return, would be allowed to build their own forts and settle where they pleased in the country. The Texas Congress, led by an aroused Sam Houston, defeated the measure.

Mexico, which had virtually abandoned hope of recovering her lost province, began to take a renewed interest in affairs north of the Rio Grande. The already strained relations between the two countries deteriorated even more when citizens of Texas traveling in Mexico were imprisoned on false or trifling charges and Texans of Mexican ancestry were unjustly harassed.

The Whigs in the United States were triumphant. Former President John Quincy Adams, now enjoying a distinguished career as a member of the House of Representatives, declared on the floor of Congress, "The cautious refusal of this nation to admit Texas to the Union has proved itself correct. Texas demonstrates an inability to govern herself that grows worse with each passing month. Let Americans beware lest we burden ourselves with the support and protection of unprincipled, bankrupt brigands."

At the Hermitage outside Nashville, Andrew Jackson picked up his quill pen and wrote in the shaking hand of an aged man, *"General Houston, it would be presumptuous of me to offer you advice in the conduct of Texas' affairs. I can only tell you, sir, that the lack of responsibility displayed by the Executive Department in Austin places in the gravest jeopardy that project which is so close to your heart and mine. The reaction throughout the United States, even in those quarters where annexation is favored, has been so bad that, unless the present catastrophic trend of events is reversed, the Democrats will join the Whigs in condemning any new attempt to win the admission of Texas to the Union."*

The chaotic situation continued to worsen, and Lamar, growing panicky, handed the burdens of guiding Texas to Burnet, but refused to give up the title of President.

Sam, showing his bride the city of Houston for the first time, held a series of quiet, emergency meetings with other leaders of the Texas Congress, and a letter was sent to President Lamar requesting that he summon the Senate and House for a special session. As anticipated, Lamar refused, so the Congress called itself into session, claiming that technical faults had invalidated its adjournment.

The rumor quickly spread that Representative Houston intended to address the House, and when Margaret appeared in the visitors' gallery of the unfinished Capitol for the first time, Senators as well as Representatives crowded into the chamber. The galleries quickly filled, and such a huge throng gathered in front of the building that, at suggestion of several apprehensive Congressmen, the company of Rangers stationed in Austin was called out to prevent possible rioting.

The House was called to order, and as the chamber became quiet, Sam appeared at the rear and walked slowly to his seat in the front row. Attired in black except for a waistcoat made from the skin of a mountain lion, the gift of an admirer, he appeared lost in thought and seemed unaware of the cheers that rocked the building. He glanced up at the galleries, saw Margaret and smiled at her before taking his seat.

The sergeants-at-arms finally quieted the assemblage, and the Speaker threatened to clear the galleries if another demonstration occurred.

Then Congressman Houston rose, and immediately was recognized. "Mr. Speaker," he said, "it is no secret to anyone that we are in debt, that our standing among the nations of the world has declined to the vanishing point, and that the government of this land cannot continue to function without the imposition of taxes so great that they would crush us all.

"What is to become of us, God only can tell. All human wisdom, or at least Texas wisdom, seems to fail us. We have many patriots in Texas, as well as Congress, but it seems that every measure proposed by those most able in finance cannot devise a plan by which the nation is to be extricated from its present difficulties.

"Every attempt made by the Congress to salvage Texas and prevent her ruin has been defeated by the Executive, which uses the veto indiscriminately. I am familiar with the veto as a weapon,

Mr. Speaker, as members of this august body with long memories can readily testify. At no time, however, did I use my veto power to the detriment of Texas.

"I do not stand here today to criticize, to vilify, to attack. The situation in which we find ourselves is too serious, and mere accusations accomplish no positive good. You can't kick a dead mule back to life.

"The exertion of all the talents and all the industry of all our people will be necessary to restore us to the situation in which the present administration found the country when it took office. But I say again that this is not the appropriate time to speak of the failures of the Executive Branch. We must turn our eyes to the only subject that can and should claim the attention of the people of Texas.

"We must cultivate our soil, raise our crops, rear our cattle, increase the products of our factories, and do everything that will make us comfortable and independent when we are in our homes. We will still be a people, if we cannot be a government, though I hope devoutly we will remain a people and a nation."

A storm of applause interrupted him, but Sam, looking surprised and displeased, held up both hands for silence.

"I ask for no approval," he said severely. "If I were making a political speech, I would charge that useless extravagance and the most unprincipled profligacy have characterized the present administration and have caused our sad plight. I would charge that recklessness, the most palpable and bare-faced, has been practiced to such an extent that the members of the administration can neither blush for their crimes, nor relent at the calamities they have inflicted upon a generous, poor and confiding people.

"If this were a political speech, I would charge that the sole object of President Lamar is to insure, to secure the election of his crony, Vice-President Burnet, to the highest office of trust that the voters of this nation can bestow upon any man. If this were a political speech, I would remind you that the country is being forced to pay dearly for the experiment in reckless, irresponsible government that is being practiced by Lamar and Burnet.

"But this is an hour when the needs of Texas require statesmanship, not name-calling. This is an hour when all Texans, working together, sacrificing what we must, will restore us to dignity, honor—and financial solvency.

"When things get to the worst, they must mend, as the old adage goes. Our situation, if the adage is true, must soon be in a better condition. We must seek the day when it once again becomes reputable to hold a post in the government. We must seek a day when the Congress, which meets too often and tries to do too much, will restore its partnership with the Executive.

"We must dedicate ourselves to the achievement of the great potential that, as all Texans realize, belongs to us. With patience and industry let us strive toward that goal."

Bowing to the Speaker, then to Margaret, Sam walked slowly up the center aisle. So great was his hold on his listeners that they obeyed his injunction not to applaud, and he left the chamber in silence.

Thomas Rusk, sitting beside Margaret, leaned toward her and whispered, "Sam won't have to campaign. This talk has re-elected him, and if there are any dead mules to be kicked, their names are Lamar and Burnet."

Margaret nodded, secretly proud of her husband for a reason she could tell no one. In the hours he had spent writing and refining his speech, it had not once crossed his mind to leave their hotel room and go to the tavern on the ground floor for a drink.

SEVEN

1841–48

Cedar Point, the new house in Chambers County, was a handsome dwelling, and even Sam was satisfied that it was suitable for Margaret. He had sold some of his land in order to build and furnish the new place. The soil was rich, livestock thrived there, and, in spite of the unstable financial conditions prevailing in Texas, Cedar Point promised to become a profitable operating farm within a year. Tables and chairs, rugs and beds had come from New Orleans, and a carriage sturdy enough for a lady to ride in comfort on rutted roads was ordered from Galveston.

Only Margaret was displeased, and repeatedly urged her husband not to spend so much money on her. But he ignored her protests, and sold an additional property in order to enlarge and improve their cabin in the city of Houston. Sam was so busy he had virtually no time to campaign for office until midsummer of 1841, when the demands of his friends became so insistent that he finally consented to make a few speeches. On September 6 the voters went to the polls, and to the surprise of no one, Sam defeated Burnet by the overwhelming margin of three to one.

Former neighbors in Nacogdoches gave a feast in honor of the Houstons, and when Sam saw the food being prepared, he commented dryly, "We may be bankrupt, but we're sure not starving."

Thirteen hogs were barbecued, and four sides of beef, two of oxen and six of venison were roasted. No one bothered to count the number of chickens that were fried, but Anna Irion estimated that more than two thousand potatoes were baked and four thousand ears of corn either boiled or roasted.

The older boys and men in their early twenties engaged in wrestling matches and free-for-all fights, and all men were invited to take part in a shooting contest. Efforts were made to persuade Sam to enter, although he was busy discussing Cabinet appointments with Thomas Rusk and Anson Jones, whom he had already named his Secretary of State.

Finally he consented to "try a few rounds" provided his score did not count. He scored seven out of ten shots with pistols at fifty feet, and eight out of ten bull's-eyes with a rifle at fifty paces, which prompted several delighted veterans of San Jacinto to suggest that he might be happier serving as a General than as President.

"No," he told them. "Only a miracle gave me the use of my arm after the Creek campaign, and my leg will ache every day until I die to remind me of San Jacinto. I've seen enough of war, and don't want to lead any more fine youngsters to their death. I'll fight again only if it becomes necessary, as a last resort, to protect us from our enemies."

His sober declaration dulled the festivities for a short time, but spirits revived when several carts piled high with kegs of whisky, rum, and ale arrived. The President-elect drank only cold water, but seemed as animated as he had in earlier times.

Only Dr. Irion had the courage to ask him whether he was finding it difficult to abstain from drinking.

"I'll be honest with you, Bob," Sam said. "When I feel myself getting all tight inside, I develop a powerful thirst. Then I think of Margaret, and nothing tastes as good as water or coffee. The best way for any drunk to reform is to marry the right woman—if she'll have him."

Eyebrows were raised when Margaret did not accompany her husband to Austin for his inauguration on December 13, and Sam gave his political foes personal ammunition to use against him when he appeared in a hunting shirt, faded work trousers and a magnificent, broad-brimmed hat of white beaver. "The man's only genius," ex-President Lamar told a reporter from the new Austin *Daily Bulletin*, "is for showing off. I predict he'll wear something outlandish to his own funeral, just so people will talk about him."

Sam made no reply, and buckled down to work. He and Secretary of the Treasury William Daingerfield flooded the Texas Congress with bills designed to restore the nation's financial stability, and when both the Senate and House balked at some of the more stringent measures, he threatened to keep them in continuous session until they passed the bills. He won every battle, and the *Daily Bulletin* said in an editorial, "Like him or not, Texans know we have a President again."

At the end of February, when he permitted Congress to adjourn, he and the other members of the Executive Branch transferred their activities to the city of Houston, where Margaret was waiting for him. Refusing to accept more than one social invitation per week, Sam thought nothing of working eighteen to twenty hours per day. Refusing to be distracted by Mexican raids across the Rio Grande, he sent two regiments of his best troops to the border and devoted his principal efforts toward the restoration of prosperity and his dream of persuading the United States to admit Texas to the Union as a state.

Margaret fell ill, and when she failed to respond to treatment, Dr. Irion suggested she visit relatives in Alabama, where her strength would not be sapped by the responsibilities the wife of a President was expected to fulfill. Sam escorted her to Galveston and saw her off, then returned to his crushing work load in Houston. Burnet and other enemies predicted he would start drinking again, and even friends like George Hockley became apprehensive.

The Texas Congress reconvened and, angry over the worsening situation on the southern border, authorized the dispatch of a punitive expedition into Mexico. The newspapers were filled with articles on the resumption of war, bonfires were lighted in every town and village, and volunteers appeared at every Army post, wanting to enlist.

Sam calmly vetoed the measure. *"Texas cannot afford the luxury of a war on foreign soil,"* he wrote, *"and I can see no need for the waging of offensive war at the present time. We are strong enough to repel an invasion, and therefore our borders are secure. By a return to sound prosperity, by husbanding and developing our resources, we will become still stronger. I am, therefore, unalterably opposed to military adventure for its own sake."*

Some of his closest political friends turned against him, and virtually without exception the newspapers attacked him with unprecedented venom. But he remained firm, and wrote to Margaret, *"I will not be budged. The President must do what he believes right, and under no circumstances can allow himself to be swayed by the inflamed demands of an ill-informed public.*

"My love, I miss you, and count the days until your return. I have tasted not one drop of liquor, and want none. Your affection has cured me, for all time, of the drink habit."

For the first time in years the cause of Texas was improving somewhat in the United States, and the chances of winning the Republic's admission to the Union were becoming brighter. The death of President William Henry Harrison one month after taking office brought Vice-President John Tyler into the White House, and Tyler, although elected by the Whigs, frankly favored annexation. "The slavery issue must not be allowed to influence this question," he declared. "Texas, from President Houston to the newest immigrant who has crossed from our soil into hers, is populated almost exclusively by Americans. A single glance at a map will show that a marriage between the United States and Texas is desirable, necessary and inevitable. Let there be no more unseemly delays. Texas must and shall be annexed!"

"Our cause improves," the ailing Andrew Jackson wrote from the Hermitage to Sam. *"May it be accomplished while I still live on this earth."*

Sam, believing himself unable to influence the situation in the United States, confined himself to keeping informed. He knew that Secretary of State Daniel Webster was opposed to annexation, and was elated when Abel P. Upshur of Virginia succeeded to the Cabinet post in 1843. "From what I hear," Sam told Jones and Rusk, "Upshur is as anxious as we are to see the American flag raised beside the Lone Star."

Margaret returned to Texas, her health improved, and her mother arrived for an extended visit in time to spend Christmas 1842 with the President and his lady. Sam ordered a long list of household goods from New Orleans, including a bolt of linen cloth which, he insisted, would be used for "making towels."

The *Telegraph and Texas Register* obtained a copy of the list, and amused its readers by indulging in drawn-out speculation. Why, it asked, had President Houston made such a point of saying the cloth would be used for toweling? Didn't he and Mrs. Houston already own enough towels? Might it be possible they intended to use the cloth for some other purpose? And why was Mrs. Nancy Lea of Alabama paying her first visit to Texas at this particular time? Might her visit be more significant than people realized?

Other Texas newspapers picked up the scent, as did the American press, and the bolt of linen became the most celebrated cloth on the North American continent. Sam maintained a dignified silence on the subject, both publicly and privately, and refused to be goaded into replying. And Margaret, who was conserving her health, was refusing all invitations, and therefore could not be questioned by the curious.

Sam Houston, Jr., was born on May 25, 1843, in a small second-floor bedroom, while his father tried in vain to study and sign a new series of Executive orders. At the sound of footsteps on the stairs he threw down his quill pen, and warning himself to remain calm, leaped to his feet, upsetting a pile of books in the tiny, cramped chamber he was using as his office.

"Congratulations," Dr. Irion said, extending a hand. "You have a son."

Sam discovered he was trembling, and wiped a film of perspiration from his forehead. "How is Margaret?"

The grinning physician rolled down his sleeves. "See for yourself, but don't stay in the room long."

Sam bolted up the stairs two at a time, and almost collided with his mother-in-law.

"Gracious," she said, "you'll tear down the house if you aren't careful."

He hugged her exuberantly, raced down the corridor and threw open the door. There he stopped short. Margaret was lying in the big bed, looking pale but happy, and beside her on the pillows of fine calico, wrapped in a blanket, was a small, animate object. Overwhelmed, Sam tiptoed into the chamber.

His movements were so cautious, so exaggerated, that Margaret laughed. "We won't break, dear," she said in a weak voice. "We're very sturdy."

He was still diffident as he approached the bed, and felt clumsy as he reached out a hand to pat her before leaning down to kiss her on the cheek. "You're really feeling all right?"

"I wouldn't want to go through this again for a day or two, but I'm fine."

Sam straightened and examined the baby, feeling a momentary sense of disappointment. "He looks like an old man."

Margaret was indignant. "He looks like you, sir!"

"We're saying the same thing." He shook his head. "My God, I've become a father at the age of fifty!"

"You're the most active man I know—of any age."

"The world will soon belong to that rascal." Sam was fascinated by the round, wrinkled face. "Are all of them this plump?"

Again Margaret smiled. "No, dear. Only ours."

He chuckled, then sobered. "I wish him all that's good and noble. May he become anything but a loafer, an agitator—or a demagogue."

The financial recovery of Texas was so swift that all but the most bitter of Sam's foes admitted he had worked miracles. In his private statements to friends, however, as well as in his public declarations, he insisted that the common sense of a resilient people had asserted itself, and that the citizens, not he, deserved the credit. In any event, with stability restored and economic growth assured, he was able to devote more of his attention to the burning issue of annexation.

The question was both delicate and explosive. A treaty that would have given the United States the authority to "adopt" Texas was strongly opposed by the Whigs, and failed to pass the Senate by the necessary two-thirds majority. The cause of annexation, American and Texan newspapers trumpeted, was dead.

Sam held a long, private meeting with Secretary of State Anson Jones, and then left Austin for a brief visit to his family for reasons officially called "of a personal nature." Then the newspapers learned, when Jones, seemingly by accident, let it be known that the British chargé d'affairs in Texas, Charles Elliot, was Sam's house guest.

By a strange coincidence, President Tyler received a letter soon thereafter from one of Sam's closest associates, Washington D. Miller. Expressing the hope that annexation might yet be achieved, Miller went on at length to praise Elliot. Not only was he an able diplomat, Miller said, but he was accomplishing the many purposes of the British government. He had succeeded in nullifying the influence of France in Texas, and was doing a great deal to cushion the blow that Texas had suffered when the United States Senate had failed to pass the annexation treaty.

Texas newspapers close to the Houston administration predicted that a closer association with Great Britain soon would be formed. A few even dropped the hint that the independent Republic might forge a new, mutually profitable trade treaty with the British, and was considering accepting the protection of the Royal Navy.

American proponents of annexation were alarmed, President Tyler immediately ordered a new chargé d'affairs to take command of the American legation in Austin, and Andrew Jackson, believed by many to be teetering on the edge of his grave, issued a series of sharp statements opposing the candidacy of Martin Van Buren and of Henry Clay for the presidency of the United States because both had been equivocal on the subject of annexation.

The Foreign Office in London added fuel to the fire by making a discreet announcement to the effect that Her Majesty's government was trying to mediate the dispute between Texas and Mexico. The young Queen Victoria herself was said to be taking a personal interest in the negotiations.

As the furor mounted, Sam sent a letter to Elliot, and allowed it to be published by the eager Texas press. In it he said:

"Texas once evinced a willingness, amounting to unexampled unanimity, to become annexed to the United States. We sought the boon with humble supplications. In this posture we remained in the outer porch of their Capitol for many months.

"Our solicitations were heard with apathy. Our urgency was responded to with politic indifference. Apprised of this, I directed our Minister in Washington to withdraw the proposition. This I did from a sense of national dignity.

"Since that time Texas has not renewed the proposition; and the United States now, in order to create a posture that would be creditable to them, desire, no doubt, that Texas should again come forward soliciting the boon.

"They have not as yet received such indications as they desire. If we were to respond to their desire, it would place the subject before the political parties of the United States in a position different from that in which it now rests.

"In that event there would be but one question to ask: Shall the annexation of Texas to the United States take place?

"As it is, there are two questions: First, is Texas willing to be annexed? Second, in that case, shall it be annexed?"

The fury of the storm redoubled, and many Texans, until now firm advocates of annexation, began to wonder whether an association of some sort with Great Britain might be desirable.

Sam, who dined with Anson Jones on the day the communication was made public, summed up the matter succinctly. "Wait until the American newspapers reprint the letter. The fat is really frying."

The new American chargé reached Austin, only to learn that the President had gone to the city of Houston, and followed him there. Sam was eating alone in the enlarged house, going through a sheaf of state papers, when a servant told him that an American visitor had arrived, but had been told to return in an hour.

Refusing to be inhospitable, Sam went out into the corridor. "Andy Donelson!" he shouted, and embraced Jackson's nephew, pounding him on the back. "Why didn't you let me know you were coming? And what are you doing here?" Not waiting for a reply, he turned to the surprised servant, who was lingering in the corridor. "Set another place at the table, and tell the cook we have a guest who eats like a Texan!"

"I didn't know I was coming myself," Donelson said, "until I got orders. I was visiting in New Orleans, and I came straight here as fast as I could. I'm the new American chargé, Mr. President."

Sam allowed himself a tight smile. "Tyler and his State Department must be worried. But I've got to give them credit. It hadn't crossed my mind that they'd appoint an old and dear friend."

Donelson proved himself a diplomat by changing the subject and inquiring after Sam's growing family. They spoke of Andrew Jackson's declining health, the sudden and tragic death of Emily Donelson and their mutual interest in horse-racing, and by then the meal was ended.

"Maybe you'd like to try some of our Texas brandywine," Sam said, "although I'd better warn you that our grape growers haven't really learned the knack of making it yet. But they will. People down here can do anything when they set their minds to it."

Donelson hesitated.

Sam grinned at him. "Unless you mind drinking alone, it doesn't bother me a damn. If I felt like it, I could rub brandywine on my face after I shave, and I still wouldn't feel like drinking it." He went to a sideboard and poured his guest a glass of dark, potent liquor.

"To the annexation of Texas by the United States, Mr. President!"

Sam nodded politely, but did not raise his water glass in a token gesture.

"I've been a little surprised that the news from home hasn't reached Texas yet, although I suppose your newspapers will be printing it in the next day or two. After Secretary Upshur died so unexpectedly, President Tyler deliberately took his time finding a successor, and he finally found the right man. John C. Calhoun is our new Secretary of State."

"The right man?" Sam grimaced. "This pretty much guarantees that Texas will make a treaty with Great Britain!"

"My uncle sent me a note by the special courier that reached me just as I was sailing from New Orleans," Donelson said carefully. "He asked me to tell you that if he were in your boots, he'd make a bargain with the devil if it meant Congress would pass an annexation bill."

In spite of himself, Sam chuckled.

"President Tyler appointed Secretary Calhoun because there's no more devoted an advocate of annexation in the United States."

"So I've heard, but if Tyler is as sincere in his declarations as he seems, he made a mistake. The people with whom Calhoun is friendly already favor annexation. The White House should be worrying about northern Senators whose minds can be changed, and no man who believes the states have the right to defy the Federal government and leave the Union if they like is going to influence them in favor of annexation."

Donelson couldn't tell his host he had a blind spot, and was giving Calhoun too little credit. "I think you'll be pleasantly surprised, Mr. President."

Sam shrugged. "We'll see," he said curtly. "Let me refill your glass, and you can take it into the parlor, where we'll be a mite more comfortable."

The American diplomat again resorted to his most potent weapon. "My uncle," he said, "swears you're an American patriot. He's convinced you're flirting with England for only one reason, to put pressure on the United States and hurry annexation."

Sam refused to be trapped. "I'll admit to you that I'd favor annexation if all factors were equal, but Texas can't be put in the position of a beggar asking for alms."

"Oh, I understand, but—"

"And we can't wait forever. We're starting to produce more cotton than we can use, and there's a great demand for it in the British mills. We're going to have a surplus of corn and wheat and potatoes this year, for the first time. The British Isles need more food than they can grow. I'd like to show you some figures on our cattle raising. It has more than doubled in the past year, and will double again in the next twenty-four months. I'm not even mentioning our apples and pears, which are the finest grown anywhere. American tariffs are so high we can't send in any of our products, and mind you, we're an agricultural country."

"We appreciate your position, Mr. President, but I believe, as my uncle does, that annexation is inevitable."

"I can't deny it," Sam said vigorously, pounding the table. "But how long must we wait? A year? Two? Three? Our economy could be crippled, permanently, while the United States Senate goes through the tortures of a Hamlet trying to make up its mind. I love the land of my birth, and I'd give my life to preserve the Union. But I'm under oath to serve the interests of this Republic, and a trade treaty with the British looks mighty attractive to me. What's more, I've had problems with my own Congress getting appropriations for warships, and with Mexico showing no signs of wanting a fair, final peace with us, I'd sleep better nights knowing our coast is protected by the Royal Navy. If I can't get what I want—within a reasonable period of time, and I've been very patient—I'll take what I can get!"

Anson Jones announced his candidacy for the presidency of Texas, and Sam's enemies, uniting behind Edward Burleson, declared that Jones would be a puppet manipulated by Sam. The voters remained complacent, and many of them seemed comforted by the charge. "No elected leader of a democratic people has ever been as popular as Sam," Thomas Rusk told Margaret. "What he wants, the people want. What he believes, they believe. He can do no wrong."

Apprehensive American advocates of annexation were less certain of him, and fears that he would make an agreement with England continued to grow. Santa Anna emerged from his enforced retirement to seize control of Mexico again, and Texans reacted by taking their rifles from their mantels and oiling their pistols.

"If I were Sam Houston," Andrew Jackson told Representative Cave Johnson, who was chairman of the Tennessee delegation to the 1844 National Democratic Convention that would nominate the party's candidate for President of the United States, "I'd accept an offer from Great Britain to guarantee the independence of Texas. I won't support Van Buren, because his stand on annexation hasn't been strong enough. Tyler has done his best, but he isn't a Democrat. You've got to support a man who'll go whole-hog for annexation—in a hurry!"

The Whigs nominated Henry Clay, who, trying to win favor with everyone, issued so many contradictory and confusing statements that he lost the support of all but the most rabid Whigs. President Tyler, realizing the Democrats would not nominate him, announced his candidacy for re-election as an Independent.

Texans were distracted by their own campaign, and their interest in events across the American border temporarily declined. Sam campaigned actively on behalf of Anson Jones, and no one was surprised when Burleson was defeated.

"At last I can look forward to retirement," Sam wrote from Austin to Margaret. "For the first time in my life my finances are solvent, the farm earns us a handy income, and, after I have rested for a time, my law practice will add substantially to our capital. How I long to be with you and the little rascal!"

"Only the cloud of the annexation question darkens the sky, and until it is settled, I cannot take my ease. Something must be done, soon, before Santa Anna crosses our borders and Texas is forced to fight another war alone."

American Chargé Donelson was kept apprised of events in the United States by couriers who raced to Texas with every scrap of news favorable to the cause of annexation. He was a regular visitor, so Sam, attired in his nightshirt, was not surprised when Donelson appeared late one evening at the door of his Austin hotel room.

"Come in," Sam said, "and help me find my damned slippers."

The President of Texas and the head of the American legation scrambled around the room on their hands and knees, taking care not to pick up splinters from the rough floor. At last Donelson found the slippers behind a pile of books in a far corner.

Sam put them on his bare feet, offered his visitor the only chair and sat on the bed. "I don't do much entertaining here, so I can't offer you anything but a cup of apple juice."

"I hope you'll let me buy you the best meal in Austin tomorrow to celebrate, Mr. President."

"What is there to celebrate?" Sam asked cautiously.

"The Democrats have nominated their candidate for President. Governor Polk."

Sam completely forgot that, as Chief Executive of his Republic, he was expected to maintain a neutral stance in a foreign election. "By God, that's tremendous! How did it happen?"

"The convention was deadlocked, and the Tennessee delegation offered a dark horse."

"I can see the hand of Old Hickory in this."

"I imagine he may have written a few letters to the right people, Mr. President."

"There's nobody I'd rather see in the White House than Jamie Polk."

"I don't need to tell you where he stands on annexation."

"I've hoped Van Buren and the other mealy-mouths could be stopped, but I didn't know how. Trust Jackson. I wonder if you could do me an undiplomatic favor. I want to write Jamie, but I can't send it through my own legation in Washington, and I don't trust the ordinary mails. If the Whigs got hold of it, they'd claim I was interfering in American politics, and it might win votes for Clay."

"I can promise you Jamie will get your letter promptly, with the seal unbroken."

"Thank you." Sam was beaming. "There must be something special in the Tennessee air that makes statesmen. But even if Jamie is elected," he added, his elation fading, "how can he push an annexation treaty through the Senate?"

James K. Polk was elected the 11th President of the United States, but John Tyler was determined to win the honor of admitting Texas to the Union before his retirement from the White House, and proposed a remarkably ingenious legislative device for the purpose. Since it was impossible to win a two-thirds majority in the Senate favoring annexation, he suggested that Congress accomplish the feat by means of a joint resolution, which would require only a majority vote.

Sam, who retired from office in December 1844, was privately delighted. "Tyler makes sense," he told Anson Jones just before leaving Austin. "Now I think there's a real chance we'll win."

Enjoying his first real holiday in years, Sam took his wife and baby son to Bastrop, where the prominent citizens of Texas were gathering for a round of barbecues and races featuring four-, three-, and two-year-old horses. The occasion was enlivened by the first entries from the Houston stables, Sam having thought it beneath the dignity of the presidency to have submitted entries the two previous years.

No one was surprised when his three-year-old, Sam Houston, easily lead the field. President Jones summed up the crowd's reaction when he said, "With that name, how could he lose?"

A surprise entry in the two-year-old class drew a roar of approval from the throng when he was announced as, "Big Drunk, from the stable of General Houston."

He came in second to last in a field of fourteen, and Sam, as usual, had the last word. "I gave the poor beast too big a handicap when I named him. Drunks always lose."

The Houston family returned home two days later, and Sam settled down, ostensibly, to look after his own, long-neglected affairs. But the eyes of Texas and the United States remained fixed on him when the climactic debate began in Washington on the joint resolution. It was almost universally recognized that he alone would determine the response of Texas to any move the American government might make, and even his foes were content to leave a matter of such magnitude to his judgment.

Seemingly unaware of the attention riveted on him, Sam went hunting for two days with Elliot, the British Chargé, and feigned astonishment when the press speculated on the possible hidden meanings of the trip. He became so close-mouthed that no one knew what he really thought, and a disturbed Donelson wrote to the State Department in Washington: *"I thought I knew General Houston's mind, but he has withdrawn. I have just returned to Austin after spending two and one half days as his guest. He was a generous, genial host, and Mrs. Houston was charming, as always, but I could draw no word from him on his views regarding our present efforts to bring Texas into the sisterhood of our Union."*

The debate in Washington was becoming protracted, so Sam broke his silence late in January 1845. In a letter written to all of Texas' major newspapers, he expressed his admiration for the President-elect of the United States, his old friend. But James K. Polk, he said, was mistaken in his assertion that the claim of the United States was better than that of Great Britain to the huge Oregon Territory that stretched from the Pacific to the Rocky Mountains. The claim of Texas was infinitely the strongest and most valid, he insisted, and predicted that Texas, occupying the western half of the continent, would become mightier than the United States.

Many Americans dismissed his stand as absurd, but no one in Washington laughed. The people of Texas greeted their former President's idea with enthusiasm, it was conceivable that the Texan Army could wrest California and the vast New Mexico Territory from Mexico, and the leaders of the American Congress realized that a man as zealous, daring, and imaginative as Sam Houston, who had created one country, might be able to enlarge that nation until it rivaled the United States in power. Certainly it was possible that Great Britain might be willing to relinquish its Oregon claims to Texas in return for an extension of its own influence. President Tyler and President-elect Polk joined in urging Congress to speed its deliberations.

The House of Representatives, voting in late January, approved the joint resolution. The Senate moved more slowly, although prodded mercilessly by Thomas Hart Benton of Missouri, and not until February 27, after an all-night debate, did the joint resolution pass. On March 3, less than twenty-four hours before leaving the White House, John Tyler signed the measure which authorized the annexation of Texas, provided the people of Texas gave their consent by January 1, 1846.

Before the word reached Texas, Sam was blithely making personal plans for a family journey beyond the borders of Texas, and wrote to Andrew Jackson that he hoped to bring his wife and son to the Hermitage for a visit in the summer.

News of the American adoption of an annexation bill reached Mexico City almost as rapidly as it did Texas, and Santa Anna suddenly but belatedly realized he had made a grave error. An independent Texas would be less of a threat to Mexico than a Texas incorporated into the United States. Trying to rectify the mistake, the Mexican dictator offered, through British and French diplomatic channels, to recognize a permanently independent Republic of Texas. London and Paris, which had no desire to see the United States expand, offered to guarantee the treaty.

Sam pondered the problem at length, and made a trip to Austin to see President Jones. "The American offer isn't particularly generous," he said. "The United States has as much to gain as Texas, but the joint resolution specifically spells out that our public debt won't be assumed by the American government. I'd like to see Washington change its tune, and if I were you, Anson, I'd be in no hurry to answer the American proposal."

Word of the Mexican offer became public knowledge. Jones did nothing more important than send the Texas Congress a message proposing the building of several new roads, and everyone waited for Sam's reaction. Oblivious to the furor, he took his family to a comfortable house on a property he had purchased at Huntsville, in Walker County, and spent virtually all his time prior to his departure for Tennessee supervising the development of the ranch.

For the first time in years he was tanned, he spent so many hours each day roaming around the farm that he lost weight, and Margaret wrote to her mother that he was sleeping as soundly as the baby. But insomnia in Washington was widespread, members of the American Congress began to mutter that the honor of the nation had been slighted, and only the Whigs unalterably opposed to annexation were pleased.

One afternoon in late May, while Sam, stripped to the waist as he wielded a shovel and demonstrated to a gang of hired men how to fill in a ravine dangerous to cattle, saw a horseman galloping across the field toward him. He paid no attention until he heard someone call his name, and, shielding his eyes from the glare of the hot sun, recognized American Chargé Donelson.

One look at his friend's face indicated to Sam that this was no ordinary visit, and he stifled a cheerful greeting.

Donelson dismounted, hastily throwing the reins to a hired man.

Sam, still clutching his shovel, came forward to him, wiping his right hand on the side of his trousers.

For a moment neither spoke, then Donelson said, "I came from Austin myself. An exchange of letters would have taken too long. Sam, this is a strictly personal visit. Forget that I represent the American government and tell me straight out. Where do you stand on annexation?"

"Hold on, Andy. This is a complicated question, and I can't—"

"Damnation, this isn't an official visit!" Donelson spoke savagely, then fought for self-control. "I'm sorry. I've been living with this, and you don't know anything about it. My uncle is dying."

Although Sam was covered with sweat, he suddenly shivered.

"I had a very short note from his godson, Ed Butler. He says General Jackson keeps asking him, 'What will Houston do?'"

For a moment Sam was very still, then he stood erect. "I've been bargaining for better terms, of course. Since the day I first came to Texas it's been my dearest wish to lead her into the Union, and I've never for a moment changed. I thought Old Hickory knew it. He can't—he mustn't die until he knows."

"I've brought a courier with me."

"Good. We'll go up to the house, and I'll give him one of my best horses. I'll send along a short note, and I'll follow as fast as my family can travel. I've—got to see him again—before he goes."

On June 6, 1845, late in the afternoon, a dust-covered messenger arrived at the Hermitage, and Mrs. Andrew Jackson, Jr., read the brief note he brought to her father-in-law. The old man sighed, smiled, and closed his eyes. Forty-eight hours later General Andrew Jackson, 7th President of the United States, hero of the Battle of New Orleans, the conqueror of Spanish Florida and of the Creek, died of natural causes at the age of seventy-eight.

At nine o'clock that evening of June 8 a carriage pulled up at the main entrance to the Hermitage. Sam, helping Margaret to the ground and reaching inside to pick up his sleepy son, knew before anyone told him that he was too late. There were other coaches standing on the gravel driveway, and more than a score of horses were clustered at the hitching posts, but lights were burning in only a few rooms of the mansion, and the quiet was ominous.

Sam took his wife's arm, and, still carrying his son, followed a servant into the house. A number of gentlemen and ladies were gathered in the main parlor, and the few who were conversing muttered in low tones. Sam knew all of them, members of Mrs. Jackson's family, Congressmen and former ministers to foreign lands, two retired Senators and several distinguished judges. Among them were men who had been his close associates before he had resigned the Governorship of Tennessee to live with the Cherokee. He had not seen them since that terrible time, and knew that many of them had gossiped about him maliciously. But old wounds were no longer painful, and the tragedy at the Hermitage reunited him with them. They bowed to him, and to Margaret, and Sam inclined his head.

Andrew Jackson, Jr., came toward the newcomers, his face pale beneath his farmer's tan, his eyes red-rimmed. Sam embraced him, and Margaret, who had never met him, kissed him on the cheek.

"It just happened this evening, General, at six o'clock."

"Did he get my note?"

"Two days ago."

Sam felt a surge of relief, then was beset by fresh anxiety. "He was—conscious?"

"My wife read it to him, and he knew." The younger Jackson drew a deep, tremulous breath. "Just before he—left us—he whispered a message to you."

Sam stiffened, and Margaret, steadying herself by holding her husband's arm, dug her fingers into his coat.

"He said, 'Tell Houston I'll meet him in that special part of Hades reserved for old reprobates.'"

Sam blinked rapidly.

"'Tell him I thank God for what he's done. Tell him, now that I'm going, that I'm relying on him to preserve the Union he's helped to create.'"

Unable to speak, Sam bowed his head.

"Would you like to see him, General?"

Sam nodded, and they started to follow the younger Jackson toward the main staircase.

Margaret looked at her husband, a question in her eyes.

"I know he's very young," Sam said, "but I want him to come with us."

Long tapers, set in pairs, burned at the head and foot of the old-fashioned fourposter bed in the large room on the second floor of the Hermitage. The windows were open, but there was no breeze, and the flames glowed steadily. On one wall was a portrait of Rachel Jackson, and over the mantel were two crossed swords, one the blade that Old Hickory had carried at New Orleans, the other George Washington's dress sword, which had been a gift from the Marquis de Lafayette.

The still figure on the bed looked very small, almost insignificant, and it seemed strange to see the cragged features in repose. Jackson's son, unable to remain in the room, turned away, and the Houston family was alone.

Margaret reached out and took the little boy from his father.

Sam walked toward the bed, scarcely able to breathe. Suddenly, inexplicably, he dropped to his knees and wept without shame.

After what felt like a very long time he realized that his son was watching him curiously.

With a great effort Sam pulled himself to his feet, took the child and stood him on the floor. Then, holding his hand, he led the boy to the bed. "My son," he said, "try to remember that you have looked upon the face of Andrew Jackson."

Sam and Margaret took the longest holiday they had known since their marriage. They visited his relatives in various parts of Tennessee, then went to see her relatives in Alabama before returning to Tennessee. They traveled at a slow, easy pace, and Sam refused all speaking engagements out of courtesy to the late President Jackson. When pressed by old friends to deliver an address in Nashville, he consented to give the sermon at the First Baptist Church, and spoke on the subject of temperance, using his own case as an example.

After the service he and Margaret stood outside with the clergyman, shaking hands with departing churchgoers; among them were people he had not seen in years, and he had to search his mind for their names. The last in the line were a couple dressed in conservative but expensive clothes, and Sam blinked at the slightly faded but still attractive woman who stood before him now.

"Don't you remember me, Sam?" she asked.

"I've never forgotten you, Eliza," he replied, and felt Margaret start.

Eliza introduced her husband, Dr. William E. Douglas, a physician, and Sam presented both to Margaret.

"You've done well in the world, Sam," Eliza said.

"Better than I've deserved, maybe." He felt no emotion as he looked at the woman he had once loved, and was grateful she had become a total stranger.

Eliza managed to meet his gaze. "I couldn't forgive myself for years. I hope you bear me no malice."

"None."

Eliza glanced at Margaret and smiled. "You're fortunate, Sam."

"I still wonder, sometimes, how I could have been so lucky."

Dr. Douglas bowed. "It's obvious, General, that both you and Mrs. Houston showed good judgment."

"I paid for my mistakes," Eliza said, "but I've learned what happiness is, too."

"I'm pleased for you," Sam said, and meant it.

There was a brief, awkward pause, and then the two couples went their separate ways. Sam and Margaret said their farewells to the embarrassed clergyman, then walked off toward the McEwen house, where they were staying.

Margaret was the first to speak. "She's very attractive."

"She was prettier when she was younger, but there's more character in her face now."

"Meeting her gave me a strange feeling. It never bothered me, knowing she existed, but seeing her was—different."

"You have no cause for worry."

"Did you love her very much, Sam?"

"Not in the way I love you."

"That's no answer!" Margaret didn't realize her voice was tight.

"I thought I loved her a great deal," Sam said patiently. "It took years before I understood I really loved the image of myself that I thought Eliza was reflecting. When that was destroyed, nothing was left, and I was shattered. I didn't know real love until you came into my life."

Margaret sighed gently and pressed his arm. "Is Dr. Douglas the man who—"

"No. They met and were married fairly recently. The other one —I can't remember his name—died of consumption while trying to work a plantation in Mississippi, and Eliza stayed single until she married the doctor."

"You know the whole story."

"I heard it a year or two ago." Sam tipped his hat to some passing acquaintances.

"But you never mentioned a word to me!"

"It must have slipped my mind. Be sure you get the McEwens' recipe for chicken gumbo soup. They always serve it for Sunday dinner, and after you've tasted it you'll see why I've been talking about it all these years."

Margaret glanced at him and saw he was sincere in his total indifference to Eliza. Perhaps it was because they had not really lived together that Sam had been able to dismiss her from his mind. Or it might have been that his travail when he had floundered for years in the Cherokee wilderness had enabled him to find himself and see the tragedy of his first marriage in its proper perspective. In any event, Margaret knew he had no regrets and was not looking back.

So the few moments of discomfort she had suffered during the brief encounter were well worth the small price she had paid. The most mercurial and complicated of men had found genuine peace in his life with her, and she was content.

Sam kept up a lively correspondence with his friends and associates in Texas, but refused, both publicly and privately, to discuss her future course with Americans. There was consternation in Washington, where the failure of Texas to respond at once to the annexation bill was creating a ceaseless stir. Only President Polk was unconcerned, which puzzled the members of his Cabinet and the Senators who raised the Texas question when they visited the White House. No one knew he had received a secret letter from Sam, assuring him that Texas would enter the Union in the fairly immediate future.

President Jones called a convention to meet on July 3 for the purpose of discussing the "alternatives of peace with the world and independence, or annexation and its contingencies."

Thomas J. Rusk presided, and after a token debate, the convention voted, on July 4, 1845, in favor of annexation. There was only one dissenting vote.

In the next two months a state constitution was prepared, and so many members of the convention were writing to Sam for advice and receiving long, detailed replies from him that the suggestion was made on the floor, only half in jest, that time and effort could be saved if General Houston wrote the document and sent it along for the formal approval of the convention.

Sam and Margaret returned to Texas with their son in October, just in time for the popular referendum on annexation. *"I'm sure there is no need for me to make a speaking tour before the ballots are cast,"* Sam wrote to President Jones just before coming home. *"I feel positive that Texas has made up its mind."*

As usual, he was right, and the voters ratified the decision of the convention by an overwhelming vote. On December 29 the United States Congress gave its formal approval, and on that date

Texas legally became a state in the Union, although formal ceremonies were not held until six weeks later.

It had been taken for granted since July that Texans would join
either the Democratic or Whig parties, and it was automatically
assumed that Sam would be a Democrat. No one who knew him
could imagine that anyone who had been so close to Andrew Jackson could belong to any other party.

It was also believed inevitable that he would seek and win a
seat in the United States Senate, but he himself was privately
ambivalent on the subject. "I'd like to go off to Washington and
work with Jamie Polk again," he told Margaret. "I'm particularly
concerned about Oregon, and I'm afraid a war between the United
States and Mexico can't be avoided. But I'd like to stay at home
with you, too."

She smiled at him. "I wouldn't try to make this sort of decision
for you, Sam. You know that. You'll have to do what you think is
right."

"Damnation, what's right and what I want aren't always the
same." He thought for some time, then said, "Maybe I can arrange
to let the problem solve itself. If I refuse to make any speeches
or do anything to seek a place in the Senate, maybe I'll be left
alone."

He kept his word to himself, would not permit friends to tender
him a banquet in the city of Houston, and politely declined offers to speak in Galveston, Washington-on-the-Brazos, San Antonio,
and Nacogdoches. When he went to Houston to discuss the terms
of a loan from bankers to improve his property, he calmly told a
group of newspaper representatives who asked him about his
plans, "I'm finally in a position to do what I came to Texas for
in the first place. I intend to raise cattle."

The press refused to take his announcement serious, and the
Texas National Register, owned by his good friend, Miller, flatly
predicted that he would become one of the state's Senators. Even
his foes forced themselves to accept the unavoidable.

Judge James P. Henderson, a Houston follower, was elected
the first Governor of Texas, and immediately said he believed
the General and Rusk, both "good Democrats," would be sent to

the Senate. The new Legislature voted on February 21, 1846, and the Governor proved himself an excellent prophet. Sam received seventy votes, Rusk won sixty-nine and the other candidates, three in all, were given a grand total of four votes.

Margaret went with her husband to Galveston to see him off, and not until they were riding together toward the dock where his ship was berthed did she bring up a subject of considerable mutual interest. "How long will the session of Congress last, dear?"

"That's difficult to say. If there's war with Mexico, we may be held in Washington for some time. With luck, I'll be home in August. Otherwise it could be as late as October or even November."

"You'll want to be here by September."

He stared at her. "Margaret!"

She nodded. "I'm going to have another baby then."

"If I'd known—"

"That's precisely why I didn't tell you, dear. I couldn't let your family life interfere with your duty. Nearly everyone in Texas wanted you to sit in the Senate."

Ignoring the occupants of other carriages, horsemen, and pedestrians, he kissed her. "No matter what may be happening in the world," he said, "I'll be home by September."

The United States, although vastly increased in territory by the annexation of Texas, seemed to be shrinking, thanks to new and improved methods of travel. Sam left Galveston by steamship on March 12, traveled up the Mississippi from New Orleans to St. Louis on a steam-propelled vessel, and, after going to Pittsburgh by stagecoach, made the final leg of his journey on a railroad train. He reached Washington at noon on March 29, after a journey of only two and one-half weeks; only a few years earlier he would have spent at least a month and a half in travel on the same route.

Newspapermen, alerted in advance to his arrival, were astonished to see a giant in a broad-brimmed hat of white beaver, and wrapped in a voluminous, multi-colored Mexican blanket called a serape, alight from the train. Senator-elect Houston had not forgotten the sensation he had created on his first visit to Washington, when he had arrived in Cherokee attire.

With infinite patience he refused to answer the questions of the newsmen. "I'll make my position clear on Oregon, Mexico, and every other issue in the appropriate forum, gentlemen, the Senate. I hope to pay my respects to President Polk as soon as I can. And I'm afraid I have nothing else to tell you today."

"Do you intend to support the President, sir?" a reporter wanted to know.

"I'll have to familiarize myself with his stands, won't I?" Sam countered, and grinned. "Let me just say that James K. Polk is one of my oldest and closest friends, and we've thought alike for many years. I doubt that we'll disagree often."

The baggage handlers started down the long platform with Sam's luggage, and he followed them, but the newspaper representatives still clustered around him.

"Senator," the Washington correspondent of the Hartford *Courant* said innocently, "there's been some confusion here about your party affiliation."

Sam recognized the man's New England twang, and knew the statement was not as bland as it seemed. "I don't wonder. We've had no formal parties in Texas."

"But in the Senate, sir, members are seated according to party," the reporter from the Whig newspaper persisted.

"In that case, you'll find me sitting with the Democrats, but voting as my own conscience, the interests of Texas, and the security of the United States dictate."

"Does that include the slavery issue?" the man from the *Courant* wanted to know.

Sam halted abruptly. "I deplore the injection of the slavery question into politics, and I believe nothing is more dangerously devisive than making it a sectional problem. Personally, I own no slaves and disapprove of the institution. But I can sympathize with men who didn't create the system, but whose economy is based on it. Virtually all of our cotton, most of our tobacco and rice, and approximately sixty percent of all American vegetables are grown by slave-owners. If some way could be found to adjust our nation's first industry, agriculture, to the wrenches created by the abolition of slavery—and I include the matter of giving slave-holders appropriate compensation for their losses, I'll become an active abolitionist. Until then I won't. I believe the issue can be solved by men of good will, but I can offer no easy, painless formula. Until one is found, and I wish I could discover it, I'll work with men of every belief to achieve an equitable solution."

He paused, waiting until the newsmen stopped scribbling their notes, and then spoke slowly, so they would not misquote him. "Gentlemen, I have no desire to win honors greater than those already accorded me, or powers more sweeping than my constituents have granted me in past years. I have come to take a seat in the Senate for one purpose. I am obliged to keep the trust handed to me by President Jackson. No matter what the cost, I am here to work for the preservation of the Union."

Some of the furniture in the little suite at Brown's Hotel was new, and so were the rugs, but otherwise everything was unchanged. The years rolled away, and Sam stood at the window of his sitting room for a quarter of an hour, looking out over the low rooftops at the White House. Had his life been different, he, rather than Jamie Polk, might be occupying the Executive Mansion now. But he felt no regrets, and, ignoring the vague stirring of an old ambition, he sat down to write a brief note to the President, announcing his arrival.

Senator Rusk, who had arrived several days earlier and had already taken the oath of office, was waiting for him in the tavern, on the ground floor, and they ate a light meal together as they discussed their joint recommendations for Federal posts in Texas, and other problems. Before they had finished their meal, Sam's messenger returned from the White House with a three-line reply that Polk had scribbled: *"Sam—It is good you are here at last! Can you drop over at six this evening, and stay for supper? Sarah begs me to assure you there will be no other guests. J.K.P."*

Sam changed into a conservative dark suit and cravat, and promptly at six o'clock presented himself at the White House.

The President, looking surprisingly wan and tired, came to the anteroom himself as soon as his guest's presence was announced. Dropping the reserve their positions demanded, the two men greeted each other boisterously, and repaired to the President's office for a pre-dinner chat. Since neither drank alcoholic beverages, Sarah Polk sent in a pitcher of her husband's favorite drink, sweetened tea and lemon juice.

For a time they indulged in the talk of men who had known each other well, making light of their advancing age, exchanging family anecdotes and reminiscing. Then, abruptly, Polk became crisp. "What's our situation with Mexico, Sam?"

"If Texas hadn't been annexed, you might have bought California from Santa Anna. He needs cash so badly that he might have been willing to sell you the New Mexico Territory, too. But no President of Mexico can tolerate the insult of annexation. You mustn't forget that Texas is still regarded as a province that must be recovered, and Santa Anna thinks of himself as a Napoleon. His vanity is insufferable."

"Then he'll go to war against us?"

"There's no doubt of it, Mr. President. But he wants the tacit support of England, France, and the sympathy of Spain and the new Pope, Pius IX, who is said to hold liberal views. Santa Anna'll send raiders across the border and sink American shipping, but he'll try to make us appear in the wrong."

"We'll have to declare war, then, instead of waiting for him to do it."

"If you like, I'll spell out our position on the floor of the Senate at the right time, for the benefit of the foreign legations."

"I'm going to find it exceptionally helpful," Polk said, "to be supported by a Senator who is qualified—uniquely qualified—to understand the burdens the elected president of a democratic nation must carry. What's your view on Oregon?"

"I'd like the United States to take as much of the Territory as she can get, of course," Sam replied. "Where do you stand, Mr. President?"

"Confidentially, I'll accept a British offer to split the West at the 49th parallel. Officially, I've got to keep my campaign pledge, and press for a boundary at a latitude of fifty-four degrees and forty minutes."

"We won't get it. They don't want a war with us any more than we do with them. But they're a wealthy, expanding nation with a tremendous national pride, so I'm sure we'll have to compromise."

"If we reduce our terms now, we'll get less than we want. They seem to be shrewd bargainers," Polk said.

"They are. One of the reasons I couldn't work out a treaty with them was their demand for too many concessions from Texas. They'll be wondering how I feel, so, if you like, Mr. President, I'll make a speech in the Senate insisting the United States demand the Fifty-four forty boundary. That'll make an impression in London, even though the Prime Minister, Lord Russell, will know as well as I do that we're bluffing." Sam chuckled.

"Your experience shames me, Sam. I'm just beginning to realize that in this office the shadow of power, carried to its logical conclusion, often becomes the substance. Once it becomes common knowledge that you're so familiar with the tools of the presidency, the party will insist you succeed me in '49."

"You'll serve two terms."

"I'll be lucky if I survive one."

Sam wondered if Polk was ill, but the President offered no explanation.

"Come along to supper. Sarah must be waiting for us." Polk guided his guest into the corridor. "And although this might be premature, I wish you'd think of the future."

Sam glanced at the portrait of Andrew Jackson between those of John Quincy Adams and Martin Van Buren. "I'll concentrate on the country's future. At fifty-three, I've got to live my own life one year at a time."

The galleries for the press, diplomatic corps, distinguished visitors and public were filled, and thirty or forty members of the House of Representatives stood at the rear of the United States Senate chamber. Promptly at noon Vice-President George M. Dallas walked to his desk on the rostrum, the chaplain read a brief prayer, and the presiding officer declared the Senate in session. Senator Thomas J. Rusk of Texas rose from his new desk in the rear row on the left side, and was recognized.

"Mr. President, I have the honor to present to this august body my colleague, the Honorable Sam Houston."

There was a sustained roar of applause as Sam, escorted by the Majority Leader, Thomas Hart Benton of Missouri, came down the center aisle. It had been rumored that he would appear in his serape, and people in the galleries stood and jostled one another as they peered down at him. His suit and cravat were conventional, but he managed not to disappoint them, and maintained his reputation for eccentricity by wearing a Texas rancher's field boots and a waistcoat of leopard skin that had been given to him, just prior to his departure from home, by a ship's captain who had acquired the skin in Algiers.

Rusk presented Sam's credentials, and the Vice-President administered the oath of office. "The junior Senator from Texas," Dallas said, "is now a member of this body."

Senators on both sides of the aisle stood and applauded.

The presiding officer rapped for order. "Since one-third of the membership of the Senate must submit itself to the will of the electorate every two years," he said, "one Senator from Texas will serve a full six-year term and the other a two-year term. If agreeable to you, gentlemen, I suggest you draw these straws to determine the length of your terms."

The Texans drew, and Sam found himself holding the shorter straw.

"Senator Rusk will serve six years, and Senator Houston will serve two years," Dallas said.

Majority Leader Benton chuckled. "I don't feel sorry for you, Sam," he said. "I have an idea Texas will keep sending you back here as long as you want to come."

There was a hearty laugh, and Sam started toward his seat at the rear.

His colleagues rose to shake his hand, and the first to reach him was a balding, square-faced man in his sixties who held a seat in the front row on the Democratic side. "It's good to know we'll be working together, Sam," he said, addressing the younger man by his Christian name for the first time.

Forcing himself to remember that John C. Calhoun had served the country in many capacities, with distinction, for almost a half-century, and that he had labored incessantly for the annexation of Texas, Sam smiled. "I hope we'll be working together, John," he replied, and those who heard the chill in his voice knew he never forgot old grudges or the principles he held dear.

New members of the Senate were expected to keep silent on the floor of the Senate during their first terms, deal with matters of home state patronage, accept minor committee appointments and learn from those who held seniority. But no one was surprised when the junior Senator from Texas paid no heed to protocol; his position was unique, since it was generally accepted that he was responsible for the admission of the largest of states to the Union, and he was treated accordingly.

Senator Henry Clay of Kentucky, the Whig leader, invited him to dine on his third night in Washington, and he was often seen in the company of another distinguished Whig, Senator Daniel Webster of Massachusetts. Members of his own party were equally anxious to win his favor, and, since he accompanied Tom Benton to the White House several times each week, and often was summoned there for meetings alone with President Polk, he assumed the unofficial but powerful post of Assistant Majority Leader.

The Democrats in caucus, elected Sam to posts on the three most important Senate committees, Finance, Foreign Relations, and Military Affairs. Since war with Mexico was threatening and he was the conqueror of Santa Anna, it was only natural that his colleagues decided to make him chairman of the Military Affairs Committee.

The White House sought his advice on patronage problems in every part of the country, and President Polk gave him the delicate task of discouraging the ambitions of Senator Benton, who wanted to be made commander of the Army. Sam delivered his first speech in the Senate only one week after he was seated, and expressed himself with such vigor in favor of the administration stand on Oregon that the Whigs asked for an adjournment until the following day to prepare their reply.

No man in Washington worked longer hours, or seemed less subject to fatigue. Sam appeared in the Brown's Hotel tavern every morning at six o'clock for a breakfast of steak, eggs, potatoes, and pancakes, sometimes substituting fish for the eggs when he wasn't hungry. He reached his office on Capitol Hill before seven, and after working all morning on correspondence and attending committee meetings, he ate lunch with other Senators and then went to the Senate floor for the afternoon.

He held himself available for the President at five every afternoon if summoned to the White House, invariably dined with a colleague or two and then returned to his office to sift and consider the floods of requests from would-be Federal office holders that he received from Texas. It was usually midnight, sometimes later, before he could begin his nightly letter to Margaret, and he rarely retired before one or two o'clock in the morning.

The threat of war with Mexico dominated everything else that happened in Washington, and Sam's counsel was sought by Cabinet members, chairmen of House committees and his own fellow Senators. Late in April a corps of Army troops commanded by General Zachary Taylor landed in Texas, and within the next few weeks there were several sharp skirmishes, with each side claiming the other had invaded its soil.

On April 23 the Mexican government declared war on the United States, and word of the action reached Washington on May 9. Sam went at once to the White House, conferred with the President and helped him begin a draft of a message to Congress declaring that a state of war existed. The Military Affairs Committee of the Senate gave the President firm support, and in two days reported a bill creating an Army of fifty thousand men and requesting munitions, supplies, and uniforms worth ten million dollars.

On May 12 Senator Calhoun delivered an address questioning the advisability of passing such a bill. There was insufficient evidence, he declared, that Mexico's unilateral declaration meant a state of war really existed.

The moment he took his seat Sam rose and was recognized.

"Mr. President," he said, "the honorable member from South Carolina has held his seat in this chamber intermittently for many years, and has also served as Secretary of State and Secretary of War. Therefore it is not my intention to ridicule one who has, at still another period, been the presiding officer of this body in his capacity as Vice-President of the United States.

"But I would like to acquaint him with some hard facts. A state of war between Texas and Mexico has existed for ten years. No final peace treaty has ever been signed. The United States, by annexing Texas, has assumed her burden, and we need not issue a new declaration of war for hostilities to exist. The United States is already at war with Mexico!

"This is a time for action, not speeches." He sat, and was applauded by both Democrats and Whigs.

Late in May, Senators Benton and Houston were called to the White House for a private meeting with the President. Everywhere in the country men were volunteering for military duty in such large numbers that the Army and Navy could not accommodate them, Congress was being asked to pass a large number of bills that would enable the administration to prosecute the war vigorously, and Polk, who had been working twenty hours a day, was exhausted.

But he greeted his visitors warmly, then sat down with them behind the closed doors of his office. "I want your advice," he said. "First, the British are stiffening their stand on the Oregon question."

"I'm not surprised," Benton replied. "London thinks we're too preoccupied with Mexico to press our claims in the Oregon Territory."

Sam nodded. "I must admit that if our positions were reversed, we'd be less inclined to grant any British demands."

"Of course." President Polk rested his elbows on his desk. "So the dilemma that faces me now is whether to keep pressing for a Fifty-four forty boundary, or to offer an immediate division of the Territory at the 49th parallel."

"I'd be inclined to make a realistic offer," Benton said.

President Polk turned to Sam, whose face was wooden.

"Let's put ourselves in the position of the British. They'd believe we were acting from a position of weakness, and they'd be right. If we ask for the 49th, they'll insist that the Columbia River, at the 46th, is the more natural boundary, and we might have to take it. We'd leave ourselves no room for bargaining."

Polk ran a finger inside his high, stiffly starched collar. "If we refuse to change, though, and keep claiming the Fifty-four forty line, they might be tempted to break off negotiations."

"In which case," Benton said somberly, "we'd have to fight Mexico and Great Britain at the same time."

"I'll concede that London might feel tempted to tell us to go to the devil, but I don't believe that will happen. They don't want a war over Oregon any more than we do. So, if we hold firm, we'll get our compromise boundary at the 49th."

The others were silent for a few moments, then Benton said, "There's a risk we'd be running."

"Granted." Sam's broad grin relieved the solemnity of the discussion. "The British are every damned bit as proud a people as we are, and if we're arrogant, if we rub their fur the wrong way, they'll have to fight. But I learned when I was dealing with them in Texas that they always prefer compromise."

"It's true there are more Americans than Englishmen settling in the Oregon country," Polk said, "and we're closer to the Territory than the British, so it would be easier for us to take full possession than it would be for them. All the same—"

"If I were sitting behind that desk, Mr. President," Sam said, "I'd issue a statement refusing to yield one inch of the Territory. But I'd tell Secretary of State Buchanan to invite the British Minister, Mr. Pakenham, to dinner. I'd instruct him to avoid the subject of Oregon until they start passing the bottle of port at the end of the meal. Then I'd tell him to hint—without saying it in so many words—that no matter what our public position, we'd be willing to be reasonable. That's the kind of gesture they appreciate."

"Suppose you're wrong, Sam, and they won't budge," Benton said.

"Between the 49th parallel and the 46th are about seventy thousand square miles of rich land, west of the Rocky Mountains alone. The rivers are filled with salmon, the soil is wonderful and the timber is worth a tremendous fortune. In the Rockies there are furs and minerals that will make the United States richer for hundreds of years. I say that—if we must—the area is worth a war with the British, even though we're fighting Mexico at the same time!"

"Those are my sentiments," President Polk said. "I wanted to hear them supported."

Benton stiffened. "I'm cautious, but you'll find my patriotism as great as any man's if we find ourselves in trouble."

"I'm not questioning your patriotism, Tom," the President replied quickly.

Benton was slightly mollified.

"My other problem is just as delicate," Polk continued. "General Taylor is competent, and is doing well, but he lacks the experience to assume full command in the field. I've just about made up my mind to organize a major expedition that will capture Mexico City, and need a commander-in-chief capable of taking over-all charge in the field. I needn't tell you Scott wants the post."

"Winfield Scott is in the right place now," Benton said firmly. "He's completely at home sitting behind a Washington desk and wearing those gaudy uniforms he designs for himself."

Polk shook his head. "The field command is his by right of seniority, unless I appoint a lieutenant general from civilian life who would outrank him."

"I'd certainly be willing to resign my seat in the Senate to accept it," Benton said. "I'm at your disposal, Mr. President."

Polk was embarrassed. "I'm sure you'd be a very able field commander, Tom. But I was thinking more in terms of someone who has a natural reputation as a military hero, someone who has already fought and beaten the Mexicans."

Sam felt his face growing hot.

Benton glared at him, then turned back to the President. "I've had a longer military service record than any other civilian in the country. I don't know if the public thinks of me as a hero, but I'm sure the people would have no complaint against me after I captured Mexico City!"

Sam knew what was going through his colleague's mind, and realized that it would be a grave error for the President to antagonize the Senate Majority Leader. Now, of all times, Polk needed the undeviating support of Thomas Hart Benton in order to obtain the legislation the administration needed to mobilize the country for war.

The urge to go back into the field once more was overwhelming, and he felt certain he could lead an expedition to victory. But this was not a time to think of his own desires, his own yearning for greater glory. The good of the country made it imperative that the President and his Senate Majority Leader remain friendly, working together.

"I suppose I qualify as a hero," he said with a faintly self-deprecating smile, "and I believe I could accomplish your objectives in the field, Mr. President. But Tom is right about his own seniority. He was my commanding officer when I was a young ensign holding a new commission. I know how he feels. When a man has worn his country's uniform, he sometimes gets a hankering to wear it again. I'd sure like to be a member of that expedition—serving, maybe, as Tom's deputy. But I'm afraid our place is in the Senate, where the voters sent us. We need Tom there. I don't know of anyone else who has his talent for guiding bills. I don't know how much good I do, but I feel I ought to stay there, too, to help as best I can."

The sensitive Polk immediately realized he was ruling himself out of consideration for the post of Army field commander in order to preserve harmony between the White House and Benton. "It's true," he said, "that I need both of you right where you are."

Benton's grunt indicated that he accepted the inevitable with a marked lack of enthusiasm.

The President pretended to be unaware of his attitude. "Will you stay for a bowl of soup and some cold beef, gentlemen?"

Sam agreed, but Benton was still miffed. "I'm expected at a meeting in my office, Mr. President," he said, and took his leave.

"I'm afraid," Polk said, after the door closed behind him, "that I've made an enemy, Sam."

"I think not, Mr. President. He may not be your friend until he calms down, but he won't break with you. He enjoys being Majority Leader too much. We've all been hearing rumors that you might appoint a civilian as field commander, and it's plain he had his heart set on the post."

"Too plain. And I've lost you as a major general, Sam."

"I'm probably too old, anyway."

"I appreciate your sacrifice, and I just wish there were some way I could make this up to you."

Sam shrugged. "Thank you, Mr. President, but when we're at war, we've got to make sacrifices. It seems to me that giving up a personal ambition is doing a good deal less than risking my life in battle. Besides," he added, trying to make himself feel better, "my wife will be happy I'm not rejoining the Army. We're expecting another child in September."

The 29th Congress of the United States was kept busy through the summer, and did not adjourn until late August. Sam remained in Washington for an additional thirty-six hours, and spent the entire time at his desk, disdaining sleep as he cleaned up his desk, answered necessary correspondence and sent two long reports to the President. "We've accomplished very little here," he told Senator Rusk as they boarded a train together for the first stage of their long journey back to Texas. "When there's a war, Congress must take second place to the President. I just hope we get home in time for me to be with Margaret when our new son is born!"

On September 6, 1846, Margaret Houston gave birth to her first daughter at the family home, Raven Hill. Seventy-two hours later her husband arrived, and was astonished.

"I'll be damned," he said. "As anybody who knows the life I've led realizes. But it never crossed my mind we'd have a girl." He peered at the infant in the bed beside her mother.

"I hope you're not too disappointed." Margaret's voice hinted at her anxiety.

"Certainly not!" he replied, his voice too hearty. "But we have a problem."

Her concern became greater.

He reached into his tailcoat pocket and drew out a sheet of paper, which he unfolded. "I made out a list of names for boys. But I wouldn't know what to call a girl!"

Margaret felt slightly relieved. "I thought we might name her after our mothers."

"Nancy Elizabeth. Not bad." He made a great effort to hide the feeling of having been cheated.

"Would you like to hold her, Sam?"

"Lord Almighty! I've never held a baby girl!"

Margaret sat up higher in bed and carefully wrapped the infant in a soft blanket. "Here."

Sam hesitated.

Margaret had never seen such consternation and fear in his face, but managed to stifle a laugh. "She won't hurt you. And she won't break in two, either. Even girls are indestructible, you know."

He took a deep breath, reached for the bundle and held the baby awkwardly.

Nancy Elizabeth stirred.

"Well," he said with an air of discovery. "Her eyes are blue!"

Margaret carefully refrained from telling him that all newborn infants' eyes were blue.

His excitement growing, he bent closer to the baby. "By God, she's smiling at me!"

"Really? Then you're the first. She hasn't paid me any notice yet."

"Is that right? Well." Sam chuckled, and bent his face still closer. "Nancy Elizabeth Houston, your pa is an old scoundrel and a reprobate. He's too damned vain for his own good or anybody else's, he's a reformed drunk who would have killed himself with whisky if it hadn't been for your ma, and he's mean clear through. He doesn't understand women, and never will, so you'll have to make allowances for him. But I won't be surprised if you and I become friends, Nancy Elizabeth. I think I'd like that."

Margaret lay back on her pillows, her fears vanishing.

On December 1, 1846, the members of the Texas Congressional delegation left together for Washington. Just before his departure Sam bought a new pony for his son and another for his infant daughter, Margaret gravely assuring him that she would teach the baby to ride as soon as she could stand. When they arrived in the capital Sam was surprised to find his waiting mail included scores of invitations to act as the speaker at dinners, banquets, and other public affairs in all parts of the country.

The Oregon compromise had been effective, the President having not only employed Sam's tactics but giving him full credit for them, and people everywhere were singing the praises of the junior Senator from Texas. *"Sam Houston not only brought Texas into the Union, but has balanced the addition of a slave state with the acquisition of the Oregon Territory at the 49th parallel,"* the Hartford *Courant* declared in an editorial. *"He is a patriot who deserves the thanks of every American."*

"Don't be surprised," Rusk told his colleague, "if a movement starts soon to run you for President."

They were sitting together in the new dining room at Brown's Hotel that was reserved for the exclusive use of Senators, Congressmen, and high-ranking administration officials. Sam looked around, made a quick but careful count, and shook his head. "Even if Jamie Polk retires, and I've never known him to break his word, and they try to stand me for President, I'd refuse. I've just added up seven states that would switch from the Democrats to the Whigs, for the simple reason that I come from the South. They ask me to their dinners and praise me in their newspapers because I put the Union ahead of sectionalism, but they wouldn't vote for me, Tom. They like me because I don't agree with the followers of Calhoun that the rights of a state are more important than those of the whole Union, and they like to show me off because they think I believe as they do.

"Well, I don't," he continued. "I'm going up to New York and

Boston to speak, maybe to Philadelphia, in the hope I can make people see that the North is as guilty of sectional feelings as the South. I hope to God it won't be too long before citizens everywhere realize there must be an understanding deeper than the regional truce that's been worked out because we're at war. My candidacy would make all the hatreds between the Northern free states and the Southern slave states worse, not better, so I'd do more harm than good.

"I'd be a liar if I told you I didn't want to be President of the United States, but I'd rather give up my chances than see the Union destroyed."

By early January 1847 preparations were well advanced for the dispatch of a powerful expeditionary force to Mexico. A corps of ten thousand to fifteen thousand men, armed with the most modern weapons and carrying ample supplies and equipment, supported by cavalry, artillery and engineers, and transported by the strongest squadrons of ships the growing Navy could provide, was being mobilized. But President Polk had not yet appointed a commander-in-chief for the corps, even though most of the planning had been done by Major General Winfield Scott.

Senator Benton of Missouri, still yearning for the command, introduced a bill in the Senate authorizing the President to appoint a lieutenant general. His friends, in and out of Congress, spoke openly of his candidacy, and he felt the post was as good as his.

But the majority of his colleagues disagreed. It became common knowledge that Whigs as well as Democrats intended to vote for the bill because they supported Senator Houston for the post. The Baltimore *Sun* spoke for the people of the country as well as the majority of Senators when it said, *"Should a Lieutenant General be appointed, there is only one candidate worthy of the President's consideration, the General who beat Santa Anna once and can beat him again, Sam Houston of Texas."*

On the eve of the day the vote on the bill was scheduled in the Senate, Secretary of State James Buchanan paid a quiet visit to Brown's Hotel. The tall, dapper bachelor, a former Senator from Pennsylvania, took his horse to the rear of the building and climbed the back stairs in order to escape notice by the guests in the dining room.

Sam, who was not expecting company, was in his nightshirt and stocking cap when he greeted his visitor. His bed was littered with correspondence, committee reports, notes for speeches and reference books, which overflowed onto all three chairs in the bedroom. He cleared a chair, took a jug of whisky, a glass and a pitcher of water from a shelf and placed them beside his guest.

"Help yourself, Jim," he said. "I'd do the honors for you, but the smell of that stuff makes me ill."

Buchanan, who had found it difficult to believe he had really stopped drinking, saw that he was sincere. Pouring himself a mild drink, the Secretary of State smiled. "This is a private call, Sam, but it isn't personal. A mutual friend asked me to stop in for a little chat with you."

Sam grinned. "Our mutual friend is a very high-minded man who hasn't changed since the days I first knew him as a lawyer in Tennessee. I often wondered how he'd get his dirty work done if ever he held very high office. I don't reckon you have many evenings to yourself, Jim."

"Very few, Sam," Buchanan admitted. "Our friend is interested in your stand on the Benton Act."

"Oh?"

"You haven't announced your position on it."

"I told him what I thought when Tom Benton and I paid a call on him one day last year."

"Then you'll vote in favor of the appointment of a lieutenant general."

"I doubt if there will be many votes opposed. Even Zachary Taylor's Whig friends will vote in favor of it, hoping he'll get the appointment."

"Taylor won't be appointed. He's already the Whigs' leading candidate for the presidency, and there's no sense in making him more popular."

Sam rubbed the scar on his leg; his old wound still ached when the weather was damp. "Let's not play boys' games, Jim. Why does it matter to the President how I vote on a bill that's sure to be passed by a vote of five or six to one?"

"He remembers your conversation of last year, and wonders if you're still disinclined to accept the appointment."

"Disinclined? That's too mild. Jamie Polk knows I can't and won't accept it."

"He has no intention of making Tom Benton our lieutenant general."

"Why not?"

"For one thing," the Secretary of State said incisively, "he's too old. He's sixty-five. For another, no matter how good an opinion he has of his own talents as a military man, the Army doesn't share those views. His experience is limited to Indian campaigns, and he's never led a real Army in a formal war."

The President's objections to Benton were valid, Sam thought. "I've been assuming that Scott would be promoted."

"He's already the top-ranking Regular Army Major General. There's no need to promote him, which might set a precedent that future Presidents wouldn't necessarily care to follow."

There was one aspect of the situation that was being left unmentioned, Sam realized. Scott, although a competent officer, already held such a good opinion of himself that his conceit might become intolerable if he should be promoted.

"The President would prefer to appoint no one," Buchanan said, "but he feels—and the Cabinet agrees with him—that the country might become less enthusiastic about the war if he ignored the will of Congress. From all we hear, the House will support the Benton Act by an even bigger majority than the Senate."

"I've been told the same thing."

"So, if he must appoint someone, it will be you."

"No!" Sam was emphatic. "Tell him, Jim. If I must, I'll stop off at the White House in the morning and tell him myself."

"That won't be necessary. I'm reporting back to him this evening."

Sam pulled off his nightcap and ran a hand through his gray hair. "Damnation! This creates a very awkward situation for me."

"I'm sure you understand the President's position is uncomfortable, too."

"What can I do about it, Jim?"

"The President doesn't want to interfere with the operations of the Legislative Branch of the government, Sam. He just thought you should be acquainted with the facts."

Vice-President George M. Dallas was in the chair for what members of the Senate expected to be a routine session. Several appropriations measures were on the calendar, which guaranteed the attendance of virtually every Senator, anxious to insure that his own state was not overlooked, but the atmosphere was relaxed. Whigs and Democrats chatted amiably as they strolled to their seats, and some worked on correspondence as they waited for the significant business of the day.

The clerk read the Benton Act, which had been introduced at a previous session, and Sam was on his feet at once. "Mr. President!"

"The chair," the Vice-President said, "recognizes the junior Senator from Texas."

"Mr. President, I intend to confine myself to a few remarks." Sam, standing beside his desk at the rear of the chamber, saw that most of his colleagues had not bothered to look up. "I want to assure our distinguished Majority Leader that I have the greatest respect for him as a Senator, as a man and as a military officer. For the information of those who may be unaware of the origins of our old friendship, Colonel Benton was my commanding officer at a time when I was a very young ensign in the Regular Army. I found his courage, gallantry, and sagacity second to none.

"Therefore it grieves me, Mr. President, to announce that I will find it necessary to vote against his bill today."

Other Senators stopped writing and sat upright in their seats.

Benton, on the aisle in the front row, twisted around and stared incredulously at Sam.

"I would welcome the appointment of Colonel Benton to the post of Lieutenant General and commander of the force the United States intends to send off to Mexico in the immediate future. It is my understanding, however, that the War Department plans to assign that role to General Winfield Scott, and while I cannot presume to speak for the White House, it is my personal view that the President will confirm the appointment of General Scott."

All heads were turned toward the speaker now, and the galleries subsided after a brief, whispered flurry.

"I object to the appointment of a Lieutenant General from civilian life. I have many reasons, chief among them the fear that such an appointment would destroy the incentive of the professional soldier at a time when his skills, training, and valor are most needed.

"As one who has himself served in the uniforms of the United States and of Texas, I believe I am familiar with the character of the professional soldier. So I put it to you this way, Mr. President. Let us suppose you were a Colonel, or even a Brigadier or Major General. Would you not feel cheated if, instead of seeing your commander promoted from within your own ranks, an outsider was brought in and placed above you? Would you try as hard to defeat the enemy, no matter how great your own patriotism, if you knew your own efforts would be unrecognized and unrewarded?

"You would falter, Mr. President, and so would I. Therefore I must make it finally and conclusively clear to you, sir, that should this measure be passed by both Houses of the Congress and signed into law by the President, and should the President then see fit to tender me the appointment as Lieutenant General, my conscience would make it necessary for me to refuse, with regrets."

The chamber was silent when he sat down, then Tom Rusk stood and was recognized. "Mr. President, I support the stand taken by my distinguished colleague and fellow Texan."

Senators on both sides of the aisle began clamoring for recognition. If Sam Houston had no intention of accepting the post of Lieutenant General, the bill creating the new rank lost its meaning, and both Democrats and Whigs wanted to go on record as opponents of such a measure.

After fifteen Senators of both parties had announced they would vote against the bill, Thomas Hart Benton rose. "Mr. President, I withdraw my Act," he said stiffly, and started toward the rear.

There was a commotion in the galleries, and Vice-President Dallas gaveled for order.

Benton stopped at Sam's desk. "I knew I didn't have much chance of winning the appointment and that you stood first in line," he said. "But I was hoping I could smoke Polk into the open. Maybe you were helping me just now, or maybe you were trying to protect the administration. I'm not sure which, but—"

"I was doing both," Sam said, "and I was protecting myself. I couldn't accept an appointment under your Act, with you left out."

Benton studied him. "I believe you—unless I learn otherwise. So you and I can keep our friendship, anyway."

Before Sam could ask what he meant, Benton left the chamber.

Less than an hour later a note was handed to Vice-President Dallas. Visibly disturbed, he said he would entertain a motion for an hour's adjournment, and, after it was forthcoming, he summoned the Democratic Senators to a party caucus in his office. Benton, he announced, had resigned as Majority Leader.

A committee of three immediately went to the Missourian's office in an attempt to persuade him to change his mind, but he remained adamant, revealing that he had also sent a copy of the message to the White House.

Senator Rusk nominated his fellow Texan for the post of Majority Leader, and Sam was elected without a dissenting vote.

"Thank you for your confidence, my friends," he said. "Now, let's go back to work."

Bludgeoning and persuading, threatening the termination of patronage and promising greater influence in Federal appointments, Sam moved unprecedented numbers of administration bills through the Senate. The successes enjoyed in Mexico by the expeditionary corps under General Winfield Scott's command made the new Majority Leader's task easier, and only Benton, who now called himself an Independent Democrat, refused to cooperate with him.

John C. Calhoun, who had been ill, returned to the Senate, and he, too, appeared to be following his own inclinations, but Sam called on him in his office at the end of the South Carolinian's first day in Washington.

"You voted against two administration bills today, Senator Calhoun," he said.

"I didn't approve of them, Senator Houston."

"You and I have known each other for a great many years, and since our relations have never been friendly, this is a bit embarrassing," Sam said.

Calhoun refused to ease the strain. "I'm sorry you're embarrassed, Houston. I'm not."

"I was taught by my mother to show respect for my elders." Sam spoke quietly, almost casually. "You were a prominent member of Congress while I was still a boy, sir. But times do change, as the saying has it, and I'm charged with certain obligations by our fellow Democrats. I'm assuming, of course, that you're still a member of the party, Senator."

"Naturally." Calhoun seemed to be enjoying himself. "Andrew Jackson couldn't read me out, and James Polk is no Jackson."

"I'm sure the idea hasn't even occurred to the President. I just wanted to know, for my own sake."

"Now you know, Houston."

Sam took a sheaf of papers from his inner coat pocket and spread them on the desk. "I assume you recognize these."

Calhoun's aplomb vanished. "They're recommendations I sent to the White House this noon for military appointments and a new circuit court judgeship!"

"So it appears. We worked out a new system, you might call it, while you were away, Senator. The President isn't in good health, so he channels all requests for appointments through me. It saves him time that he can devote to the direction of our war activities."

"I see." Calhoun stared hard at him. "It has always been customary for the President—any President—to honor the patronage requests of a Senator within his own state."

"There has been no basic change in the custom." Sam was more relaxed now. "I've yet to recommend that the President reject any legitimate request made by a Senator who is a member in good standing of the Democratic party."

"What are your criteria?"

"Obviously," Sam said, "I'd be wrong to interfere when a Senator casts his vote as a matter of conscience. Our form of government would collapse if we didn't have that right. But a Senator who claims he belongs to the administration's party and wants to enjoy its benefits must prove his loyalty to the administration. It's very simple, Senator."

Calhoun was shocked. "Not even Jackson dared to go this far, sir!"

"The United States wasn't engaged in a major war with a foreign power during President Jackson's terms of office, Senator."

"I'll protest to Polk!"

"You have as much right as any other Senator to seek an appointment with the President, sir. And I speak only for myself, not for the White House, but I believe I can assure you, Senator, that the new system won't be changed. Shall I keep these requests for appointments until you've seen President Polk, or would you prefer to take them back to the White House yourself?"

"You've done what no one else has ever done in all the years I've held office, Houston. You've skinned me." There was a trace of humor in Calhoun's rueful tone.

Sam was surprised to discover that he could not keep old hatreds alive. "I'd rather work with you than skin you, sir," he said. "I've spent less than two years in the Senate, and it will take me a long time to learn what you know about this place."

His graciousness was so unexpected that Calhoun was taken aback. "I think it unlikely that I can teach you much about politics, Senator."

There was a moment's silence, then Sam grinned and extended his hand. "I'll fight you to the death when you try to weaken the Union, sir, and I'll gladly debate your theory that the rights of the individual states are greater than those of the Union as a whole. But I'm damned if I know why we can't get along on everything else."

Calhoun shook his hand. "You're a bully, Houston, but I can't help admiring your technique. When you press a loaded pistol to my heart, you do it as a gentleman."

It would be strange, Sam thought, not to keep up the long feud, and it seemed odd, too, that his victory gave him no sensation of pleasure. "There will be no need for you to take these requests back to the White House, Senator. I'll approve them right now and send them along to the President. If you have any others in mind, perhaps you'd let me have them this evening. They serve a tolerably good dinner at Brown's, and if you'd join me, I might be able to bring you up to date on pending legislation."

"I gladly accept the invitation, sir. But I'm curious."

Sam waited, not knowing what to expect from the old fox.

"You're approving my requests for presidential appointments before you actually know that I'll vote with the administration. Is this another form of pressure? If it is, you're the most clever parliamentarian in Christendom!"

"Frankly, Senator Calhoun, it hadn't occurred to me to obligate you, although I'll remember the trick for future use. No, once you and I made our peace, I simply took it for granted that you'd vote with the party whenever your conscience permits. I must admit that my opinion of you hasn't been flattering in the years we've been enemies, but I've always known you were a man of your word."

Calhoun bowed, then suddenly chuckled. "When you were President of Texas, Houston, what would you have done if some young officer had come to Austin dressed as a savage Indian?"

"I'd have reprimanded him, just as you once reprimanded a young fellow. Then I'd have promoted him a rank, on the spot, before he could lose his temper and resign his commission. The trouble with the young, Senator Calhoun, is that they so consistently act their age."

The victories won by Winfield Scott were as impressively decisive as those achieved by Zachary Taylor, and it became evident that Mexico City would fall within a short time. The 29th Congress ended its labors in the midsummer of 1847, and when Sam arrived home in Texas a month later, he learned that Scott's corps had just entered Mexico City. For all practical purposes the war was at an end, but there were many problems still to be solved, and President Polk summoned Congress to reconvene on December 1.

"You'll have to be late, Sam," Washington Miller told his old friend. "You're standing for re-election, and you've got to be on hand when the Texas Senate votes in January."

"Impossible," Sam said firmly. "I've got to be in Washington when the peace treaty is submitted to the Senate. If I do nothing else, I intend to make certain that Mexico officially and finally recognizes the Rio Grande boundary of Texas. And I've already made my position public on Secretary Buchanan's aim of annexing all of Mexico. I say it's enough to take California and New Mexico. To keep the rest would be an affront to civilization—and would almost certainly guarantee a Mexican revolt within five years."

If Miller disagreed, he kept his thoughts to himself. No former subordinate ever dared to argue with Sam's ideas in either foreign or domestic affairs. "If you can stay home for only two months, you'll have to campaign hard."

"I can't do that, either. My son is growing up, I'm scarcely acquainted with my daughter, and my wife and I deserve to spend these few weeks together."

"Don't you realize that four or five others are going to be campaigning like madmen? They're already accepting speaking engagements in every city and town in Texas."

"That's their concern, not mine. My record will have to do my campaigning for me."

Governor Henderson, Senator Rusk, and other close associates added their pleas to Miller's, but Sam remained adamant. "If I don't deserve another term, I'll be retired. I don't have time, so I can't and won't campaign for re-election."

On November 20 Senators Rusk and Houston left Texas for Washington, with Sam entering the 30th Congress as a "lame duck," not knowing whether he would win office again. But he was unconcerned, and plunged into the nation's business. He attacked

Buchanan's proposal that all Mexico be annexed by the United States, and spoke with such persuasive fervor that the scheme was dropped.

Senator Houston, his colleagues agreed, knew more about Mexican relations than anyone else in the country, and President Polk was willing to accept his judgment, too. Under the terms being worked out in Mexico City, the United States would extend her boundaries to the Pacific Ocean, gaining territory almost two and one half times as large as that of all France.

President Polk, whose increasingly frail health made it impossible for him to seek re-election in 1848, had kept his pledge to the American people, and the United States now spanned the continent. Taylor and Scott were the military heroes of the day, and Senator Houston, who won the President's lavish praise, was hailed everywhere as a major architect of the overwhelming victory.

In the closing days of 1847 the Texas Legislature settled down to the business of electing a Senator for a full six-year term. To the surprise of no one, Sam Houston won sixty-nine votes, while the combined total of his five opponents was only ten. Sam took the oath of office on January 24, 1848, but was too busy to celebrate, as he had to preside, that same evening, at a caucus of Democrats from both Houses of Congress, for the purpose of setting a date and time for the Democratic National Convention.

In February 1848 the United States and Mexico formally signed the peace treaty ending the war, and Majority Leader Houston of the Senate had such a busy speaking schedule in New York, Massachusetts, Connecticut, and Rhode Island, states in which the Whigs were strong, that everyone assumed he had presidential ambitions. The belief grew when Senator Rusk told the Democrats of Baltimore at a dinner meeting, "If James K. Polk could be persuaded to accept a second term, he would be the best of all possible Presidents. But, if he insists on retirement, the party is still fortunate. We have a man capable of taking his place, my renowned colleague, Sam Houston."

Sam refused to discuss politics, however, and after returning to Washington from his speaking tour, granted no interviews to the press. But the newsmen were as persistent as he was stubborn, and at the beginning of May, shortly before the convocation of the Democrats in Baltimore, he unexpectedly called a press conference.

So many reporters crowded into his Senate office that the door was kept open to accommodate the overflow in the corridor outside.

"I hadn't expected to see so many of my good friends," Sam said innocently. "Where have you lads been keeping yourselves lately?"

There was a rumble of laughter, which died away when he rose from his chair.

"Gentlemen," he said, "I asked you here today because I want to make an announcement of a very personal nature."

No one stirred, and the reporters who had wagered he would reveal his willingness to accept the Democratic nomination for President looked smug.

"I've just had splendid news from Texas. Mrs. Houston has given birth to our third child, our second daughter. We're calling her Margaret Lea, which was her mother's maiden name. Mrs. Houston and the baby are in good health, and I'm informed that my son, who is learning his alphabet, is writing me a letter to tell me he'll take care of the ladies until I return home. I think that's all I have to say, gentlemen."

No one moved, and a deep-voiced representative of the *Telegraph and Texas Register* called, "How will your family enjoy living at the White House, Senator?"

Sam pretended to misunderstand. "Billy," he said, "you ought to know, even better than these other folks, that we live in Texas."

The correspondent of the Nashville *Banner* picked up the cudgels. "We hear you're going to win the Democratic nomination, Senator."

"Then your sources of information are better than mine." Sam continued to smile amiably.

A Philadelphia newsman tried a different approach. "What's your reaction to General Taylor's nomination by the Whigs, Senator?"

Sam's smile vanished. "Like all Americans, I'm proud of General Taylor's accomplishments in the war. As one who has had a little experience fighting Mexicans, I can appreciate his problems. I sent him several letters of congratulations during the war, and I was pleased to shake his hand when he came home.

"I don't know that I'm particularly qualified to discuss his qualifications for the presidency," he continued. "As a matter of fact, I don't know that he is capable of judging whether he'd be a good or bad President. Just because a man has been an effective General in combat operations doesn't necessarily mean he'd be an effective President." He paused, modestly refraining from mentioning the obvious record that he himself had compiled. "There aren't many George Washingtons and Andrew Jacksons in our history."

"Or Sam Houstons, Senator?" a bold young man from the newly founded Chicago *Tribune* called.

Sam joined in the general laugh. "My opinion of him would be biased in his favor, I think. But we were speaking of General Taylor. Since I have no way of guessing his talents as the principal administrative officer of the United States, I prefer to trust in the common sense and good judgment of the Democrats. You'll find me supporting the candidate of my own party."

"Who will that be, Senator?" two newsmen asked simultaneously.

"Come to the convention in Baltimore, and I'll tell you as soon as I know. Thank you for calling on me, gentlemen, and I regret that I must end this little chat now, but I'm expected on the Senate floor." Gently but deftly, Sam ushered the reporters out of his office.

Both the Whigs and Democrats were embarrassed by the slavery question, which was becoming increasingly important in both the Northern and Southern states. The acquisitions from Mexico made the problem even more urgent, and whether these new lands would be administered as free or slave territories became the paramount issue of the day.

The Whigs neatly evaded the dilemma by the nomination of Zachary Taylor, whose war record had won the admiration of the North, but who, a Southerner and slave owner, was certain to receive support in the South.

The Democrats were equally anxious to find a candidate acceptable to both sections of the country, and, on the eve of the convention, Senator Houston and Postmaster General Cave Johnson were sent to the White House in the hope they could persuade the President to change his mind.

"You're the only man in the country who is sure of beating Taylor, Mr. President," Sam said. "He beat the Mexicans in battle, but you won our new territories from them. And you also won Oregon without a war."

"We know you're tired and want to go back to Nashville, but the country needs you, Mr. President," Johnson added.

"My decision," Polk said, "is final."

They looked at each other, surprised by his unexpectedly brusque manner.

"There are some things I'm reluctant to discuss with anyone," the President said, "but I believe I can trust two of my oldest and closest friends. Since I've said nothing to anyone, including my wife, I must ask you to be equally discreet."

Sam braced himself.

"I'll be fortunate," Polk said, "if I live to finish my term. I've been examined by more physicians than I'd care to number, and all of them tell me the same thing. I'm praying that I can fulfill my obligations to the people, and that I can go home to die in peace."

The hard-bitten Cave Johnson walked to the windows overlooking the White House lawn, and seemed to be removing something from his eye with a large bandanna handkerchief.

"A damned idiot of a doctor told me I'd never walk again after San Jacinto," Sam said gruffly. "I don't have faith in a single one of that breed." He knew that what he had said was weak, but it was the best he could muster.

Polk's fleeting smile indicated his appreciation of his friend's difficulty and loyalty. "I intend to keep my mouth shut and support no one at the convention," he said, "unless you want to run, Sam. If you do, I'll send a letter that Cave can read at the appropriate time. I can promise you it will be strong and unequivocal."

"I'm not going to be a candidate, but thank you," Sam said.

Johnson turned back into the room from his place at the window. "You could beat Taylor, I think."

"Maybe so. But I'm not going to be stuffed down the voters' craws just because I happen to fit a formula. I'm a Southerner, I fought my own war with the Mexicans and I brought Texas into the Union. That's history, though, and so are Taylor's accomplishments. I'm worried about tomorrow." Sam looked at Polk, who was watching him closely. "Mr. President, it looks as though you and I are the only men in the United States who dare to speak our minds freely on the slavery question—in favor of preserving the Union. I'm going to wait until after the convention, and then I plan to talk plain sense to the people. When I do, I'm sure neither party would want me as its candidate, but that isn't important. Somebody has got to stop these sectional feuds before the Union is seriously hurt."

The Democrats nominated a former Senator and Secretary of War, Lewis Cass of Michigan, as their candidate for President, and Sam, keeping his word, supported him. But the campaign was mild, principally because neither Taylor nor Cass would comment on proposed Congressional legislation that had come to be known as "the Wilmot Proviso." Representative David Wilmot of Pennsylvania, an ardent anti-slavery Democrat, had repeatedly offered an amendment to appropriations bills in the House, providing that slavery be forever abolished in all territory acquired by the United States.

The measure had passed in the House in 1846 and again in 1847, but had failed to gain enough support in the Senate. Daniel Webster and other outspoken anti-slavery Senators had supported the Wilmot Proviso, John C. Calhoun and other Southerners had opposed it, but most Senators had tried to keep silent. Now, with the campaign moving toward its climax, Senator Houston announced that he intended to make some remarks on the subject.

The galleries were crowded and every member of the Senate

was in his seat on the hot August afternoon in 1848 when Sam rose to make his address. Visitors in the crowded galleries saw that, as always, he spoke without the aid of notes.

"Mr. President," he said, "I have remained silent on certain subjects because of my hope, a vain hope, that passions would subside and reason prevail. Now I must speak, and appeal to my fellow Senators, and, through them, to their constituents, the people of the United States.

"I stand here as a representative of the people of Texas, and I trust I may be forgiven if I call her the first state in the Union, not only because of my love for her, but because her sons are men who migrated there from virtually every other state represented in this chamber. I am, then, a Southerner. And make no mistake, I'm proud of it!

"I would be the last man to wish to do anything to prejudice the interests of the South, but I do not think that on all occasions we are justified in agitating sectional feelings. I am not one who feels alarmed when the word 'slavery' is mentioned. I do not believe that the mere mention of the subject is a crime, and that the Union is about to be dissolved.

"I have too much confidence in the integrity, intelligence and patriotism, not only of gentlemen upon this floor, but of the people of this Union. The agitations that may arise in this hall or elsewhere are not calculated to affect the great interests of the Union—unless we insist they are so affected.

"Our institutions are too valuable and have cost too large a price to be easily parted with or disturbed. The intelligence of the people has taught them to appreciate those institutions. They consider them a sacred legacy left them by their fathers, and they will not allow the schisms and agitations which may prevail for a time among politicians—note, if you please, politicians—to endanger their safety.

"Lest it be claimed that I speak only in safe generalities, let me become specific, Mr. President. I can offer no magic nostrum, no medicine, no formula that will cure the illness eating into the heart of our Union. There are some who are opposed to slavery in any form. There are some who defend the slave system of the South on economic grounds. I know of no man who defends the institution for any other reason.

"It is my conviction that the Congress arrogates to itself powers it does not possess when it tries to decide the question, 'Shall the United States be part-free and part-slave, all free or all slave?'

"It is my conviction that this complex, painful and inordinately difficult question can and must be determined by the Supreme Court.

"I believe that the endless debate on the question of whether slavery should be banned in the Oregon Territory is absurd. Northerners are migrating to Oregon in large numbers. No person from the South has migrated there. No person from the South will migrate there at any time within a future we can see. So why do we beat at one another?

"Only free men are migrating to California. There, too, the issue is settling itself. So why do we beat at one another?

"Am I still being too general in my comments? Very well, I shall become more specific. I own no slaves. I personally cannot own the body or bodies of other human beings. However, that does not give me the right to forbid my Texas neighbor to own slaves. It does not give such a right to any man from the free states, either. Should my neighbor be required to grant freedom to his slaves?

"It is not the prerogative of the Legislative Branch to determine this issue. The Judicial Branch of the government, and it alone, has the authority to determine whether the institution of slavery shall exist, and if so, where it may be allowed.

"It is true that we, the Legislative Branch, can rightly influence the Judicial Branch. Let us do this by counseling together, by uniting in mind, spirit and heart to find equitable and honorable solutions to a problem we cannot solve by shaking our fists under the noses of those who hold views unlike our own.

"As for me, the Union is my guiding star, and I shall fix my eyes on that star to guide my course. I say, with the greatest of men it has ever been my privilege to know, 'The Federal Union, it must be preserved.'"

Margaret was dozing before the fire in her second floor sewing room when strong hands closed over her shoulders and she felt herself being kissed. "Welcome home, General Houston," she murmured before opening her eyes.

Sam drew her to her feet and embraced her. "I curse myself every day I'm away from you. I'm a fool not to stay right here for the rest of my life. You're looking well."

"I've completely recovered from the ague I wrote you about in my last letter."

"The children didn't catch it?"

"No, they're fine. Sam is reading now, and this morning he climbed to the top of the big apple tree behind the house."

"I've brought him a new pair of riding boots," Sam said, chuckling. "Do you think Nan will know me?"

"Of course, and so will Maggie, but you mustn't wake them up, or they'll be too excited to sleep."

Sam grinned at her. "You're very expert at reading my mind, Mrs. Houston."

Margaret had no intention of discussing the delicate subject. Looking at him carefully, she raised a hand to his face. "You look tired, dear."

"I'm always tired after that long trip from Washington. It becomes more wearing every time I make it."

"You're hungry."

"We can go down to the pantry after a spell. I just want to look at you and talk to you." He eased her into the chair and sat on its arm. "Tell me all the news."

"Nothing has happened here except domestic trifles."

"Those trifles are my meat and drink, Margaret."

"It's your news that absorbs us. Every Texas newspaper reprinted the text of your speech in the Oregon debate."

He nodded. "So I've been told."

"They also printed Senator Calhoun's charge that you're a traitor to the South!" She always reddened when she became indignant.

"I'll answer Calhoun at the next session, and I'm writing to the press, too. He means me no personal harm, you know."

Margaret stared at him. "You've changed."

"I'm growing too old to carry grudges, and so is he. We ate dinner together the night I left Washington—just a few hours after he attacked me."

"How could you sit at the same table with him, Sam?"

"We have different goals, and he was using me as a club to beat some life into his. He still favors the rights of the states over those of the Union. I intend to answer him by saying that he represents South Carolina, not Texas, and that he has no mandate to speak for the whole South. I'll take particular pains to point out that there are countless patriots in the South."

"How can you be so calm?"

Sam patted his wife's shoulder. "I thought I understood all there was to know about politics, Margaret, but I've learned something in this past year. A statesman fights for principles—"

"So you've told me many times."

"—and, when he must, he smears dirt on men who believe in other principles. If I can remember the lesson, it's possible I won't lose my temper in politics again."

Margaret could not imagine him remaining benign when provoked.

He saw her expression, and added, "But don't make any wagers on it."

"I won't, I promise you. Now let's go down to the pantry. I baked bread this afternoon, and some of the hams that have been curing in the smokehouse are ready to eat."

Sam realized she wasn't taking his protestations seriously, and couldn't blame her. Senators and Congressmen from the North had been treating him with consideration in their public statements, but he suspected that Calhoun's attack might be the beginning of a campaign launched by his colleagues from the South to discredit him. Men everywhere were becoming increasingly emotional on the subject of slavery, and he was afraid they were becoming indifferent to what he regarded as the most fundamental of issues, the preservation of the Union. Whether he could maintain his new-found objectivity if the United States should be threatened with dissolution was highly dubious.

EIGHT

1852–59

Sectional feelings continued to mount with each passing year, and Sam believed he was virtually alone in his attempts to safeguard the Union. James K. Polk died three months after leaving the White House, and Zachary Taylor, who had tried to stem the rising tide of hatreds, succumbed to an attack of typhus on July 9, 1850, after only fifteen months in office. His successor, Millard Fillmore, tried to placate both North and South, and succeeded in satisfying no one.

Gold was discovered in California, which was admitted to the Union as a free state, the slavery question in the New Mexico Territory became the principal topic of bitter debate, and the national cleavage grew wider.

"The fundamental issue," Sam declared repeatedly in speeches on the Senate floor, public addresses and statements issued to the press, "is Union or disunion. I subscribe neither to the mad fanaticism of the North nor the mad ambition of the South."

In 1852 the death of Henry Clay, "the Great Compromiser," gave him an opportunity to express his convictions from another point of view. "Clay and I seldom agreed, but I respected him as a patriot," he said in a memorial address. "On one question he believed, with me, however, that no compromise was possible. It

249

was our unalterable stand, and remains mine, that the Union is sacred, and that the future of this nation depends upon our adherence to the provisions of the Constitution."

Few men agreed, and the only recruit to Sam's cause was an old friend, Congressman Andrew Johnson of Tennessee, who, in spite of his sincerity, lacked national stature. The burden became heavier, and Sam's weariness was unrelieved.

His family was growing still larger, Margaret having given birth to two more daughters, Mary and Antoinette. On his brief sojourns in Texas the head of the family bought more cattle, planted additional acres of corn, wheat and oats, and, for the first time, seriously began to consider his future in new terms.

"I'm tired of trying to put out fires when others are fanning the flames," he told Margaret. "All I seek for myself is retirement, so I can spend more time with you and the children. Whenever I come home I find the children and I are strangers to each other, and we've got to become acquainted all over again. I pray to God the country will have become sensible again by the time my term is up."

"No matter how anyone feels, haven't you done enough?" she asked.

Sam shrugged. "If I don't protect the Union, who will?"

The question was rhetorical, no one else appeared and Sam reluctantly allowed himself to stand for re-election late in 1852. Again he refused to campaign for himself, but made several speeches on behalf of the Democratic candidate for President, Franklin Pierce of New Hampshire. The Whigs having succeeded when they had run one military man, tried another, but Pierce overwhelmingly defeated General Winfield Scott.

In Texas there were no political parties on a state level. The *Telegraph and Texas Register* explained the situation to its readers in a succinct editorial, saying, *"Our situation is unique. We have few Democrats and few Whigs. We are divided into two camps of another sort. There are those who stand with Sam Houston, which is to say, most Texans, and a small, lonely handful opposed to him. The latter is of little consequence."*

On January 15, 1853, the members of the Texas Legislature cast their ballots for United States Senator; in the Senate, Sam received nineteen votes out of twenty-two, and in the House he won by a margin of forty-five votes to a scattered twelve for several opponents.

Newspapers throughout the United States were speculating that Sam would be offered a post in the Cabinet of President-elect Pierce, some of whose friends indicated to him that he could have any place he wanted. But he told Margaret he had no interest in a Cabinet appointment.

"Pierce has too little backbone for my taste," he said. "In one breath he appeases the anti-slavery people, in the next he makes promises to the South that no President can keep."

"Couldn't you strengthen him, Sam?"

"No, a Cabinet member carries out the policies of the President. He doesn't make policy. I don't know that many people are listening to me, but I'd completely lose my voice if I joined the administration. Besides, I'd never get home. I'd have to move you and the children to Washington for four years."

But the pressure increased, and Pierce himself wrote to the Texan, asking for his advice in the selection of his Cabinet and hinting broadly that he was anxious to include the illustrious Senator Houston in his official family.

Sam replied immediately. *"A Cabinet of irreproachable and unapproachable integrity, if intelligent and industrious, is all you want; the rest depends upon yourself. I am able to express my reflections to you freely and without stint because no consideration would induce me to accept an official position in Washington other than that to which the citizens of my own state have elected me."*

The temper of the times was changing rapidly, and nowhere was the new spirit more evident than in the United States Senate. The three men who had been symbols of the Senate to millions of Americans, Daniel Webster, Henry Clay and John C. Calhoun, were all dead. Younger men, like Stephen A. Douglas, a Democrat from Illinois, were drawing up bills to organize the

Kansas-Nebraska country, which was being opened by the extension of railroads to the Pacific.

Anti-slavery men and Southerners prepared for a new and bitter battle, and Sam found himself alone. "In a sense," he said at a caucus of Democratic party Senators, "I'm responsible for a possible new crisis. It was I who introduced the bill to build new railroads in the West. Now all the old fights threaten to break out again. I'm determined to use every parliamentary means and every trick of rhetoric I know to prevent a new battle in the Senate—and the inevitable battle that will be fought throughout the country after all of you have spoken your minds. Use common sense, I beg you, and don't tear the United States apart."

No one listened to him, and, in January 1854, a bill was introduced in the Senate making Kansas-Nebraska a free Territory. The expected senatorial fireworks promptly erupted. Sam remained silent for more than a month, having discovered in the previous session that his parliamentary tactics and rhetoric had no effect on his colleagues. He watched in growing dismay as Senators from the North and South became more violent in their exchanges of mutual, vitriolic abuse.

Finally, unable to tolerate the deteriorating situation any longer, he notified his colleagues that he intended to make a major address. He began speaking on the morning of February 14, and no one familiar with the details of his life was surprised to hear him attack Democrats and Whigs, Northerners and Southerners for their wanton disregard of the rights of Indian tribes that had settled in the Kansas-Nebraska Territory.

These savages, he declared, had settled in the area under the terms of treaties signed with the United States government. But, "not for the first time and, I fear, not for the last," he said, "the supposedly inviolable rights of Indians once again have been violated. While we quarrel with each other, we jointly grind into the dust the hopes, the aspirations, the very existence of the Indian nations to whom the United States is obligated. In our anxiety and zeal to solve problems which, as I have so often stated in the past, are in this hall insoluble, let us not forget that we are breaking our solemn word to helpless people who have accepted our pledges and whose future depends upon our willingness to honor our promises!"

Becoming increasingly exorcised, he devoted the rest of the day to a passionate defense of Indian rights. Not until the next morning, still holding the floor, did he concentrate on the subject of the Kansas-Nebraska Territory. Then, in his best rhetorical form, he addressed himself to the galleries, particularly the section in which newsmen were sitting, rather than to his fellow Senators.

"What must be the consequence if a new attempt is made to upset the balance that has permitted North and South to live together peacefully in recent years?" he demanded. "Will it produce no excitement? Will it strengthen the ties that bind together the component parts of our sacred Union?

"Depend upon it, if the Kansas-Nebraska free territory bill is passed by the Senate, that action will convulse the country from Maine to the Rio Grande, from the Atlantic Ocean to the Pacific!

"I do not urge that the measure be defeated any more than I want to see it passed. I request—nay, I demand—that it be tabled!

"As a Democrat, and as one elected to this chamber from the South, my own sympathies lie with my party and my own section of the country. But I am, I trust, more than a Democrat, more than a Southerner. I am an American!

"I trust I am also a realist, which is more than I can say for the majority of honorable gentlemen with whom I share membership in this distinguished body.

"As a realist, I well know that the preponderance in favor of Northern influence and Northern votes is every day, everywhere, in progress of increase, and must continue so in after times. It will not cease in our time.

"The vast northwestern portion of our continent, unadapted to slave labor, will not be filled up by Southern men with slaves. Northern people will increase that preponderance until the entire North is connected, from this seaboard to California.

"Our children have two alternatives here presented. They are either to live in after times in the enjoyment of peace, of harmony and prosperity, or the alternative remains for them of anarchy, discord, and civil broil. We can avert the last if we are wise. I trust we shall.

"I do not ask that we bury our heads and ignore the problems of the settlement of Kansas-Nebraska. I have in my own lifetime lived in two pioneer lands. I went to Tennessee as a child, and in the years that followed I saw her develop from a wilderness into a civilized land. I went to Texas as an adult, and saw her grow from a raw frontier land into an independent Republic, which, of her own free will, joined this Union.

"Neither in Tennessee nor in Texas were the pioneer settlers hampered by rules and regulations made by the Congress. Nature took her own course. She will do so in Kansas-Nebraska, if so allowed.

"As a realist, I know that only men from the North will settle in Kansas-Nebraska. I can imagine no practical circumstances that will encourage men from the South to settle there. Consequently, in the name of Almighty God, let us not set up artificial obstacles to domestic harmony.

"The North will get what she wants, new free territory. The South, although effectively denied that territory, will not be subjected to the totally unnecessary humiliation of being forced to grovel in the dust at the feet of a larger, more powerful section of the country.

"Therefore, I say, let the Kansas-Nebraska question—which is already solved for all practical purposes—let it rest on the basis of that which is, not that which might be, should be or would be in a set of hypothetical circumstances.

"Let us not continue to tear at the fabric of this Union. No nation is capable of tolerating such strains for all time. The fabric might tear if it is not treated with respect by men of every persuasion.

"Stir up no more agitation, gentlemen! In the name of God, let us have peace!"

The galleries applauded, some men standing to cheer, but the members of the Senate sat stonily silent.

Andrew Jackson Houston was born in the late spring of 1854, while his father was busy in Washington, and Sam quietly celebrated the event at dinner with Senator Rusk. But he had virtually no other reason to rejoice; everywhere his Senate speech was misunderstood. It was praised by Abolitionist groups in New England, who promised him support if he wanted to run for President in 1856, but the South was coldly furious.

Even in Texas, where Sam had been able to do little wrong in the eyes of his constituents, he was attacked. The Marshall *Meridian* called him a snake, the Brenham *Inquirer* was even less complimentary, and the press of the larger communities, embarrassed and unable to grasp the fundamentals of what he was trying to say, retreated into silence and pretended he no longer existed.

Some months later the Dallas *Herald* found the courage to declare in print what many men had been saying privately. *"Sam Houston,"* wrote the editor, *"is a traitor to the South."*

Sam made a desperate attempt to persuade his fellow Southerners that their approach to the vital issue was suicidal. At a special caucus of Senators and Congressmen from the Southern states he said, "The established political parties are falling apart, and unless you put the interests of the Union first, you're guaranteeing even more trouble for the South. The new Free-Soil party is growing stronger every day, and is certain to run a candidate for President in '56. Then—and it won't be long, mind you—they'll join forces with the Abolitionists, who'll take control of the party. I predict that, in '60, they'll elect the President of the United States.

"It's a matter of simple arithmetic. They're strong and growing stronger in the states that have the largest electoral votes—New England, New York, Pennsylvania, the fast-growing states in the Middle West, like Illinois. We'll be outnumbered and helpless.

"Never fight a battle unless you know you can win it. The new states and territories are moving into the free soil camp, and there's nothing you or I can do to stem the tide. So far, but only so far, no one is seriously trying to abolish the slave economy of the South. Continue on the path you've chosen, and the Abolitionists will gain complete control of the United States government.

"When that day comes, the tocsin of war will sound, and everywhere in the South there will be a cry for secession from the Union.

"Do you honestly believe we could win such a war? Gentlemen, stop fooling yourselves. The North has more men. The North has fifty industrial plants for each isolated factory that we've built. The North has great shipyards. The North has fertile soil that can produce enough food to sustain her people in time of war.

"We have cotton. The North can do without our cotton for a time, and cotton can't be eaten by hungry Southerners.

"You're being impatient. Wait, and a formula will be evolved that will enable you to preserve your way of life.

"Stay on your present, blind course, and you will destroy yourselves, your homes, all that you hold dear. I'm not speaking to you as an outsider. I'm a Southerner by birth, and have been a Southerner all my life. My affection for the South is as great as that of any man here. It is because I feel as I do that I have chosen the one course that will enable us to survive this senseless quarrel. Put your faith in the Union, as Andrew Jackson did before us.

"But, if you refuse to change, there will be war, and I shall see my beloved South go down in the unequal contest, in a sea of blood and smoking ruin."

There was a heavy silence, and then the Senators and Congressmen began to hiss. Someone at the rear of the hall jeered, and in a moment the legislators' mood became ugly, almost menacing. Sam was abused and cursed, his colleagues shouting epithets and shaking their fists at him.

He remained on the podium, his head erect, refusing to yield to his scornful fellow Southerners. Finally Alexander Stephens and other men of courteous good will managed to re-establish order, and Sam walked back to his seat in a quiet that was in itself ominous.

Violence broke out in Kansas in 1855 as both Northerners and Southerners tried to gain control of the Territory. Farmers were attacked at night, and they and their families were driven from their homesteads, subjected to harsh treatment and sometimes murdered. Each side set up its own Territorial government, and each waged a vicious war in miniature on the other.

Sam was heartsick. When his renewed pleas to the South were rebuffed, he turned to the North, making long speaking tours as he pleaded for reason and justice. Everywhere his theme was the same: "I do not advocate slavery in the abstract. I am not here to discuss it as an abstract question. It is an existing fact that is causing far too much discord and agitation.

"The people of the South did not create slavery. The South does not love it, but it exists there, and, as an economic necessity in the present condition of the South—mind you, I stress *present* condition—it must be used, but guarded from abuse. The South should not encroach on the rights and institutions of the North, nor the North upon the institutions of the South. Union is what is needed, and freedom for every man to hold and express his own opinion.

"Our country is too glorious, too magnificent, too sublime in its future prospects to permit domestic disruptions or political opinions to produce a wreck of this mighty vessel of state. Let us hold on to it, and guide it; let us give it in charge to men who will care for the whole people, who will love the country for the country's sake, and will endeavor to build up and sustain it, and reconcile conflicting interests for the sake of all Americans. This can and must be done. Let us not despair. Let us not break up the Union!"

The Northern audiences received him politely, applauded him at appropriate rhetorical pauses and totally ignored his advice.

With each passing month his isolation became more complete, and in the late spring of 1855, just before Congress adjourned for the summer, he was made to feel the full weight of his colleagues' wrath. He had spent the whole day in his office, catching up on his correspondence after his return from his most recent speaking tour, and walked into the private dining room of Brown's Hotel at a late hour.

All of the tables were occupied, and most of the legislators and other government officials were finishing their meal. It was the custom for a late-comer—or for any man arriving alone—to find a place where he could, and according to the informal custom of the "club," anyone was entitled to sit where he pleased. "Politics ends at the entrance to the dining room at Brown's," Henry Clay had said when the place had first opened, and everyone had behaved accordingly.

But in the past few years subtle differences had begun to manifest themselves. Northern Democrats and Northern Whigs still sat together, but were rarely joined by Southerners of either party, who remained at tables of their own. The Free-Soil men congregated at one end of the room, near the few who openly accepted the label of Abolitionists. To an outsider the hum of conversation appeared vivacious and the general atmosphere cordial, but Sam knew the difference: there were hidden tensions, and when men spoke of legislation and the attitudes of voters, they addressed one another in low tones so they could not be overheard by those at neighboring tables.

There had been a time when Sam would have moved to the first vacant seat he saw, but he was careful now, partly because there were some present he disliked, in part because he, like everyone else, had to be cautious. He had no desire to join the Abolitionists, who were fanatics, able to discuss only one subject, and the Free-Soil people were little better.

At last he saw a place at a table of Democrats from the North, between Senators Cass of Michigan and Douglas of Illinois, and moved toward it. They nodded amiably enough, but quick glances were exchanged, and the burly Cass looked embarrassed. "You're late tonight, Sam," he said.

"I had a desk piled almost to the ceiling with letters, Lew."

"Then you must be starved, so you won't want to join us. We're just finishing our coffee, and we'll be leaving very shortly."

Sam understood the rebuff. Cass was considered somewhat too pro-Southern by his constituents, and it was rumored he would face heavy opposition in his campaign for re-election the following year. His enemies would make capital of the fact that he had dined with a Southerner, even the one man who was undeviatingly in favor of the Union.

Only Douglas looked slightly regretful. It was rumored that he had strong presidential ambitions, for 1860 if not 1856, and needed support from Democrats of every faction.

Sam bowed to him, then to Cass, and crossed to a table at which Secretary of War Jefferson Davis, a former Senator from Mississippi and a hero of the Mexican War, was presiding. Davis, a graceful and courtly man, almost as tall as Sam but far more slender, rose at once from his seat, a napkin in his right hand.

They exchanged bows, and Sam realized that, because Davis was holding the napkin, they could not shake hands.

"I've read that your appearances in New York and Connecticut were well attended, Senator," he said.

"The theaters and auditoriums were tolerably well filled, Mr. Secretary." Sam knew that the formality of Davis's pose made it impossible for him to take the one vacant place at the table without first being invited.

"The War Department is pleased you're back, Senator." Secretary Davis spoke impersonally, his tone indicating that his own feelings were not involved in his statement. "We sent you a report two days ago, and we'll appreciate your comments on it before you leave Washington for home."

"I read it this morning," Sam said, and waited for the next move.

"Then perhaps we can meet tomorrow, either at your office or mine. I'll accommodate your convenience, Senator Houston." Again Jefferson Davis bowed, smiled coolly and resumed his seat.

The rebuff was as complete as it was clever, and Sam salvaged what he could of his pride by turning and walking out of the dining room. He stood in the corridor for a moment, tugging at his vest of panther skin as he composed himself, and then walked to the office of Brown's. "I'll be obliged," he told the clerk on duty there, "if you'll have a bowl of soup and some bread sent to me in my room."

The young man saw the hurt in his face, and was stricken, but recovered swiftly. "I'll get it for you myself, sir," he said, and hurried out to the kitchen.

Sam mounted the stairs slowly, his legs heavy. Times had changed even more than he had recognized, and he smiled wryly as he recalled how naïve he had been when he had told Margaret that the political differences of statesmen in no way influenced their personal feelings or relationships.

It was true he and John C. Calhoun had made their peace, but he suspected that Calhoun, if still alive, would be one of the first to snub him now.

Andrew Jackson had been right, as always. A man divided all people into two categories: they were either his friends or his enemies, and he treated each faction accordingly. Removing his boots and his blue swallow-tailed coat of semi-military cut, Sam sighed and stared down at the floor. There was a significant difference between his situation and Jackson's. Old Hickory had never lacked friends, but it appeared to Sam that he stood alone because he refused to put sectional partisanship above the cause of the Union. But, no matter how difficult his situation, he could not and would not change. The principle at stake was far more important than his own comfort.

When his soup arrived he discovered he had lost his appetite, and let it grow cold.

Texas' Senators traveled together, as they had for years, and were met at the state border by a delegation of citizens inviting them to appear together on the platform before a mass meeting in Nacogdoches. Sam still thought of the town as home, and was delighted to accept, even though the stop meant a brief delay in his arrival home. But he quickly discovered that the atmosphere, even in the place he considered the friendliest to him, had changed drastically.

He was invited to spend the night with Dr. and Mrs. Irion as their guests, but only Robert and Anna were cordial to him. Scores of others, among them people who had been close associates since he had first arrived in Texas, either snubbed him or greeted him with icy reserve. Their silence was more damning than outright condemnation, and Anna Irion was embarrassed when twenty of the twenty-four people she invited to a barbecue supper preceding the Senators' public appearance made flimsy regrets.

Sam, although accustomed by now to unpleasantness elsewhere, was unprepared for the hostility of his former neighbors, and had to force himself to attend the rally in a pasture just outside Nacogdoches. More than three thousand Texans had gathered by the time he arrived with the Irions, flares tied to stakes providing the illumination, and the buzz of conversation died away as he mounted the platform to join Rusk, who had arrived a short time earlier. The applause that had greeted every public appearance he had made in almost twenty years was lacking, and the farmers, ranchers, and townspeople who had gathered for the occasion stared up at him with strangers' eyes.

"We can call off the meeting, Sam," the sympathetic Rusk said. "If you'd like, you might want to prepare folks for your stand through newspaper interviews before you make a public appearance."

Sam wiped his face with a bandanna. "I hadn't realized feelings here were so strong, so the sooner they hear the truth, the better it will be for both Texas and the country."

"I don't agree with you, remember."

"Speak your mind, Tom, and I'll do the same."

Rusk was introduced first, and made a brief address. Although he was classified elsewhere as a moderate, every mild statement he could make that seemed to favor the cause of the South was cheered, and he was given a standing ovation when he finished his address.

When Sam walked to the podium after being presented, there was only scattered applause, and Robert and Anna Irion, who had risen from their places in the front row to cheer him, fell silent when their neighbors glared at them.

Sam delivered the same speech he had made in so many Northern cities, larding it with local references, but the reaction was unique—and frightening. Open, hostile anger would have been preferable to the unmoving, almost indifferent silence of the throng. People who had twice elected him President of Texas and thrice sent him to the United States Senate refused to dishonor him or themselves by attacking him, but their lethargy was even more damning.

When Sam's plea to support the Union fell on deaf ears, he turned to subjects of domestic concern, including legislation he and Rusk had sponsored in the session of Congress just concluded. Although the subject matter was of vital interest, no one seemed to care.

"You'll want to hear," Sam said, seemingly unaware of the quiet, "that the entire Texas delegation introduced bills providing for the building of railroads that will link us with those parts of the United States already possessing such railroads. We secured the backing of other states, and Texas soon will enjoy the benefit of such rail transportation."

The audience came to life, cheered Rusk and then, in turn, each of Texas' members in the House of Representatives. Although Sam himself had written the bill and had guided it through Congress, his listeners gave him no credit for the vital role he had played.

He waited until the hubbub subsided, and then, to the astonishment of his listeners, he laughed with genuine amusement. "I've traveled on a great many railroad trains since I've been a Senator. I've made more trips on them than I can count. But I don't think I'll ever ride on a railroad in Texas."

He paused, surveyed his audience and laughed again. "If I don't get rode on a rail, I'll come off pretty damn well."

The audience was stunned, and then responded with a roar of approval. Virtually no one present agreed with Sam Houston's ideas, but he had demonstrated that, although rebuffed, he had not lost his sense of humor. No matter how inimical his views to his constituents, the waves of ever-rising applause indicated that he was still Texas' favorite son.

Sam's re-establishment of rapport with the electorate that had supported him for so long was brief. While resting at home with his family, he received news of the most startling reverse he had ever suffered during his long political career. The Texas Legislature, meeting in Austin, vigorously condemned the position taken by Senator Houston on the slavery question and related subjects. The vote was an astonishing seventy-seven to three. Even Ashbel Smith and others who had supported Sam in all matters through the years had parted company with him.

"This ends it," Sam told Margaret after reading the official message to her. "Times are out of joint, as someone wiser than I am once wrote, and this repudiation ends my usefulness to Texas. It castrates me, so I can do little good for the country, either."

"Will you resign from the Senate?" She placed her hand over his.

He needed no time for reflection. "No, I'll keep my seat until they throw me out. If I can calm just a few hotheads, if I can persuade just a few men to listen to reason, the living hell of tomorrow may be postponed for a short time." He freed his hand and placed it over his eyes, his head bowed.

Margaret was afraid he might be weeping, but couldn't be sure. "Don't feel too badly because of the Legislature's vote," she murmured.

"That isn't what bothers me. I've been lucky all these years. Eventually everyone in politics stubs his toe or sees a door slammed in front of his nose. I've been supported by many friends, and I've made few enemies." He stood suddenly, went to the nearest window and threw it open.

Margaret watched him as he stood before it, the breeze sifting through his thinning, white hair. She wanted to comfort him, to hold his head in her arms, but realized that now, more than ever before, his pride made it necessary for him to rely only on his own inner resources.

"I've always been in command of my own destiny," he said, breathing in fresh air and looking out across the pastures and fields of growing grain. "Even when I ran away from Tennessee —and myself—it was my own doing. In the more than twenty years I've been in Texas, I've always believed I could influence events, and so I have.

"But now the tide is too strong. I know what's right, and I've done everything in my power, but my hands are tied and there's a gag in my mouth. We're racing to our doom, to the disruption of the Union, and there seems to be nothing I can do to stop this terrible disaster."

"You've done all that any one man could do, Sam."

He turned, his face anguished, and pounded a fist into the palm of his other hand. "Andy Jackson would have found some way of stopping certain tragedy!"

"If you were President, you'd have more authority—"

"In odd moments I dreamed of becoming President of the United States, but it's too late for that. Men who want war will have no part of someone who demands peace." Sam's shoulders drooped, and when he spoke again, his tone was spiritless. "It looks as though I'm going to retire to private life at last—and under circumstances that will leave me frustrated until I die."

Senator Houston drank large quantities of coffee at his desk in the Senate chamber during the opening session of the 34th Congress, but abstained from comment in the acrimonious debates on Kansas and Nebraska that swirled around him. Privately, in the offices of his colleagues, he continued to use reason in vain attempts to curb the rising tempers that threatened to engulf the United States in a civil war, but he seemed resigned to the inevitability of failure.

Unable to support the Democratic nominees for President and Vice-President, James Buchanan of Pennsylvania and John C. Breckinridge of Kentucky, Sam gave his support to the candidates of the new American party, former President Millard Fillmore and Andrew Jackson Donelson. He campaigned for them in Texas, but was not surprised when Buchanan and Breckinridge won the overwhelming favor of his constituents, and won enough votes elsewhere to be elected.

"Jim Buchanan," Sam told Margaret when he came home after the inauguration in the spring of 1857, "is the weakest two-faced compromiser in the country. And I'm doing no good for anyone in the Senate. I've been discredited at home, I have no influence and I'm wasting my time there."

"You'll retire?"

"Maybe, maybe not. That depends on the voters of Texas."

Margaret caught her breath.

"Ever since we founded the Republic of Texas, people have

been saying that I'm the only issue here. Let's find out if that's true. The Democrats are running a full slate for state offices this year. Hardin Runnels, their candidate for governor, parrots every other war-hungry Southern Democrat. I aim to run against him —and I'll base my whole campaign on a stand in favor of the Union and the Constitution. There's a chance, maybe just an outside chance, that I'll win. If I lose, the whole country will know that Texas has been fooled by the hysteria of others. But one way or the other, I'll stir up some excitement."

Ignoring his sixty-four years, Sam conducted the most vigorous campaign of his life. Where roads were adequate, he traveled by buggy, and where necessary he used a horse. In towns where hotels or other lodgings were available, he slept in a bed, but most of his nights were spent in the open, rolled up in a blanket. He cooked most of his own meals, frying bacon or beef or venison in a pan over a fire he built for himself.

It was his aim to visit every county in the state, and, not sparing himself, he achieved his goal. In just one town did he fail to make an address. He and Senator Rusk, who was supporting the Democratic ticket, were scheduled to debate in Nacogdoches, and a huge crowd turned out to hear them. Both arrived on time, and met as they approached the podium from opposite directions.

Sam, bronzed after his travels, stopped short, and his heart went out to his old friend, who looked pale and wan after the recent death of his wife. Rusk halted, too, and the expectant crowd suddenly fell silent, aware that the drama they were witnessing was even more intense than they had anticipated.

Before them stood the only men who had ever represented Texas in the United States Senate, the conqueror of Mexico who had won Texas' independence and his closest associate. Now they stood on opposite sides of a high and bristling political fence, but the fiery rhetoric that the people of East Texas had hoped to hear did not develop.

Sam and Rusk moved toward each other, advancing slowly, almost warily. They shook hands and then, suddenly, embraced. Neither spoke, and there was no need for words. These two, who had worked in such close harmony for so many years, realized it was impossible to attack each other from a speakers' platform. No matter what their different political convictions, their friendship ran too deep.

With one accord they turned, walked to Rusk's carriage and climbed in. To the disappointment of the crowd they drove away together, still silent.

Sam had forgotten his horse, and Dr. Robert Irion took it home with him.

Not until the following morning did Sam arrive at the Irion house to retrieve his mount, and offering no explanation for the previous evening, left Nacogdoches within the hour. Neither he nor Rusk made any addresses in the town during the entire campaign.

On August 3, 1857, the impossible came to pass. The voters of Texas went to the polls, and Sam Houston lost his first election, winning 28,678 votes to Runnels' 32,552. No one was surprised that he had been beaten, but his foes and the press were astonished that he had made such a good showing. Elsewhere in the country men of every political persuasion asked a question no one could answer: Did Senator Houston's followers believe as he did, that the preservation of the Union was the paramount issue of the day, or were they merely demonstrating undeviating loyalty to him as a man?

Sam returned to Washington for the completion of his term in the Senate, and seemed to have accepted his defeat with good-humored resignation. "Texas didn't repudiate me," he said on several occasions. "She preferred somebody else, that's all. But I got enough votes to make it a real horse race."

He was looking forward to retirement, he said, and intended to spend the rest of his days living peacefully with his family. But the chances that any American would be able to lead a peaceful existence were becoming increasingly remote. The shrill, angry voices of the extremists in both the North and South were becoming louder, and even the moderates were saying that only a miracle could prevent a civil war.

Even the Senators forgot the Senate was one of the world's foremost gentlemen's debating societies, and exchanges became so acrimonious that Vice-President Breckinridge found it almost impossible to maintain order. Fights broke out on several occasions, and the distinguished gladiators had to be separated by embarrassed sergeants-at-arms.

Sam remained quiet as long as he could, realizing the futility of an appeal to reason, but at last he decided to make one more effort. He appeared in the Senate chamber wearing a vest of leopard skin, and announced to his colleagues that, like the leopard, he was incapable of changing his spots. His humor was appreciated, but his subsequent plea to save the Union was ignored.

Senator Rusk had died in midsummer of 1857, and his old friend paid glowing tribute to him in a moving eulogy. Thereafter Sam himself fell ill, and wrote to Margaret, "*I find it almost impossible to sleep, and when I finally drop off for short periods, I suffer frightful nightmares. Nothing in this world remains constant, other than my love for you and the children.*"

The family continued to grow. William Rogers Houston was born in May 1858, and late the following month his father came home for the summer. Sam looked into the possibility of moving to Chambers County, where the climate might impose less of a strain on Margaret, who was suffering from asthma, and with his ultimate retirement only a few months distant, he tried to concentrate on his own affairs as a farmer and rancher.

But he was interrupted by a steady stream of visitors from all parts of Texas, a bewildering mixture of judges and lawyers, newspaper publishers and factory owners, and, above all, ordinary citizens who claimed the right to a quarter of an hour of his time.

"They plague me," he told Margaret, "but I can't turn them away."

"What do they want?"

He could not meet her gaze. "They're disillusioned with Governor Runnels, all of them. And I'm surprised how many of them are afraid the Union is going to break up. They—well—they're all asking me to run again for governor when I come home to stay in March."

"No!" Margaret said. "You've done enough!"

"How much is enough? I know what you think, but don't nag at me, my dear. It may be that conditions will improve by next year, and we can spend all our time together."

In mid-December 1858, Sam left Texas on his final journey to Washington, arriving there soon after the New Year, in time for the reopening of Congress. A few days later he was surprised to receive an invitation to dinner from the President, written in Buchanan's own hand. For the better part of a year Sam had eaten lightly in the evening, having discovered that a heavy meal interfered with his sleep, but he could not refuse a request from the White House, and appeared on the appointed night, wearing a new suit of semi-military cut and his leopard vest.

The cares of office had aged the bachelor President. His hair was white, his face was lined and his complexion was pale, that of a man who seldom left his desk. But he was still dapper, and exerted himself as a host. Remembering that Sam drank no liquor, he offered his guest a glass of plum juice before they adjourned to the dining room, and he kept up a steady, inconsequential chatter.

The meal made Sam shudder, and he knew he would be awake all night. They began with a thick, peppery soup made with tripe, a Pennsylvania specialty, which was followed by platters of roasted Chesapeake Bay oysters made with a sauce that Buchanan, an enthusiastic amateur cook, had concocted himself. The main course was a roast of beef, served with dumplings and potatoes; they ate a salad of raw vegetables, then a pudding filled with raisins, and ended the dinner with cheese and fresh fruit. Sam would have been more than satisfied with nothing but the cheese and fruit.

Forcing himself to eat enough for the sake of politeness, he waited for Buchanan to bring up the subject of the meeting. But the President continued to reminisce about Jamie Polk and others they had both known, and when there was no change in the light tenor of the conversation by the time he poured himself a glass of port, Sam realized that he intended to discuss nothing of importance. The invitation had been extended as a graceful gesture to a senior member of the Senate who was on the verge of retirement.

Sam had no intention of losing the opportunity he had been given, however, and as soon as the President fell silent for a moment, he stirred. "I wonder, sir, if you'd think it improper to hear some advice? Whether you choose to heed it is another matter."

Buchanan had no choice, and knew it. "I'd be glad to hear anything you want to say to me, Sam."

"The country is drifting into anarchy, Mr. President, and unless something is done quickly—damned quickly—the North and South are going to leap at each other's throats. I've never believed in the inevitability of war, but I've found there's a point men reach that make it inevitable. Neither side is even listening to the other any more, and once their positions harden, they let their guns speak for them."

"I'm doing everything in my power to prevent a war," Buchanan said bleakly, "but for each forward step toward a reconciliation we make, there are several big leaps in the opposite direction. I'm well aware of my position, and I don't want to be known as the man who destroyed the United States, but nothing I've done has stopped the growth of these damnable hatreds."

"I don't believe any President is capable of stopping men from hating one another," Sam replied. "And it won't do much practical good to urge the whole country to start attending church more regularly. In the Mexican War, I'm sure the enemy prayed as hard as we did. Each side asked God to help them—and He helped the victors, as usual. No, something else is needed." Sam paused, then leaned forward. "I didn't spend much time here during Andrew Jackson's terms of office. How well did you know him, Mr. President?"

"I wasn't close to him, but I did enjoy a certain measure of his confidence, and I attended all of his regular meetings with the Democratic leaders of Congress."

"That's good enough, then. You knew him. I found it a great help to me, when I was President of Texas, to think about Old Hickory whenever I had a problem that I couldn't solve. I always asked myself what he'd do in a similar situation. And then I'd do it."

"What do you suppose he'd do if he were in office right now?" Buchanan carefully poured himself a little more port.

"First, he'd strengthen the Army garrisons in the trouble spots. New York. Philadelphia. Chicago. Richmond. Atlanta. Charleston."

"And Houston?"

"Maybe, maybe not. I'm still hoping I may be able to put out a few fires in Texas, although I'm none too sure I'll succeed." Sam frowned, and was lost in his own thoughts.

Buchanan had to prod the old man. "And then?"

"If necessary, I'd call more troops to the colors. I'd depend completely on volunteers, and I'd mix up my regiments. Put New Englanders and boys from Alabama and Georgia in the same units. I wouldn't trust a regiment of men from Massachusetts alone, any more than I would one from Mississippi alone. Balance them, if you see what I mean."

The President nodded.

"You'd hear protests from the different cities, of course. But offer no explanations, no excuses, no apologies. Just increase your garrisons until they're strong enough to handle any riots, any disturbances of any kind."

The President started to protest.

"I'm just telling you what I think Andrew Jackson would do if he found himself in your situation, sir."

Buchanan sat back in his chair again.

"Find an occasion to make a major public address, Mr. President. If there isn't a convenient one in the near future, create one. Invite the press. Make certain that every newspaper in the country knows you plan to make a speech of great importance. It doesn't have to be a long speech. In fact, the shorter you make it, the better."

"Jackson wasn't much of a speaker."

"He didn't have to be," Sam said grimly. "I'd inform the whole country it was my duty—that is, if I were Jackson—to uphold the Constitution. I'd tell them I wouldn't tolerate any more talk of secession in the South, or any more of that 'good riddance' rubbish that's being spewed out in the North. I'd tell them the Union is indivisible, and is going to stay that way."

"Strong medicine, Sam, and bitter."

"It's better than a war that ruins the country, Mr. President. Then I'd call in all the political leaders of every party—Senators, Congressmen, and the Governors of every state. I'd insist that each faction appoint a committee to negotiate. I'd take that committee off somewhere, away from public pressure, and I'd lock them up. Maybe in a hotel off in a seaside resort, or up in the mountains. I'd keep them there until they worked out a compromise that would make it possible for the North and South to live together in peace."

"Do you really think anyone would be satisfied with such an agreement?"

"You'll be criticized and damned by everyone. They may hang you in effigy in the Carolinas—and in Vermont and New Hampshire. But they'll abide by the compromise. The Army will see to that. Once the country has become a little accustomed to working together again, the men who worked out the agreement should submit it to Congress. Their own reputations and political futures will be at stake, so they'll work hard for the passage of the bills."

Buchanan smiled in appreciation of his guest's knowledge of the ways of politicians.

"You won't be popular, and neither will they. Any compromise made under duress very probably will have to be changed and modified later, perhaps several times. But the Army will continue to keep order, the hotheads will be gagged, and the crisis will simmer down. Even a drunk becomes sober for a spell when you pour a bucket of cold well water over his head."

"You're suggesting a form of national martial law," the President said.

"The kind Jackson established in New Orleans to keep order there during the War of 1812."

"I'm not sure it would be Constitutional."

"You'd be exercising your authority—under the Constitution —as commander-in-chief."

"But the Supreme Court might—"

"I haven't practiced much law for a great many years, Mr. President, so I wouldn't care to predict what the Supreme Court might rule. But the worst would be ended by the time the justices made a ruling."

Buchanan continued to look dubious.

"I'm just telling you what I—that is, what Andrew Jackson— would do." Sam knew that Buchanan was too timid to accept his bold suggestion, but made a final effort. "The Union is in peril, sir, under circumstances we've never before faced. That's why I beg you to do whatever you can, whatever you must, to save her."

The danger grew worse. Federal arsenals in both North and South were raided by masked men, and firearms disappeared. The cause of Abolitionists became respectable in the North, and men of standing helped in the efforts to spirit runaway slaves out of the country. It was rumored that wealthy Southerners were buying muskets in England by the thousands for "hunting trips," and gunpowder plants in Delaware and Massachusetts received more orders from private individuals than they could fill. The worst disaster in American history threatened the United States.

On March 3, 1859, the day prior to the end of his term, Senator Sam Houston asked for the floor of the upper chamber of Congress to make a final statement to his colleagues. Other Senators expected him to berate them, as he had done in the past, and the galleries, as always, were filled when the press, the diplomatic corps, and the public learned that the most colorful man in government service intended to deliver a valedictory address.

The first surprise of the day was Sam's appearance. He was dressed in unrelieved black, and when newsmen who met him on his way to the Senate chamber asked whether he was in mourning, he replied, "I hope it never will be necessary to mourn the death of the United States."

The galleries applauded when he appeared on the floor, and

Breckinridge could not quiet the crowd, so Sam raised his hands in a mute appeal, and the crowd obeyed him. There was more cheering when he was recognized, and again he had to ask for silence after the Vice-President's efforts to obtain order failed.

Abandoning his usual pose, Sam stood quietly beside his desk, and spoke in a low, calm voice. "As a Union man," he said, "I have ever maintained my position, and ever shall. I wish no prouder epitaph to mark the board or slab that may lie on my tomb than this: 'He loved his country. He was a patriot. He was devoted to the Union.'

"If it is for this that I have suffered martyrdom, it is sufficient that I stand at quits with those who have wielded the sacrificial knife."

The new junior Senator from Texas, Matthias Ward, interrupted to say he preferred disunion to the violation of the rights of states under the Constitution.

Sam glanced at him with momentary scorn, but spoke compassionately. "I hope that my honorable colleague does not suppose that I would submit to any infraction of our rights. Our rights are rights common to the whole Union. I would not see wrong inflicted on the North, or on the South, but I am for the Union, without any 'if' in the case, and my motto remains, 'It shall be preserved.' "

Those who had expected a long and fiery speech were disappointed when he bowed to the Vice-President, picked up a sheaf of papers from his desk and quickly left the Senate chamber.

Sam left Washington on March 10, 1859, and reached home on the first day of April. Word of his arrival spread rapidly, and within a few days the house was besieged by newsmen from Houston, Dallas, Austin, and a dozen smaller communities. All were welcomed by a youth who bore a striking resemblance to Sam and who, if he continued to grow, promised to be taller than his father.

"General Houston is seeing no one, gentlemen," he told them. "He's enjoying the first holiday of his life, and he has no statement to make on any subject."

"Is he going to run for Governor?" the reporters demanded.

"I don't know."

"What's your opinion?"

Sam, Junior's grin was infectious. "General Houston makes up his own mind at all times," he said. "My opinion would be worthless."

"We'd still like to hear what you think."

"Well, I'm not old enough to vote. But I'm willing to bet my one-year-old colt worth seventy-five dollars against one of those new one-dollar gold pieces from California that if the General decides to be a candidate, he can beat Governor Runnels or anyone else who runs against him."

The brief interview was reprinted in virtually every Texas newspaper, and Sam, who was spending most of his time in the fields, interrupted the supervision of the ranch to summon his eldest son into his study.

"Boy," he asked severely, "who authorized you to make a statement to the newspapers?"

"Nobody, Pa."

Sam was secretly pleased that his son showed no fear. It was far better to make a courageous mistake than to cringe before superior authority. "You realize that most people believe I was responsible for what you said, and that they think I'll run."

"I'm not surprised that's how they interpret it."

"Your ma is mighty upset."

The youth was immediately contrite. "I'm sorry for that. I hate to see her worry. But she always frets about you, no matter what you do."

Sam had to admit he was right. "What makes you so sure I could beat Governor Runnels?"

"I've listened to the fathers of my friends when they visit school. I've listened when I've gone cattle buying for you. People are scared, Pa. They talk big and proud, but they've paid attention to all you've been saying in your speeches for years, and they're afraid that if there's secession in the South—and war— that we'll lose."

"There's no chance we'd win. It would take the South one hundred years to recover."

Sam, Junior, hesitated. "I've made up my own mind, Pa. If war comes, I'll fight for the South."

"I'm not surprised." Sam wanted to throw a protective arm around his son's shoulders, but forced himself to refrain. "You've got to live with your own conscience, boy, and if you felt it was right to fight for the South, then it would be right for you."

"What would you do, Pa?"

"Pray for you."

"Thank you, sir. But that's not what I mean. I've heard it said all over that you'd be offered a commission as a Major General in the North's Army."

"I'm too old."

"If you were younger," his son insisted, "would you accept?"

"I wouldn't fight against the South, and couldn't bear arms against Texas, if she joined in the secession movement. You know that, boy."

"Would you accept a commission in the Southern Army, then?"

"I'd rather be hanged from the nearest tree than do anything to destroy the Union!"

Sam, Junior, smiled. "Now you know why I talked to the newspaper people, Pa. I've understood right along how you feel."

Sam raised a white eyebrow.

"You're going to run because you hope you can keep Texas in the Union, no matter what the rest of the South might do. And there are so many men who are willing to follow your lead in a time of crisis, men who have followed you for many years, long before I was born, that you'll be elected."

"A feeling for politics is in the Houston blood," Sam said. "It may be I'll give you a chance to find out if your hunches are right."

"You'll run," his son repeated. "I know you will, because you've never in your life backed away from a fight."

On June 3, 1859, after a holiday of two months, General Sam Houston issued a brief statement announcing his candidacy for

Governor. He refused to campaign actively, however, saying that after a generation of active service for Texas, everyone knew where he stood. He consented to make only one campaign speech, at Nacogdoches, the only major town in which he had not spoken two years earlier.

There, using none of the oratorical tricks which had added to his renown, he spoke in stark, simple terms. His record, he said, was his campaign platform, and the whole state knew what to expect from him if he was elected. There was only one issue, he declared, union or disunion.

Returning home after making the address, he devoted all of his time to his family and the affairs of his ranch. Regardless of what might happen in the election, he said, he had to think of his family's future, and he expanded his holdings, bought more cattle and planted another three hundred acres of corn.

The election, held in August 1859, returned Texas' most favored son to public office. Sam received 33,475 votes to 27,487 for Runnels. "*Astonishing though it may seem*," wrote the *National Intelligencer* of Washington, "*Sam Houston has won his greatest triumph. Those who were ready to bury him will soon discover there has never been a livelier, more stubborn, more determindedly patriotic 'corpse.'*"

Sam took the oath of office as Governor of Texas in Austin on December 21, in the presence of his entire family. Since the quarters provided for the state's chief executive were inadequate for such a large brood, however, Mrs. Houston and the younger children returned home soon after the Christmas holidays, and only Sam, Junior, remained in Austin with his father. But they came back to Austin sooner than they anticipated when Margaret found she was going to have another child.

"This time," her husband said, "we're going to be together," and rented a house large enough to accommodate the family.

In the handling of the state's domestic affairs Governor Houston's hand was firm and sure. He knew Texas better than anyone else, and the Legislature indicated it would accept his recommendations on taxation and internal improvements, boundary surveys and the granting of charters to railroads.

But storms began to develop in other areas. Only forty-eight hours after Sam took office he learned that bills were being prepared in both the Senate and House to enlarge the corps of Rangers from three companies to four regiments, each to consist of eight hundred men.

"What reasons do the sponsors of the bills give for the expansion?" he asked Washington Miller, who had returned to work for him as his executive assistant.

"They claim they're concerned about the security of our borders."

"Against Indians or Mexicans?" Sam asked, his voice heavy with sarcasm.

"They didn't say, Governor."

"It's plain enough. They want to have a military force ready for duty if there's a war between the South and the North. Well, I'll have no part of such tomfoolery."

"They know you'll veto any bills they pass, but they think they may have enough votes to override your veto."

"Tell them from me not to waste their time," Sam said. "They're dealing with Sam Houston now. If they enlarge the Ranger corps over my veto, I'll veto every appropriations bill they pass to provide funds for an enlarged corps. I'll refuse to build new barracks, provide uniforms or arms or pay for more troops. I'll put so many obstacles in their way that, no matter how hard they try, they'll fail. As long as I'm Governor, Texas won't make one move toward disunion!"

He displayed an equally firm attitude on the last day of 1859, when he received a letter from Governor William H. Gist of South Carolina, asking the Governors of other Southern states to work together toward the secession that, Gist said, was "inevitable."

Sam scribbled a reply in the margin of Gist's letter, writing in large letters. "*After this,*" he wrote, "*save your ink and stationery, and don't send your seditious correspondence to me. As long as I hold office, Texas will remain in the Union!*"

NINE

1860–63

The Buchanan administration proved itself incapable of dealing with the inflamed sectional feelings that were leading the United States toward Civil War, and talk of secession was heard everywhere in the South. During this period of impending, growing crisis, the political parties held their conventions for the forthcoming presidential election. Many Northerners who favored the preservation of the Union, and who sought a candidate capable of garnering Southern votes, felt that Sam Houston was the one man who met their qualifications.

Northern and Southern Democrats were at odds, unable to agree on a candidate, and the Southerners made it plain they would not accept Senator Stephen A. Douglas. Politicians, supported by many newspapers, began to clamor for Sam, and the New York *Herald* said that if the Democrats failed to nominate him, he would be the "ideal candidate" of a new National Unity party.

The Dallas *Herald* violently disagreed, "*No man is more dangerous to our principles*," it declared, "*not even Seward or Lincoln of the new Republican party of the North.*"

Sam received hundreds of letters urging him to run, and many pro-Union men in Texas called on him. He expressed his thanks, both by mail and in person, but refused either to commit himself or withdraw his name.

"I suppose a last-minute miracle could take place," he told Margaret. "If there are enough people everywhere to form a National Unity party, I'd be tempted to become its candidate. But the party will have to be formed by the people, not the politicians, or it'll become just another sectional group."

"If you feel you can do some good, shouldn't you encourage them?"

"General Jackson didn't," he replied. "Neither did I when I was elected President of Texas. Politicians try to create public opinion instead of responding to the genuine will of the people, and I'll have no part of such trickery. If the Union is to be saved, it will be because there's a mass of voters everywhere in the country who want it saved. A President is no stronger than the principles of the men who elect him."

The Democrats were unable to agree, and their convention, which was being held in Charleston, ended in confusion. The Northerners adjourned to Baltimore, where they nominated Stephen A. Douglas, and the Southerners went to Richmond, where they made John C. Breckinridge their candidate. Meanwhile the Republicans, meeting in Chicago, nominated a relative unknown, former Congressman Abraham Lincoln of Illinois, whom the South considered its great and unyielding foe.

A group calling itself the Constitutional Union party also held a convention in May, and some of its leaders sounded out Sam on the possibility of his becoming its candidate. His hopes flared momentarily, but he lost interest when he learned that the party intended to ignore the bitter dispute between North and South. Disgusted and virtually convinced that his worst fears would materialize, he issued a brief statement:

"*If my name should be used in connection with the presidency, the movement must originate with the people themselves, as well as end with them. I will not consent to have my name submitted to any convention, nor would I accept a nomination if it were tendered me and procured by contrivance, trick or management. If such a thing were possible, that I could be elected and not in*

*harmony with the voice of the majority of the American people,
I would hold the position a single day, but retire to private station,
solaced by self-respect."*

Former Senator John Bell of Tennessee received the nomination of the Constitutional Union party to make the 1860 election a four-way race.

As the campaign progressed, Douglas became alarmed by the Southern threats of secession, and made a speaking tour through the region, urging that men of patriotic good will heed President Jackson's determined call to preserve the Union. But it was too late. Lincoln carried the North, Breckinridge won the support of nine Southern states, including Texas, while the border states cast their votes for either Douglas or Bell. Lincoln was elected, and the secessionist movement became an irresistible tide in the South.

"Now we're in for it," Sam said when he first heard the election results.

On November 8, 1860, the banner of the United States was hauled down in Galveston, and the Lone Star flag of Texas was hoisted in its place. Other cities and towns soon did the same, and Sam wrote a letter to the authorities of each community. He, more than any man, was proud of the Lone Star banner, he declared; it had been his ensign when he had won independence from Mexico, and it had fluttered proudly over the Republic he had founded. Nevertheless, he said firmly, no state had the right to secede from the Union, and men who took down the American flag were acting illegally.

His voice was unheeded, and other towns followed the example of Galveston and Houston, Dallas and Waco. But the Stars and Stripes continued to fly over the executive offices of the Governor.

On December 20, South Carolina seceded from the Union.

The following day the leaders of the Texas Legislature called on Sam and demanded that he call the state Senate and House into special session at once. He knew it was no longer possible to temporize, but said that he would not take members away from their homes during the Christmas season. So he set the date one month ahead, and issued a formal summons for the meeting on January 28, 1861.

"I'll yield to any decision the people make," he told his visitors, "but if Texas insists on seceding, I'd rather see her form a separate Republic again rather than join the rest of the South."

Sam's friends marveled at his calm. Determined to make a final effort to prevent the secession of Texas, he traveled everywhere in the state during the month prior to the meeting of the Legislature, and in Galveston, Houston, Waco, and other cities he told large audiences to reconsider before they committed treason.

Washington Miller and others who had long been close to Sam urged him to surround himself with a company of Rangers at all times, but he laughed at their fears. "Do you think Texans would lynch me? You're mad. They may disagree with me, but there isn't a man in the state who'd lay a hand on me."

He was right. The crowds that gathered to hear him speak heard him in polite silence, then cheered the cause of secession, but he went everywhere unarmed and unescorted, and was subjected to no abuse other than an occasional jeer. "*We disagree with Governor Houston in many matters,*" the Dallas *Herald* said, "*but we salute his courage. We respect all he has done for Texas in the past, even if we find his present position mistaken.*"

Sam immediately sent a letter to the editors of the newspaper, challenging them to print it. "*You refer to my 'present position,'*" he wrote, "*but I have not changed. I stand now where I have always stood, unalterably, for the preservation of the Union.*"

He returned to Austin five days before the Legislature was scheduled to meet, still unruffled, still indifferent to personal danger.

But Margaret knew his real feelings, and wrote to her mother, "*General Houston seems cheerful and hopeful through the day, but in the still watches of the night I hear him agonizing in prayer for our distracted country.*"

A tremendous crowd, described by the newspapers as the largest to gather in one place in Texas' history, assembled in Austin to watch the members of the Legislature convene. The throng was so dense that members needed the help of Rangers and constables to reach the Capitol, and each was applauded as he mounted the steps.

One man walked alone. He was recognized by all who saw him, and the crowd parted to let him pass. Hotheads who were demanding instant secession and promising death to those who stood in their way were within striking distance of him, but did not touch him. He smiled steadily, seemingly unaware of the hostility of the people, and occasionally bowed, first to the right and then to the left, as he made his way to the Capitol. The Rangers who formed a tight cordon at the base of the stairs saluted and let him pass, and he mounted the steps slowly, his back bent.

It shocked many who watched him when they realized he was an old man, that every step he took was an effort.

Then he turned, and it became evident that he intended to speak. Men began to jeer, but he raised both hands in a mute plea for silence, and there were so many in the crowd who remembered all he had done for Texas that they quieted their neighbors. At last all was still, and the members of the Legislature crowded onto the portico behind him to hear what he planned to say.

Sam's voice was resonant, surprisingly strong. "I am now an aged man," he declared. "My locks have become white in toiling, as I believe, for the liberties of mankind.

"Were I young, that I might look forward to the future, feeling that whatever danger might come my strong arm would be at hand to defend my family, I should feel less anxiety than I do at present.

"The years that I will have to endure the misfortunes of civil war will be but few.

"If I could feel that with the close of my career would end the miseries of my people, I could share your misfortunes with patience. But to feel that the perils of revolution must continue, that war with its attendant horrors of bloodshed, rapine, and devastation must still be visited upon us, would embitter my last moments.

"After living to witness the dissolution of the best government that has ever existed in the history of civilization, I would sink to the grave without a hope that freedom would be regenerated or our posterity ever enjoy again the blessings with which we have parted. Let us pause and ponder well before we take action outside of the Constitution."

He bowed slightly, and then walked down the stairs, his head high. Again the crowd parted to let him pass, and there were many who saw tears in his eyes.

On February 1 the Legislature adopted, by a vote of one hundred sixty-six to seven, an ordinance of secession. A provision was made for the submission of the ordinance to the voters of the state on February 23.

A committee of legislative leaders called on Governor Houston, carrying the original, embossed copy of the ordinance, and obviously expected that he would refuse to sign it.

Instead he picked up his quill pen and dipped it into the jar of ink that stood beside him on his desk. "I'm required by law to sign this," he said. "But let me remind you, gentlemen, that Texas is still in the Union, and until she secedes I'm bound by oath to support the Constitution of the United States."

The legislators shuffled uncomfortably, and one of them asked, "Does that mean you'll call in Union troops, Governor?"

Sam's smile was bleak. "It does not, sir! It means that I shall guard all Federal property in the state until such time as Texas is no longer in the Union. But I hope," he added, his voice rising, "that you know me well enough to realize—and believe—that under no circumstances will I be a party to the shedding of fraternal blood, Texas blood. It may be that I stand almost alone here in my love for my country, but I yield to no man in my love for Texas."

The referendum on February 23 was emphatically conclusive, although many pro-Union Texans were too discouraged to vote. A total of 46,129 cast their ballots for secession, while only 14,697 opposed it. The official tally, contrary to Texas custom, did not bear the signature of the Governor.

When Sam came home for dinner on the night of March 1 he appeared on the verge of exhaustion. He stumbled as he walked into the house, his eyes were glazed, and he scarcely heard the younger children who, after their custom, clustered around him and clamored for his attention. Nan, acutely sensitive to her father's moods, managed to lead the younger children away.

Margaret asked her husband no questions, but suggested they defer their dinner until the children had eaten and gone to bed.

"No," Sam said. "There must be no difference between this night and any other."

The family ate together, as usual. Then Sam read passages from the Bible, and the children commented on what they had heard. Their father appeared to have recovered, and displayed his usual vigor as he led their discussion. Not until he had heard their prayers, kissed them goodnight and accompanied Margaret into the parlor of the rented house for coffee did he slump.

"I'm sending a legal notice to the owners of this place, telling them we intend to vacate within ten days."

Margaret's hand was steady as she poured their coffee. "That soon, dear?"

"A state convention has been called to ratify Texas' secession, and will meet later this week. Most of the delegates are members of the Legislature, of course. It's a formality. First they'll secede, then they'll transfer Texas' allegiance to the new Confederate States of America." He mopped his face with a bandanna.

He had eaten so little in recent days that Margaret placed a platter of cookies she had baked that afternoon near his saucer.

"I'm tempted to delay them."

"Could you, Sam?"

"I've forgotten more parliamentary tricks than all of them—in their combined wisdom—will ever know."

"Why do that? They'll just hate you all the more."

"I had a letter today from President-elect Lincoln." He reached into the inner pocket of his coat.

"Tell me," Margaret said. "I never understand all that high-sounding language you use in government talk."

"Lincoln says it in language even the children could understand. He asks me to put off the secession by any means I can. Then he offers, as soon as he's inaugurated this week, to send an expedition of Federal troops to Texas by sea, and hold the state in the Union by force, if necessary."

Margaret was too frightened to speak.

"Tomorrow," Sam said, "I'll be sixty-eight. I'm too old. If I were fifty, I'd do it. The Union forces would rally, and the secessionists would calm down in a mighty hurry. But at my age I can't do a damned thing except watch the world I know fall apart." He covered his face with his hands for a moment, then sat upright and forced himself to sip some coffee. "Rubbish!"

Margaret looked at him in bewilderment.

"I tried to give up self-pity when I gave up liquor. You and I know the truth. It wouldn't matter if I were forty—or eighty. I couldn't bring in Union troops to shoot down men who served with me at San Jacinto, or the sons of the men who died at the Alamo."

She was silent for a moment. "Have you answered Mr. Lincoln?"

"I'll write him tomorrow morning."

Margaret pushed the plate of cookies still closer to him. "Will you announce what you've done?"

He shook his head. "Why make a bad situation even worse? It's already more unpleasant than you know."

She tried to appear calm as she looked at him.

"They're going to require every office-holder to take an oath of allegiance to the Confederacy. Those who refuse will be branded as traitors."

Margaret caught her breath.

"If my life depends on it—and it may—I'll never do it," Sam said. "I can't."

Texas seceded from the Union on March 4, 1861, the seventh Southern state to take such action, and joined the Confederacy. A formal ceremony was scheduled for March 16, at which time all state officials, elected and appointed, would take the oath. The galleries filled as soon as the doors were opened, and a huge crowd gathered outside to watch the arrival of the state's leaders. General Albert Sidney Johnston, who had already resigned his commission in the Union Army, was given an ovation, as was

Lieutenant Governor Edward Clark, who was expected to become the state's chief executive later in the day.

There was a murmur as a familiar figure arrived at the Capitol alone, on horseback. Sam, who had resisted the urge to wear his old uniform of Texas' military commander-in-chief, was somberly attired, and under his arm he carried a thick stick of raw pine wood. He went into the building, nodding soberly to old friends and acquaintances, and headed for the basement cloakroom, where he seated himself in a comfortable chair. Then, taking a knife from his boot-top, he began to whittle the stick of pine.

A few minutes later the gathering in the House chamber on the first floor was called to order, every word plainly audible through the open doors and echoing corridors. The purpose of the meeting was explained, and the chairman announced that the clerk would call each official forward by name to take the oath to the Confederacy.

Sam whittled steadily, his hands firm.

"Sam Houston!" The clerk's voice was loud and very clear.

There was no sound in the cloakroom but the whisper of the knife blade cutting through the soft pine.

"Sam Houston!" The clerk was more insistent.

Sam remained silent, and only his hands moved.

"Sam Houston!" the clerk called again, his impatience manifest.

The knot of men clustered at the cloakroom entrance to watch the unexpected drama saw no change in the old man's expression.

The silence in the House chamber was as prolonged as it was intense. Then the clerk called, "Edward Clark!"

Sam slipped the knife into his boot-top, carefully put the stick into his hip pocket and left the building. No one approached him as he went to the hitching-post, mounted his horse and rode off toward the rented house.

Margaret was waiting for him at the front door, as were Sam, Junior, and Nan. He had forbidden any of them to accompany him, and they had suffered agonies of dread, but tried to hide their relief when they saw that he was unharmed.

"It's done," he said, dismounting and walking toward them. "We can go home now."

Rain had fallen every day for a month, the grass in the pastures was green and sturdy, and the corn and wheat were growing tall. The dust on the road beyond the front fence had settled, the blossoms on the fruit trees in the yard were fragrant, and the quiet was so all-pervading that it was difficult to believe that elsewhere in America men were killing one another.

The old man sat in his favorite rocker on the porch, a serape protecting his shoulders from the cool breezes, and smiled at his eldest daughter, who stood beside him, a pile of mail in her hands. "I'll answer all those letters tomorrow, Nan."

"If you'd like, Papa, I'll be glad to answer them for you. I imagine you'll be saying what you've said in all the others."

Sam nodded. "I'm refusing all speaking invitations. I won't say or do anything that will make this situation worse. But I'll write my own letters, Nan. The invitations were extended to me, and this war hasn't robbed me of my good manners. The least I can do is reply to them myself."

Nan wanted to protest that the joints in his fingers were swollen and that she knew it had become painful for him to scribble more than a few lines. But she realized his pride was more important to him than the discomfort he might suffer, so she murmured, "Whatever you say, Papa."

"Put them on my desk, will you?" There was no need for him to explain that, by afternoon, he was too tired to think clearly.

A single horseman, a tall officer in the gray of the Confederate Army, was moving down the road in the direction of the house.

Sam glanced at him idly, and thought he looked vaguely familiar, but dismissed the young rider from his mind. There were so many men in uniform these days.

Nan followed the direction of her father's gaze, looked stricken for an instant, then guilty, and dashed into the house without saying another word.

Sam looked after her in puzzlement and sighed. Then, as the

horseman drew still nearer, the old man knew him from the easy way he sat his mount.

Sam, Junior, leaned down, unlatched the gate and rode into the grounds. Then he dismounted, and holding himself self-consciously erect, approached his father.

Sam should have known the boy had no intention of returning to his studies in Austin. "Stand at ease, Lieutenant Houston," he said.

"Thank you, sir." Sam, Junior, removed his hard-visored uniform cap and wiped a film of perspiration from his forehead.

"What's your unit, boy?"

"Ashbel Smith's Bayland Guards, Pa."

"Well. Ashbel is a mite old for active service, but he's a good officer. You can learn from him."

"I intend to." Sam, Junior, took a deep breath. "You're not angry, Pa?"

"You gave me fair warning before the war started, remember? I didn't try to persuade you to change your mind then, and I sure as all hell won't try now. Let me look at you." Sam beckoned him closer, then inspected him carefully. "Always carry a dusting cloth so you can keep your boots shined."

"Yes, sir."

"Don't let your brass tarnish. Once it gets bad, it'll be twice as hard to clean."

"Yes, sir."

"Now, let me see your pistol." The old man took it and examined it with the care of a professional soldier. "How does it shoot?"

"Just fine, Pa. Maybe you'd like to try it yourself, out back."

Sam shook his head, and managed to refrain from saying he could not force himself to fire a Confederate weapon. "You're the one who needs to be satisfied with it, boy." He paused for a moment. "Your ma and Nan knew what you were going to do, I reckon."

His son straightened, but made no reply.

Sam chuckled. "Just as I thought, but I won't let on that I know."

Sam, Junior, grinned weakly.

Suddenly the old man's voice became sharp. "Where's your sword?"

"I don't have one yet. I'll have to buy one."

"The pay of Second Lieutenants isn't very high. Maybe I can save you some money."

Sam, Junior, tried to thank him.

A wave of a gnarled hand cut him short. "I have two or three up in the attic, but they don't have any special significance. To tell you the truth, I can't really remember when I carried which of them. How long will you be home?"

"I've got to report back to camp tomorrow morning."

"Then tonight, after supper, we'll get the sword that's in my study."

The young man's eyes widened. "That's the one you carried at San Jacinto, Pa!"

Sam nodded.

"I—I can't take it, Pa. I mean, knowing how you feel about the war—"

"It seems to me," Sam interrupted in a harsh voice, "that when my son is going off to fight for a cause he believes in, the least I can do for him is give him my best sword."

Blinking back his tears, Sam, Junior, could only mutter, "Thank you."

"Maybe it will help balance a liability I've already given you, boy—your name. Anyone called Sam Houston isn't going to find life easy for him in the Confederate Army."

The South took the military initiative, and in the first months of the war appeared to be winning. Many of the high-ranking professional soldiers transferred their allegiance to the Confederacy, and Texas, which had contributed more volunteers than any other Southern state, dreamed of victory. But the bloodshed and devastation that Sam had predicted proved him an accurate prophet, and gradually the North's greater reserves of manpower and industrial potential began to turn the tide.

In the western theater of war the Union forces proved themselves particularly vigorous, the Confederates resisted with all their might, and in Tennessee, Arkansas, and Missouri a series of violent, major engagements were fought. In February 1862 Federal troops captured Fort Donelson, Tennessee; three weeks later a bloody engagement took place at Pea Ridge, Arkansas, and early in April both sides were exhausted by the Battle of Shiloh, in Tennessee. Confederate partisans in Texas became less exuberant as the casualty lists mounted; the price of the war was becoming painfully evident.

One evening in mid-April Sam and Margaret were sitting in the parlor of their Huntsville house, a pile of newspapers beside them as Sam tried to determine from the communiqués issued by front-line commanders just what was happening in the war.

"I've never been so torn," he said, looking haggard and very tired. "In one breath I hope the Union will win quickly, so the suffering will stop, but a moment later I find myself hoping that our Texas regiments are smashing the enemy. Who is the enemy in this damned war? On both sides we're all our own enemies." He fell silent again, and made some marks on a map of Tennessee with a crayon.

The sound of hoofbeats caused him to raise his head, and he exchanged inquiring glances with Margaret when the gate creaked open.

"Stay where you are, dear. I'll go." Margaret rose swiftly and went to the door.

Sam tried to hide his irritation. It was disconcerting, sometimes galling to realize that everyone in the family tried to save him unnecessary steps.

There was the sound of voices in the entrance hall, and then Margaret came back into the room, followed by a tall officer in a worn Confederate uniform. He wore the insignia of a Colonel on his shoulders, his expression was grave, and a spasm of fear shot through Sam.

"This is Colonel Moore," Margaret said, trying to remain calm.

The Colonel stood at attention and saluted.

Sam responded automatically, and raised his own hand in return.

"Please sit down, Colonel," Margaret said, "and let me get you some coffee. Or you might prefer something stronger."

"In a moment, ma'am, thank you." The Colonel remained standing. "I have the honor to command the regiment in which Lieutenant Houston has been serving."

"We know." Sam was finding it difficult to breathe.

"Ordinarily we notify the nearest kin of casualties by letter, but you're no ordinary citizen, General."

Margaret moved closer to her husband and touched his shoulder; he reached up and took her hand.

"Lieutenant Houston was badly wounded at Shiloh," the Colonel said. "Forgive me for putting it to you so bluntly, but I don't know any other way. I've been trying for days to—"

"We understand." Sam made an effort to steady himself. "Will he—"

"The doctors say Lieutenant Houston will recover, sir, but it will be six months, maybe longer, before he's fit for duty again."

Sam relaxed, and guided Margaret to a place beside him on the sofa.

"He's being sent home on furlough, General. I'm sorry I can't tell you when he'll be here. They'll probably hold him for another few weeks in the hospital."

Margaret found her voice. "What hospital, Colonel?"

"He's at Vicksburg, ma'am. All of the critical cases were moved there."

Margaret was not satisfied. "Is he still in danger?"

"I give you my word he'll recover, Mrs. Houston. We held off notifying you until we knew."

She dabbed at her eyes with a handkerchief she took from her sleeve.

"Now, Colonel," Sam said, "I hope you'll sit down."

Moore eased himself into a chair.

With an effort Sam hauled himself to his feet. He went to the sideboard, where he had been keeping liquor again since losing his own desire for alcohol, and poured the officer a stiff drink of whisky. "I reckon you can use this."

"Yes, sir. I can." The Colonel grinned.

Sam returned to his place beside Margaret. "Is there anything else you can tell us?"

"He was hurt leading a charge—the fourth that he led. The other officers of his company had been either killed or wounded, so he'd taken command."

In spite of his concern, Sam smiled.

"Lieutenant Houston isn't well enough to write, but he gave me two messages, one for each of you. Ma'am, he wants you to know that the Bible you gave him when he left home saved his life. He was carrying it in his breast pocket, and it deflected the bullet that hit him."

Margaret closed her eyes.

"General, he asked me to tell you that he's brought no shame on your sword."

"It doesn't sound as though he had. What's your professional opinion of his battlefield conduct, Moore?"

"I was busy in another sector, sir. But General Ferguson—who served with you at San Jacinto—had the privilege of seeing him in action—"

"I remember Ferguson."

"In his commendation sent to the War Department at Richmond, General, he said, 'Blood will tell.' And from the reports I heard, I was happy to approve Lieutenant Houston's promotion to Captain."

"A double promotion?" Sam could not conceal his pride.

"He's a little young to command a company, but he's earned the right, General."

Sam could not remember when he had been so pleased, but his joy was short-lived. His son had won glory in his own right, but had earned his reputation at the expense of fellow-Americans from the North. Even personal triumph could lead only to tragedy in a civil war.

In March 1863, after his son's return to active duty, Sam visited the city that bore his name and old friends there persuaded him to make a speech. Hundreds attended, and were surprised to see him so frail, to hear him speak in such a feeble voice. But he expressed his theme in a few pungent words. "This frightful war cannot last forever, for which I thank God," he declared. "One day—and I do not believe it is too far off—the South and North will be reunited. I earnestly urge all men of good will to prepare for that day. It is difficult, I know, to think of peace when our sons still fight in battle. But think of the future we must! It is inevitable that Americans will become reconciled, and will reunite under one flag."

In his private conversations he spoke even more boldly. The cause of the South was lost, he said, because neither Great Britain nor France, which had promised aid to the Confederacy, had any intention of entering the conflict. "The end is in sight," he said, "but I won't live to see it."

Early in April, after his return home, he made out his will, leaving his estate to Margaret, but specifying that Sam, Junior, was to keep the San Jacinto sword.

On July 4, 1863, after a campaign that had lasted for many months, the Confederate citadel of Vicksburg, Mississippi, fell to the Union forces commanded by General Ulysses S. Grant. More than thirty thousand starving, sick Southern soldiers were forced to surrender, and the entire Mississippi River was opened to Northern traffic.

"The Confederacy," Sam said, "can't survive this blow. I know now that the Union will be restored—but at a cost so great I can't think about it. My God, Margaret, how my heart aches for Texas."

Those were the last words he spoke on the subject closest to him. On the morning of July 8, only a few hours after he had learned of Vicksburg's fall, he fell ill with what appeared to be a common head cold. But Margaret, aware of a strange lethargy he had never before shown, became concerned.

Sam's condition gradually became worse, and his indifference alarmed Margaret; their eldest son, who was temporarily stationed in Texas, came home on an emergency leave of absence. Dr. Irion was summoned, but, by the time he arrived on July 15, Sam had slipped into a coma.

It was impossible to rouse him through the long day and night, and before dawn the next morning the whole family gathered in his bedchamber. The children listened as Margaret read aloud from the Bible in a voice her eldest daughter later described as incredibly calm.

At dawn Sam opened his eyes, saw his wife sitting beside him, and murmured, "Margaret."

She stopped reading, looked at him and saw the familiar expression of love in his eyes.

After what seemed like a long time, he said distinctly, "Texas."

She nodded, knowing that the end was at hand.

Sam stirred slightly, and for an instant raised the finger on which he was wearing the gold ring his mother had given him so many years earlier. "Honor," he whispered, and closed his eyes again.

AN AFTERWORD

The formidable Sam Houston, a giant among American giants, has left the student of his life a perplexing legacy. Although he was a man who habitually kept his own counsel and rarely explained his actions, the years he spent in Texas have been well documented.

Scores of books have been written on that period. Indeed, the history of Texas from the beginning of her fight for independence from Mexico until her secession from the Union in 1861 is, in a sense, the biography of Sam Houston. His valiant but vain fight to preserve the Union, and his subsequent refusal to take an oath of allegiance to the Confederacy was a gallant episode that has long fascinated historians, among them President John F. Kennedy, who described it in moving terms in his *Profiles in Courage* (Harper & Bros., 1955).

The years prior to Houston's arrival in Texas, however, are shrouded in mystery that, I suspect, may have been of his own making. Certainly he never offered a satisfactory explanation of his brief, unhappy marriage to Eliza Allen and its dramatic aftermath. At best the student can pick up small clues, fit them together as best he can and interpret them in his own way. No two scholars have drawn the same conclusions.

Since this book is a work of fiction, I have elected to write of this extraordinary relationship in the way that appears logical to me. There can be no doubt that Eliza was in love with another man, that her husband discovered it very soon after their marriage and that the blow to his ego was shattering.

It is useless—but fascinating—to speculate on what might have happened had Sam Houston not disappeared into the wilderness to spend several sodden years with the Cherokee. Would he, the heir-apparent, have succeeded Andrew Jackson as President of the United States? The question forever will remain unanswered.

I believe, however, that those years were Houston's Gethsemane. His correspondence during that time reveals little of the travail he suffered, but when he emerged from his trials and went to Texas, he was reborn. Prior to the tragedy of his first marriage he had been an exceptionally able politician. From the day he first reached Texas he became a living legend, a genius who could do no wrong, an incomparable statesman, politician, and military leader. Although his height of six feet, two inches has been proved by many historians, it is small wonder that his fellow Texans, and millions of other Americans as well, thought he stood at least six feet, six inches tall.

Moody and melodramatic, withdrawn yet renowned as an exhibitionist, sentimental but hard-bitten, Sam Houston is one of the most bewildering of paradoxes. His life becomes clear only when we see him in the focus supplied by those who most influenced his life: the father who was something of a myth to Houston himself; Andrew Jackson, the father-substitute whom he revered above all men; the mother he respected and feared; and, above all, Margaret, his second wife, who gave him the love he so desperately needed.

Inasmuch as Houston excelled in everything he did, the reader will not be surprised to learn that—at least in my opinion—he was his own best biographer. His many letters and speeches to be found in the Archives Collection of the University of Texas Library, in the Library of Congress and in lesser collections explain the man, his thoughts and deeds as no one else has been able to do in more than a century.

Texans, of course, long have recognized him as a great man. It has been my hope, in writing this biographical novel, not only to corroborate that view, to the best of my ability, but to enable other Americans to understand this enigmatic figure whom so many have known only as a name from the past.

N.B.G.

Waterford, Conn.